STATISTICAL METHODS:
A Problem-Solving Approach

Vivian Gourevitch

THE CITY COLLEGE OF
CITY UNIVERSITY OF NEW YORK

STATISTICAL METHODS:

A Problem-Solving Approach

ALLYN AND BACON, INC.

BOSTON   1965

Preface

This book is intended as an introductory text in statistical methods and their applications in psychology and related fields. Only a minimal amount of high school mathematics is assumed. The emphasis is on statistics as a research tool in the behavioral sciences, and statistical methods are presented within the context of the research problems and methodology of these sciences, particularly psychology.

One of the most frequent questions of the beginning student in statistics is, "What is it for?" For the behavioral science student for whom this book is intended, I believe the question is a legitimate one. I believe that his first statistics course should teach him primarily how statistical methods are used in his field and how they fit into the general methodology of his science. Accordingly, I have provided numerous and detailed illustrations of the role of statistics in answering such research questions as the student himself might encounter, either in the laboratory or in his reading. Most of the book follows this pattern: A research question is posed, a statistical technique is introduced to answer the question, and a discussion follows of the answer and its meaning. In this way, statistical methods are seen in context, firmly tied to sound methodology in general. So that the student will himself have the experience of applying the technique to a research question, practice problems with similarly detailed answers are provided at the end of each chapter. These problems are an integral part of the text and students should be encouraged to try them, or at least read them, even if they are not to be turned in as part of class work.

The book has been written for use as a one-semester course. It is highly suitable, also, as a second text in such laboratory courses as Experimental Psychology. Many of the statistical techniques presented are taught through examples similar to the ones encountered in such a course. A good deal of emphasis is placed on the careful

v

scrutiny of research data, the interpretation of statistical results, and permissible conclusions within the framework of the researcher's question and his method of investigation.

I am deeply grateful to Dr. George Weinberg for his careful reading of the entire manuscript, and for his continuing help and encouragement at every stage in the writing. I am deeply grateful also to my colleague, Professor John G. Peatman of the City College of New York, for his many valuable comments and suggestions. Thanks are also due to Eleanor Roehr, for her indispensable help in the preparation of the manuscript.

I am indebted to the late Professor Sir Ronald A. Fisher, F.R.S., Cambridge, and to Dr. Frank Yates, F.R.S., Rothamsted, also to Messrs. Oliver & Boyd Ltd., Edinburgh, for permission to reprint Table Nos. III, IV, and VI from their book *Statistical Tables for Biological, Agricultural and Medical Research*.

VIVIAN GOUREVITCH

New York City

Contents

ix   **CONTENTS**

STATISTICAL METHODS:
A Problem-Solving Approach

chapter 1

Tables
and
Graphs

Research is the scientist's way of finding answers to his questions. He will make systematic observations of some kind—"collect data," as it is called—then study and analyze the observations to find his answer. It is in the study and analysis of the data that statistical procedures are used. The question the researcher asks and the kind of data he collects together determine which statistical procedures will be used.

Raw data—data in their original form, just as they were collected—are usually a mass of numbers or words that represent the researcher's observations of the process or subject which interests him. The first step in a research study is to organize these raw data into a table or graph so that the results can be inspected. Sometimes the table or the graph makes the results clear immediately and there is no need for any further statistical operations. But even when this is not so, inspection of the data in some organized form is usually indispensable to a full understanding of the results.

In this chapter, examples are given of organizing and presenting three different kinds of data: (1) data classified into categories; (2) ranks; and (3) measures. For each example, we will consider also how to interpret the resulting table or graph in terms of the research problem that prompted the investigation. As will be seen, statistical answers can be properly interpreted only within the context of the research methods used by the investigator, and we shall try not to lose sight of this fact.

3   CATEGORIES

CATEGORIES   Data are classified into categories when the observations consist essentially of words or names of things. For example, if we record for each student in a class that he does or does not intend to seek a summer job we will have simply a collection of words, "yes's" and "no's." There are no numbers to sum, multiply, or divide. All we can do is classify each observation in one of the two categories "yes" or "no," and count the number of observations in each category. How to organize and present such data is illustrated in Examples 1 and 2 below.

Example 1.   An experimenter has studied the color preferences of pre-school children by having them choose, on three different occasions, among four objects which are identical except for color. One of the objects was always red (R), one blue (B), one green (G), and one yellow (Y). If the child chose the same color on each of the three occasions, he was classified as preferring that color. If he did not choose the same color consistently, he was classified as showing no preference, indicated by "O." Sixty children were tested and classified as follows:

R, R, B, G, O, O, O, B, B, Y, O, O, R, R, R, O, Y, Y, G, R, O, O, O, O, B, Y, B, B, R, R, R, R, Y, Y, O, Y, O, B, B, O, O, O, G, R, B, R, R, O, R, Y, Y, B, B, O, R, G, O, O, R, O.

• • STEP 1. To organize the data, first determine the number of categories used in classifying the observations and then list them in a column. In this case, there are five categories: Red, Blue, Green, Yellow, and No Preference. If the experimenter began with a prediction about what he would find, the order in which the categories are listed should conform to this prediction. For example, if the experimenter expected the "warm" colors to be chosen most often, red and yellow in that order, then green, and then blue, the colors should be listed in the predicted order of preference, as in Table 1.1A. If the experimenter is simply investigating color preferences without a prediction, it is more usual to list the categories in the order of frequencies found, from highest to lowest, as in Table 1.1B. Note that in both tables the "No Preference" category appears last and is separated somewhat from the color categories. This category provides important but different information about the outcome of the study, and this difference is recognized in its separation.

• • STEP 2. Count the number of individuals classified in each category, and enter the number in the frequency column opposite the appropriate category. For example, 16 R's appear in the data, which means that 16 children were classified as preferring the color red; the number 16 is therefore entered in the frequency column opposite the category "Red." There are nine Y's; the number 9 is therefore entered opposite "Yellow"; and so on, as in Tables 1.1A and 1.1B.

• • STEP 3. If the frequency distribution is to constitute a presentation of the results for inspection by others, the columns must be labeled, the categories spelled out, the total(s) entered, and a full, descriptive title should appear above the whole. There are no rules about labels and titles, but in general the table should be able to "stand alone"—that is, the headings and title together should convey enough information to allow the reader to interpret the results correctly by looking at the table alone. It should not be necessary to read a paragraph of text in order to find out what the table shows. The titles and headings of Tables 1.1A and 1.1B illustrate two acceptable presentations of the results of this experiment.

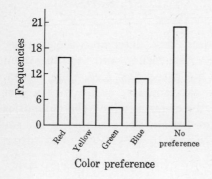

Figure 1.1A
Distribution of Color Preferences Among 60 Pre-School Children

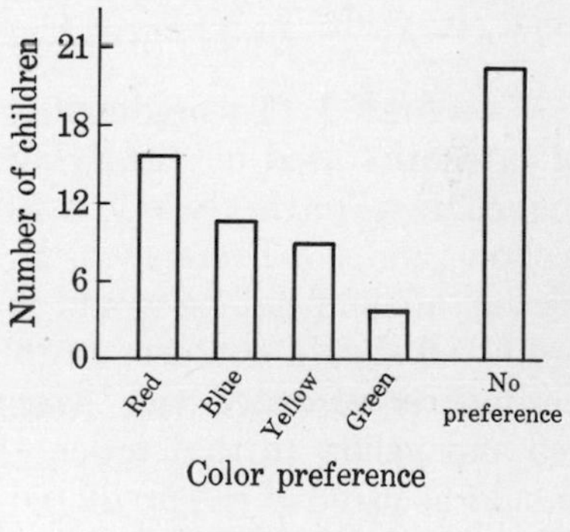

Figure 1.1B
Color Preferences Shown by 60 Pre-School Children

• • STEP 4. The *bar chart* or *bar graph* is used to depict the data of categories. Fig. 1.1A is a bar chart of the results as shown in

Table 1.1A, and Fig. 1.1B shows the results as they are given in Table 1.1B. In both bar charts, the category names appear on the horizontal axis. Frequencies, or number of children, appear on the vertical axis. There is a space between each bar, and a somewhat larger space separating the "No Preference" category from the color categories. The bars are all equal in width and each reaches to that height on the vertical axis which corresponds to the frequency for that category. Thus, the "Red" bar extends up as high as the point 16 on the vertical axis, the "Blue" bar extends up to 11, and so on. A figure number and descriptive title appear below each graph, not above as with tables.

Table 1.1A Distribution of Color Preferences Among 60 Pre-School Children		Table 1.1B Color Preferences Shown By 60 Pre-School Children	
COLOR PREFERENCE	FREQUENCY	COLOR PREFERENCE	NO. OF CHILDREN
Red	16	Red	16
Yellow	9	Blue	11
Green	4	Yellow	9
Blue	11	Green	4
No Preference	20	No Preference	20
Total	60	Total	60
(predicted order)		(ordered from highest to lowest frequencies)	

• INTERPRETING THE RESULTS

A good deal of information is already evident from the frequency distribution (or bar chart) of these data. If the experimenter predicted that the preferred colors, in order of frequency, would be red, yellow, green, blue, he must now acknowledge that his prediction was mistaken. Red does seem to be the most frequent favorite. But blue, a "cool" color, is second, and the experimenter predicted that blue would be the least frequently chosen color. If the experimenter did not begin with a prediction, he will simply note that among the children who show a color preference, red is the most frequently preferred color and green the least frequently preferred, with blue and yellow about tied in between.

What about the high frequency in the "No Preference" category? One-third of the subjects (20/60) were classified as showing no color preference. This finding would require some comment regardless of whether the experimenter began with a hypothesis. Is it true that a third of these children have no color preference? It is doubtless true in terms of the criterion set by the experimenter: that the same color had to be chosen on three different occasions to qualify the child as showing a color preference. But perhaps this criterion was too stringent. What about children who chose the same color two out of three times? Doesn't that show some degree of preference? The experimenter may counter that even if the child closed his eyes he might choose the same color two out of three times by chance alone. In other words, the child's hand could fall on objects of the same color two out of three times by accident, without his making any deliberate color choice at all, whereas we are less willing to believe it was an accident if he chose the same color all three times. There is no final answer to this controversy, though more will be said about such problems in Chapter 7. The point is that the experimenter must consider two possibilities: (1) that one-third of the children he tested really have no color preference; or (2) that his criterion for assigning a color preference was too stringent and caused him to overlook a number of children who do have some color preference. In discussing his results, the experimenter will present both possibilities, though he may choose to accept and defend one or the other of them.

Categories: Bivariate Classification

Example 2. An experimenter wishes to demonstrate the effect of "set" upon problem-solving. His subjects are two groups of 20 college students, previously matched for their ability to solve problems of the general type that will be used in the experiment. They are all asked to solve a difficult problem within a given time limit. The experimental group is deliberately given misleading instructions with the problem, while the control group receives the same problem with neutral instructions. At the end of the time limit, the experimenter collects the results and finds the following:

Experimental group: 5 solved the problem, 15 did not.
Control group: 14 solved the problem, 6 did not.

In this experiment, two observations were recorded for each subject: the group to which he was assigned (hence the instructions he received); and whether or not he succeeded in solving the problem. How the two kinds of observations vary together is of central interest. When two distinct observations are made for each subject or element in an experiment, and interest lies in how the two kinds of observations vary together, the data are cross-classified into what is called a *bivariate distribution*. Bivariate distributions are presented in two-way tables and graphs.

• • STEP 1. To construct a two-way table, list the category names of one variable in a column on the left, and the category names of the second variable across the top of the table. In Table 1.2, the variable *Instructions* (Misleading or Neutral) is shown at the left of the table, and the variable *Performance* (Success or Failure) is given across the top of the table. There is no special rule as to which variable should be listed in the column and which across the top. The researcher uses his own judgment as to which arrangement is clearer and more convenient for the reader. Again, the headings and the category names should convey specific information. Category names like "Experimental Group" and "Control Group" are generally objectionable because they convey so little information. A reader must remember or refer back to the description of the experiment in order to understand the table. It is much better to name the categories according to what was actually varied.

• • STEP 2. Enter the frequencies found in the appropriate cells. A "cell" is the space where two categories would intersect if each was extended into the table—*e.g.*, "Misleading" and "Success," where the frequency 5 is entered because five of the subjects given misleading instructions succeeded in solving the problem. The frequency 15 is entered in the cell where "Misleading" and "Failure"

Table 1.2
Problem-Solving Performance of Two
Groups Given Different Instructions

	PERFORMANCE		
INSTRUCTIONS	SUCCESS	FAILURE	TOTAL
Misleading	5	15	20
Neutral	14	6	20
Total	19	21	40

intersect; and so on, as shown in Table 1.2. When the frequencies have all been entered, they are summed separately for each row and column and these sums, called *marginal totals,* are entered in the table. A grand total is also entered, which should equal the total number of subjects.

• • STEP 3. A bar graph is also used to depict a bivariate distribution of category data. Frequencies or number of subjects (percentages of subjects, if groups are of disparate size) appear on the vertical axis. One variable appears on the horizontal axis, and the second variable is shown by a distinctive marking of the bars themselves. Clarity and ease of interpretation are again the factors which determine which variable shall appear where. A bar graph of the problem-solving data is shown in Fig. 1.2. A legend appears on the

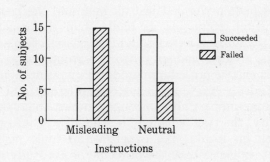

Figure 1.2

**Problem-Solving Performance of Two
Groups Given Different Instructions
($n = 20$ Each Group)**

graph explaining what the different markings of the bars mean. Note that there is no space between the bars belonging to one category, although a space separates the bars of different categories.

• INTERPRETING THE RESULTS

Looking at his table or bar chart, what can the experimenter conclude? It seems evident that a wrong "set," induced in this case by misleading instructions, does indeed inhibit problem solution. Only five subjects misled in this way succeeded in solving the problem, while 14 of the subjects left to themselves solved the problem. Ordinarily, this difference would be examined by a further statistical test (see Chapter 9) but for the moment we will assume that the test confirms our impression.

• DISCUSSING THE RESULTS

Note that the experimenter's conclusion that instructions influenced performance does not rest entirely upon his statistical findings. We would not be very impressed with his results if we did not also have reason to believe that the groups started out as equals in problem-solving ability. Suppose the groups had not been matched, suppose we knew nothing about their problem-solving ability? Perhaps the subjects in the "neutral" control group were just more able than the subjects in the "misled" group, and the results are therefore not due to the different instructions the experimenter gave but to the different abilities of the subjects. In this case, the able subjects in the control group would have performed just as well, and the poor subjects in the experimental group just as badly, had the instructions been reversed. If the subjects were a roughly representative sample of college students, divided randomly into two groups, we might be satisfied that this chance procedure could hardly result in so many of the more able students ending up in the control group. But if the groups are not random samples, and nothing is known about their problem-solving ability, the results cannot be confidently interpreted at all. In discussing his results, the experimenter must defend his conclusions with evidence that the outcome of his study is not due to factors which are irrelevant to the purpose of his experiment.

Ordinal Categories

Often the categories used in classifying data lend themselves to a natural ordering along some continuum. For example, the categories "Excellent," "Good," "Fair," "Poor" fall into a natural order from best to worst. Similarly, the categories "Agree strongly," "Agree," "Disagree," "Disagree Strongly" fall along a continuum from most to least agreement. Such ordered or orderable categories are called *ordinal categories*. Data classified into ordinal categories are presented in the same manner as other category data, except that the natural order of the categories is maintained in the table or the graph regardless of the investigator's hypothesis and regardless of how frequencies are distributed in the categories.

Ordinal categories can be ranked from "most" to "least." When the individual observations can themselves be compared and ranked, categories are abandoned and numerical ranks are assigned to the observations.

RANKS

Ranks are numerals that order a set of observations from "most" to "least" along some continuum of interest. The rank of a given observation indicates its *relative position* in that set of observations. It may not be possible, for example, to say that Jones swims two-and-a-half times as well as Smith, who in turn is three-eighths better than Brown; but competent observers may agree that in this group, Jones ranks first in swimming ability, Smith second, and Brown third. When observations can be ordered from "most" to "least" in this way, so that ranks can be assigned, the resulting numerals are *ordinal*. Ordinal numerals do not indicate the *amount* of difference between observations, only their order relative to each other along the continuum of interest.

Example 3.   Twelve persons have applied for psychotherapy to a small new clinic which will not be able to take them all at once. The therapist looks over their applications to try to judge which are most in need of help. He puts Fisher first and Irwin second; cannot decide between Carson and Davis so puts them both next; then Gordon, Allen, Bates, Harris; then a group of three—Jasper, Klapp, and Eaton—who seem about equally in need of help; and finally Levine, who is judged least in need. Placed in order from most in need to least in need, the names look like this:

> Fisher
> Irwin
> Carson, Davis
> Gordon
> Allen
> Bates
> Harris
> Jasper, Klapp, Eaton
> Levine

The therapist wishes to assign ranks to the applicants so that he may post the ranks instead of their names.

• • STEP 1. The first step in assigning ranks is to determine how many individuals or how many objects are to be ranked. This number tells how many ranks must be "used up" in the ranking. In this case, there are 12 individuals, so the ranks from 1 through 12 must be accounted for in the final ranking.

•• STEP 2. Assign ranks in a serial order, beginning with 1, until the number of ranks previously determined has been "used up." When several objects or individuals are tied in rank, each is assigned a rank whose value corresponds to the mid-point of the ranks which *would* be occupied if the several individuals had been given separate ranks. In Table 1.3, the applicants for psychotherapy have been ranked by this procedure. Carson and Davis, who have a tied position in the group, would have occupied the ranks 3 and 4 if they could have been distinguished from each other; therefore, they are both assigned the rank 3.5, which is the mid-point between 3 and 4. The next applicant, Gordon, receives a rank of 5 since the ranks 3 and 4 have been used. Similarly, Klapp, Jasper, and Eaton would have occupied the ranks 9, 10, and 11 had the therapist been able to assign them separate ranks, so they are each given a rank of 10, which is the mid-point of the ranks 9, 10, 11. Since 11 has been used, the next individual receives a rank of 12. Now the previously determined number of ranks have all been used and we have come to the end of the list. When the two events don't occur together, a mistake has been made!

Table 1.3
Applicants for Psychotherapy
Ranked in Order of Judged
Need for Help

APPLICANT	RANK
Fisher	1
Irwin	2
Carson	3.5
Davis	3.5
Gordon	5
Allen	6
Bates	7
Harris	8
Klapp	10
Jasper	10
Eaton	10
Levine	12

• INTERPRETING THE RESULTS

The results of ranking are usually self-evident. In this case, the applicants will doubtless be called in the order in which they were ranked as openings occur in the clinic. When the therapist comes to Carson and Davis, he will have to flip a coin to decide which to take first, or decide on some basis other than need for help.

• DISCUSSING THE RESULTS

The results as they stand serve the therapist's purpose, and for that purpose, there is nothing to discuss. Remember, however, that the numerals assigned in ranking represent relative positions within the particular group ranked. There is nothing absolute about them. If the group changes, so will the ranks. For example, if Allen and Bates decide to cancel their applications, everyone below them will move up two ranks. Harris, for example, will have a rank of 6 instead of 8. If three new applicants appear on the scene, all of whom need help moreso than Fisher, everyone on the present list will drop down three ranks. Harris will now have a rank of 11. Harris's need for help remains unchanged, but his rank could change from 8 to 6 to 11 to anything because ranks only refer to relative position within the group ranked.

Comparing Two Sets of Ranks

Example 4. An investigator is interested in how art teachers grade their students' work. He collects ten watercolor pictures made by high school students and brings them to two art teachers who have never seen them before. Each teacher is asked to give grades to the ten pictures on a separate sheet of paper so neither will know the grades given by the other. The investigator then compares the grades given by the two teachers and finds the following:

| | GRADES GIVEN BY | |
PICTURE	TEACHER X	TEACHER Y
A	60	45
B	60	50
C	65	65
D	95	80
E	80	70
F	75	60
G	90	75
H	85	75
I	80	70
J	80	70

In this example, the observations take the form of numbers, but the numbers can hardly be taken literally as indicators of merit since the teachers differ so markedly in the grades they assign. Obviously, the two teachers are using different grading scales. We may still examine the amount of agreement between the two teachers, irrespective of the grading scale each is using, by converting the grades of each teacher to ranks and comparing the ranks. (A more precise technique for assessing "amount of agreement" is taken up in Chapter 6.)

• • STEP 1. For each teacher separately, the grades are ranked by the procedure outlined in Example 3 above.

• • STEP 2. To facilitate comparison, the items are listed from highest to lowest following one of the sets of ranks. In Table 1.4, the letters identifying the student pictures were arranged from highest to lowest to conform to Teacher X's grades and ranks. The corresponding grades and ranks of Teacher Y were then entered in separate columns.

Table 1.4
Art Teachers' Grading of Student Work

STUDENT PICTURE	GRADES		RANKS OF GRADES	
	TEACHER X	TEACHER Y	TEACHER X	TEACHER Y
D	95	80	1	1
G	90	75	2	2.5
H	85	75	3	2.5
I	80	70	5	5
J	80	70	5	5
E	80	70	5	5
F	75	60	7	8
C	65	65	8	7
B	60	50	9.5	9
A	60	45	9.5	10

• INTERPRETING THE RESULTS

It seems evident from a comparison of the ranks in Table 1.4 that the two teachers are in very good agreement about the order of the pictures relative to each other along some scale of merit. Except for small discrepancies, the *order* of their grades is very similar even though the magnitude of their grades is very different. The investigator has found two things therefore: (1) that Teachers X and Y do not agree as to the *amount* of merit attaching to the pictures they graded; but (2) that they do agree rather well as to which pictures are better than others.

- DISCUSSING THE RESULTS

Attempts to estimate the "amount" of some quality present in persons or things often fail. The usual reason is that the quality of interest is an elusive one and it is difficult to establish criteria about which independent observers will agree. Obviously, Teachers X and Y are grading according to different criteria, weighting various factors differently. Ranks are especially useful in such cases—if it is found that observers agree at least in this. If they do not agree in the ranks assigned, then the ranks would not be useful either. In general, observations are not useful to science unless they are *reliable*. *Reliability* in this context refers to the consistency of repeated observations. This consistency must exist for any given observer (Teacher X must assign the same ranks, or nearly the same, if he were to grade these pictures again at a later date) and there must be consistency among observers (other teachers must assign the same, or nearly the same, ranks). In this situation, we would be led to conclude that the grades given to student pictures are not reliable indicators of their worth, but the ranks of those grades are reliable. Hence, the *relative* merit of the pictures has been reliably determined.

Since our investigator's interest is in the behavior of Art teachers rather than in the merit of student pictures, his discussion will center about the reliability of the teachers' behavior. He may ask them to grade the pictures again after a time period sufficient for them to forget the grades they had given originally. He will inquire into the criteria they use in grading and try to discover both the reasons for the unreliability of grades and the reasons for the reliability of the ranks.

MEASURES

We shall call a *measure* any numerical observation that is intended to convey an amount or magnitude, as opposed to simply relative position. Unlike ranks, which indicate only order, measures are truly quantitative. There are many kinds of measures. Besides the familiar inches, pounds, temperature, in Psychology there are test scores and ratings of various kinds, measures of performance like number of trials or number of errors, reaction time, rate of response, etc. All of these are quantitative indicators of the *amount* of some given quality and so will be regarded as measures. To be useful, of course, measures must meet certain standards of reliability and usually, as we shall see, other standards as well.

The student should be careful not to confuse *measure* and *frequency*. A measure is an observation. A frequency is the number of times an observation occurs. If we record that a subject made eight errors, 8 is a *measure* of his performance and constitutes one observation. If 20 subjects made eight errors, then the observation 8 has occurred 20 times. The *frequency* of the observation is 20.

The remainder of this chapter will be devoted to procedures for organizing and presenting measures.

Example 5.   A psychologist is interested in the amount of hostile or aggressive feeling among medical students. He secures a random sample* of 78 students from nearby medical schools, and as part of the study, he asks each student to make up a story about each of ten picture cards that show people in ambiguous situations. Afterwards, he counts for each student the number of "aggression" themes that appear in his stories and this number becomes the student's aggression score. Scores may range from 0 (no aggression themes) to 10 (aggression themes in all stories). The 78 students receive the following scores:

3, 6, 6, 2, 5, 5, 7, 4, 4, 4, 3, 5, 6, 6, 1, 4, 4, 3, 3, 5, 4, 4, 4, 6, 7, 2, 4, 5, 5, 4, 7, 5, 5, 5, 5, 3, 3, 6, 2, 4, 4, 8, 3, 3, 7, 4, 4, 5, 7, 5, 4, 6, 6, 7, 3, 6, 1, 5, 5, 5, 4, 2, 2, 4, 4, 2, 7, 5, 7, 6, 3, 6, 4, 3, 3, 4, 5, 5.

• • STEP 1. Since it is apparent that many observations have the same value, the first step in organizing the data is to construct a *frequency distribution*. Look over the array of scores and find the highest and lowest scores. In this case, although the scores could have ranged from 0 to 10, the lowest score is 1 and the highest score is 8. *The lowest score to the highest score of a distribution is called the range of the distribution.* Therefore the range of the distribution is from 1 to 8. List all the scores within this range in a column, starting with the highest score and ending with the lowest score, as in Table 1.5. These scores are the *classes* for which frequencies will be counted.

• • STEP 2. Going through the observations one by one, put a tally for each opposite the class into which it falls. Thus, the first observation is 3 so a tally is put opposite the class 3; the second is 6 so a tally is put opposite the class 6; the next observation is also 6

* A *random sample* of subjects is obtained by drawing subjects from a specified larger group (*e.g.*, all students attending the medical schools) in such a way that every member of the larger group has the same chance of being included in the sample. Random sampling permits us to generalize our findings to the larger group. This concept is discussed more fully in Chapter 3.

so another tally is put opposite the class 6; and so on, until all the observations have been tallied. The sum of the tallies in each class is entered in a column headed "Frequency" (sometimes simply "f"). The frequencies are totalled and the total is identified as n, as shown in Table 1.5.

Table 1.5
Distribution of Aggression Scores
Obtained by Medical Students

AGGRESSION SCORE	TALLY	FREQUENCY
8	/	1
7	₦₦ ///	8
6	₦₦ ₦₦ /	11
5	₦₦ ₦₦ ₦₦ ///	18
4	₦₦ ₦₦ ₦₦ ₦₦	20
3	₦₦ ₦₦ //	12
2	₦₦ /	6
1	//	2
		$n = 78$

• • STEP 3. The results may be depicted in either a *histogram* or a *frequency polygon*. Fig. 1.3 shows a histogram of the data. A frequency polygon of the data is shown in Fig. 1.4. In both cases, frequencies appear on the vertical axis and scores on the horizontal axis. The essential difference between the two graphs lies in how they represent the scoring classes.

Histogram

On the histogram, the scoring classes are represented by bars which correspond in width to the *exact limits* of the classes. The exact limits of a class extend from half a unit of measure below the class to half a unit of measure above the class. Thus, the bar representing a score of 1 extends from .5 to 1.5 on the horizontal axis; the bar representing a score of 2 extends from 1.5 to 2.5; and so on.

The use of exact limits conforms to the assumption that our observations are quantities measured on a continuous scale of values. Theoretically, if not in practice, a subject might have a score of 1.9 or 2.33 instead of 2. But our test does not permit such fine discriminations to be made. Use of the exact limits 1.5 to 2.5 reflects our belief that the *real* score of a subject scoring "2" falls somewhere within these limits, and not necessarily at 2.0 exactly.

Frequency Polygon

On the frequency polygon, the scoring classes are represented by their midpoints. The midpoint of an individual class has the same value which designates the class itself. Thus, the class 3 extends

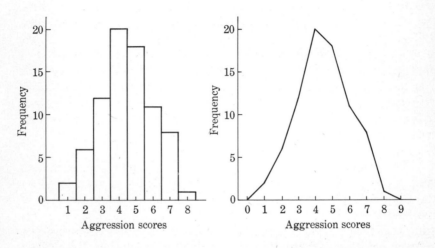

Figure 1.3

Distribution of Aggression Scores Obtained by Medical Students (n = 78)

Figure 1.4

Distribution of Aggression Scores Obtained by Medical Students (n = 78)

from 2.5 to 3.5, but its midpoint is 3; the class 4 extends from 3.5 to 4.5, but its midpoint is 4. A point is plotted on the graph for each midpoint (class) opposite its frequency, and the plotted points are connected by straight lines.

Note that the lines extend back to the baseline on both sides of the graph to form a closed figure. The extensions are not to some arbitrary point on the baseline. On the left, the line is extended to the midpoint of the class just below the lowest class in the frequency distribution. In this case, the lowest class in the frequency distribution is 1, so the line is extended to the class 0 on the baseline. (If the lowest class in the frequency distribution is 0, the line is extended to a mythical class "−1," although the numeral itself would usually not appear on the baseline.) On the right, the line is extended to the midpoint of the class just above the highest one in the frequency distribution. In this case, the highest class in the frequency distribution is 8, so the line extends to the class 9 on the baseline.

- ● INTERPRETING THE RESULTS

From an inspection of the table and graphs, it is evident that the largest concentration of scores is in the classes 4 and 5. Almost half the observations (from the table, 20 + 18 = 38) are found in these two classes. The greatest single concentration of scores is in the class 4. That is, a score of 4 was obtained more times than any other single score in the distribution. *The most frequently obtained score in a distribution is called the* **mode.** Thus, the psychologist may say that 4 is the mode among these medical students, or that 4 is the most "typical" score among them. He may also note that 1 and 8 seem to represent rather extreme, "untypical" scores for this group because they occur so infrequently. Only two of the 78 subjects scored as low as 1, and only one scored as high as 8.

The graphs show the overall form of the distribution. Although it may not be obvious from simple inspection, the area enclosed by the frequency polygon is equal to the area enclosed by the bars of the histogram. This will always be true of a properly drawn histogram and frequency polygon of the same data. In both graphs, the distribution of *area* reflects the distribution of cases. That is, a given proportion of the observations in the frequency distribution is represented by a corresponding and equal proportion of the area enclosed by the histogram or frequency polygon. Thus, the graph makes it possible to tell at a glance how the observations are distributed, where the scores are concentrated and where they are few.

- ● DISCUSSING THE RESULTS

Can the psychologist decide from these results whether the medical students as a group show much or little aggression on this test? Not with the information given. To decide whether medical students show more or less aggression than other students, the investigator must know how other students score on the test. He may find, for example, that scores of comparable students not attending medical school are similarly distributed around a mode of 3 on the test, which would make the medical students' mode of 4 look a little high. Or perhaps other students' scores are distributed about a mode of 7, which would make the medical students' mode of 4 seem substantially "below average." Or perhaps there is no difference between medical students and other students on this test. The point is that the investigator must have a known standard of comparison before he can make judgments of "more" or "less" about a group.

We have assumed without saying so that telling stories with themes of aggression indicates aggressive feelings in the subject. Even if repeated observations show the test scores to be reliable, the assumption that the scores really measure aggressive feelings cannot be made. *What* the scores measure is a separate matter. It is not enough that a test should *seem* to measure aggression or anxiety or extraversion or whatever. We want independent evidence that the measure used is in fact related to the characteristic of interest. A test may *seem* to measure aggressive feelings, while most of the time it is measuring what the subject thinks the examiner wants, or some other irrelevant thing. Therefore, it is incumbent upon our investigator to provide evidence that his aggression scores do indeed reflect aggressive feelings in the subjects, and that differences in subjects' scores reflect corresponding differences in amount of aggressive feelings. Evidence of this kind is said to establish the *validity* of a test. In general, validity is established by showing that a test measures what it was intended to measure, or that it predicts successfully those outcomes that follow logically from what the test claims to measure (for example, that subjects with high aggression scores dislike or distrust more people than subjects with low aggression scores). If the investigator does not provide evidence of the validity of his test—and even though he may have a standard group for comparison—we cannot know what his results mean and can have no confidence in his conclusions.

Measures: Grouping Data into Class Intervals

Example 6.   An experimenter has measured the extent of the Müller-Lyer illusion for one subject by the method of adjustment. That is, the subject was asked to match a fixed, standard line of given length with another line which he could adjust at will, under conditions which induce a marked error in perceptual judgment. The standard was 13 centimeters (cm) long. The subject was given 100 trials, each time trying to set his adjustable line to match the length of the standard line. He was given a rest period after 60 trials had been completed; then the experiment was resumed and the last 40 trials given. After each trial, the experimenter recorded the length of the subject's line setting to the nearest tenth of a centimeter. Beginning with the first trial, the subject's settings (length in cm) were as follows:

17.6, 17.0, 18.3, 16.9, 15.8, 17.0, 16.3, 15.7, 16.3, 17.1, 17.4, 16.3, 15.3,
15.6, 14.3, 15.1, 14.5, 13.4, 14.4, 16.8, 16.8, 16.0, 16.6, 16.1, 18.0, 17.9,
18.1, 16.2, 15.4, 15.3, 14.7, 14.1, 14.3, 17.3, 16.9, 16.4, 16.3, 17.5, 16.3,
16.0, 17.1, 16.6, 14.9, 15.5, 14.8, 15.2, 14.0, 15.0, 16.5, 15.9, 16.4, 16.4,
17.6, 15.4, 15.2, 16.5, 15.8, 15.9, 15.5, 14.8 (Rest period) 14.4, 15.4,
14.8, 13.9, 13.7, 13.5, 13.3, 13.3, 13.4, 12.9, 13.4, 13.1, 12.8, 12.6, 13.5,
13.6, 13.0, 12.6, 12.2, 12.3, 12.4, 12.4, 14.3, 14.4, 14.6, 14.0, 15.0, 15.3,
15.4, 15.0, 14.6, 14.7, 15.8, 16.2, 16.3, 15.9, 16.4, 16.5, 17.0, 16.6.

We do not proceed here as in Example 5. Scanning the data for the lowest and the highest observations recorded, these values reveal a range of from 12.2 to 18.3. There are 62 individual classes within this range, one for each tenth of a centimeter. The separate listing of 62 individual classes would hardly make for a compact table. When this is so, it is customary to group the classes into *class intervals* each of which will include several classes.

• • STEP 1. Determine the number of classes that will be grouped together into one class interval. One way to do this is to divide the total number of classes by 10, and use the result as a rough guide to the number of classes to be grouped together. In this example, $62 \div 10 = 6.2$. When the result of dividing by 10 in this way is near to 5 (roughly, between 3 and 8) it is customary to set up class intervals each of which will include five classes. If the result is close to 3, and there are many observations—say, 100 or more—set up class intervals that include three classes each. If the result is 8 or more, and there are *not* many observations—say, fewer than 100—set up class intervals that include seven classes each. (Note that only odd numbers—3, 5, or 7—have been suggested as the number of classes to be included in a class interval. An odd number of classes simplifies the procedure considerably when a frequency polygon is to be constructed or when later computations will be made from the grouped data.)

• • STEP 2. For these data, five classes give a class interval *size* of .5 cm. Since the lowest observation recorded is 12.2, we take 12.0 as the lower limit of the first class interval. If the size of each interval is to be .5, the lower limits of the intervals must go 12.0, 12.5, 13.0, etc. After the lower limits are set down in a column, the upper limits are easily added. The highest class interval must, of course, include the value of the highest observation in the data. Table 1.6 shows class intervals of five classes each for the data of this example. The class intervals appear in a column under the heading "Setting—cm," a more informative title than "Class Intervals" would be.

•• STEP 3. Going through the observations one by one, put a tally for each opposite the class interval into which it falls. Thus, the first observation, 17.6, falls in the class interval 17.5–17.9, so a tally is put opposite this interval. The next observation, 17.0, falls in the interval 17.0–17.4, so a tally is put opposite this interval; and so on. When all the observations have been tallied, the tallies are summed in the Frequency column, and the total below is identified as n, as shown in Table 1.6. The frequency distribution is now complete.

•• STEP 4. Either a histogram or a frequency polygon is appropriate for these data, and we will suppose that a histogram was

chosen. To construct a histogram, an additional column is required in the table showing the *exact limits* of the class intervals. The exact limits of a class interval, like the exact limits of an individual class, extend from half a class below the interval to half a class above the interval. Thus, the exact limits of the class interval 12.0–12.4 are 11.95–12.45. For the class interval 12.5–12.9, the exact limits are 12.45–12.95. The exact limits of all the class intervals are found in this manner and listed in a column, as shown in Table 1.6.

•• STEP 5. The column of exact limits and the column of frequencies are used in the construction of the histogram. The exact limits determine the width of the bars in the histogram, and the

Table 1.6
Müller-Lyer Illusion: Distribution of 100 Adjustable
Line Settings Made by One Subject
(Standard = 13 cm)

Setting–cm	Tally	Frequency	Exact Limits
18.0–18.4	///	3	17.95–18.45
17.5–17.9	////	4	17.45–17.95
17.0–17.4	ЖЛ //	7	16.95–17.45
16.5–16.9	ЖЛ ЖЛ	10	16.45–16.95
16.0–16.4	ЖЛ ЖЛ ЖЛ	15	15.95–16.45
15.5–15.9	ЖЛ ЖЛ	10	15.45–15.95
15.0–15.4	ЖЛ ЖЛ ///	13	14.95–15.45
14.5–14.9	ЖЛ ////	9	14.45–14.95
14.0–14.4	ЖЛ ////	9	13.95–14.45
13.5–13.9	ЖЛ	5	13.45–13.95
13.0–13.4	ЖЛ //	7	12.95–13.45
12.5–12.9	////	4	12.45–12.95
12.0–12.4	////	4	11.95–12.45

$$n = 100$$

frequencies determine their height. Fig. 1.5 shows a histogram of the data as organized in Table 1.6.

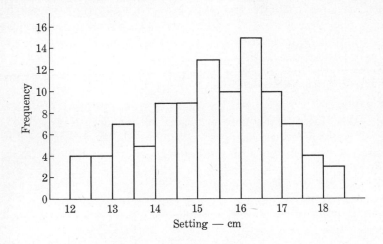

Figure 1.5

Müller-Lyer Illusion. Distribution of 100 Adjustable.
Line Settings Made by One Subject
(Standard = 13 cm)

• INTERPRETING THE RESULTS

The results certainly suggest that the subject's judgment was influenced by the illusion set up in the experiment. In 100 attempts to match the 13 cm standard, he set his adjustable line too short only eight times (the sum of the frequencies in the class intervals below 13.0 cm) while he made adjustments which were too long 92 times. In short, he showed a strong tendency to overestimate the length of the standard. (Perceptual misjudgment is usually the case in experiments with the Müller-Lyer illusion.)

The histogram shows the heaviest concentration of scores between 14.0 and 16.9 cm. The tallest bar, hence the highest frequency, is found in the class interval 16.0–16.4, which is therefore called the *modal class*. The "typical" performance, as indicated by the mode, is between 16.0 and 16.4 cm, at least three cm longer than the standard. The histogram also shows other, lesser modes (bars which rise above those on both sides of them). There is such a lesser mode at the interval 15.0–15.4, and another, still smaller mode at the interval

13.0–13.4. When there are two modes, the graph is described as *bimodal;* when there are more than two, as *multimodal.* A multimodal graph suggests great variability—which is another way of saying that the "typical" performance was not really very typical because the subject's responses varied a great deal. The three modes of the histogram, and the wide range of the settings, suggest that this subject's performance was highly variable.

- DISCUSSING THE RESULTS

Possible reasons for the subject's variability would require consideration of several factors. When observations recorded for a large *group of subjects* yield a multimodal graph, the variability can usually be attributed to the existence of several sub-groups within the larger group who differ from each other on the variable being measured. Each of the different sub-groups makes its own typical "peak" on the graph, and the peaks are at different points because what is typical for one sub-group differs from what is typical for another sub-group. But in this example there is only one subject, and it is one subject's performance which varies so much.

Great variability in one subject may occur for several reasons. The task may be so difficult that the subject is reduced to guessing, and with no knowledge of results he guesses "all over the lot," making guesses which cluster sometimes around one point, sometimes around another. A second possibility is that although the task is not so difficult, the subject is not motivated—he "doesn't try," his attention wanders, he is bored or in a hurry, or both—and he makes many careless responses. The third possibility is that the conditions under which the subject was operating became subtly changed in the course of the experiment. For instance, an unpracticed subject is no longer "unpracticed" after ten or twenty trials, and an initially energetic subject may become fatigued after forty or fifty trials. If the experimenter also made informal observations of his subject, noting comments which suggest boredom or fatigue or impatience or sudden insight, he will have some idea about the reason for the subject's variable performance. The subject's remarks are only of interest, of course, if they are accompanied by some change in his performance on the task. The first thing to do is to look at the data again.

Scanning the original data, the experimenter will look to see whether "runs" of similar values occurred at any particular time during the experiment (or in conjunction with particular remarks made by the subject). Short runs in the region of 16 cm, the major mode, are found throughout the data, and therefore did not occur at any particular time during the experiment. A run of four observations in the region of 15 cm, the second mode, is found near the end of the experiment, and several runs centering around 13 cm are found soon after the rest period. It would appear that settings made after the rest period are responsible for the two lesser modes, 15.0–15.4 cm and 13.0–13.4 cm. This discovery suggests that the conditions of the experiment were different somehow after the rest period, since the subject made shorter settings, closer to the standard. Perhaps the rest, combined with practice, enabled him finally to overcome the perceptual illusion that dominated his earlier performance.

It would be a great mistake to stop with these guesses. Now that there is reason to believe the conditions of the experiment were different after the rest period, the data should be reorganized so that trials before the rest period and trials after the rest period can be compared. The procedure for doing this is illustrated in the example that follows.

Comparing Two Sets of Measures

Example 7. The experimenter of Example 6 above has found that an unplanned event has importance in explaining his results. The subject's line settings seem to vary with two categories of trials, those made before the rest period and those made after the rest period. He wishes to examine this variation more closely.

• • STEP 1. To reorganize the data, prepare a new frequency table using the same class intervals as were used in the initial frequency distribution. (If the data have not been previously organized, determine class intervals on the basis of all the observations combined, then continue with this procedure.) For the new table, enter a separate frequency column for each category of measures that is to be compared. Thus, as shown in Table 1.7, there are separate frequency columns for the categories "Before Rest Period" and "After Rest Period." The observations that fall in each category are tallied separately (not shown in the table) and summed separately in their respective frequency columns. The totals of each frequency column are identified below as n_1 and n_2.

• • STEP 2. If the different n's are not equal, convert the frequencies of each column to proportions of the column total. Since n_1 and n_2 are not equal in this example, the frequencies have been converted to proportions of their respective totals by the formula

$p = f/n$. That is, each frequency was divided by the total of its group, n_1 or n_2. Each frequency in the column "Before Rest Period" was divided by 60 (n_1); each frequency in the column "After Rest Period" was divided by 40 (n_2). The resulting proportions are entered in new columns, headed "p" in Table 1.7.

• • STEP 3. To compare the two sets of trials, a frequency polygon of each set is plotted on the same pair of axes. To construct a frequency polygon of data grouped into class intervals, an additional column is needed in the table—the midpoints of the class intervals. The midpoint of a class interval is the value which divides the interval exactly in half. When an odd number of classes are grouped into one class interval, the midpoint of the interval is the value of the middle class. When an even number of classes is included in one interval, the midpoint of the interval is the value which falls halfway between the two middle classes. Since these data were grouped into intervals of five classes, an odd number, the midpoints have the values of the middle class in each interval. The midpoints are entered in a separate column, as shown in Table 1.7.

• • STEP 4. On the same pair of axes, two separate frequency polygons are constructed of the data. In Fig. 1.6 a frequency polygon has been plotted using the midpoints and the proportions of the

Table 1.7
Müller-Lyer Illusion: Comparison of One Subject's Settings Before and After a Rest Period
(Standard = 13 cm)

SETTING–CM	BEFORE REST PERIOD		AFTER REST PERIOD		MIDPOINTS
	f_1	p_1	f_2	p_2	
18.0–18.4	3	.05			18.2
17.5–17.9	4	.07			17.7
17.0–17.4	6	.10	1	.03	17.2
16.5–16.9	8	.13	2	.05	16.7
16.0–16.4	12	.20	3	.07	16.2
15.5–15.9	8	.13	2	.05	15.7
15.0–15.4	8	.13	5	.13	15.2
14.5–14.9	5	.08	4	.10	14.7
14.0–14.4	5	.08	4	.10	14.2
13.5–13.9	1	.02	5	.13	13.7
13.0–13.4			6	.15	13.2
12.5–12.9			4	.10	12.7
12.0–12.4			4	.10	12.2
	$n_1 = 60$	.99	$n_2 = 40$	1.01	

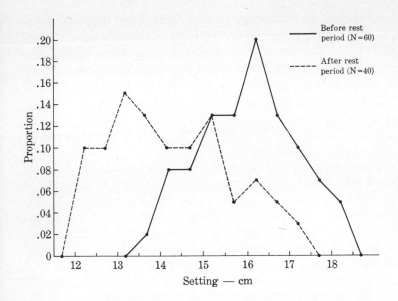

Figure 1.6

Müller-Lyer Illusion. Comparison of One Subject's Settings Before and After a Rest Period

category "Before Rest Period." A second frequency polygon was plotted independently, using the same midpoints but the proportions of the category "After Rest Period." The plotted points belonging to each category are connected by straight lines, and the lines are made differently—one solid, one dashed—in order to distinguish the separate categories. A key on the graph explains which line represents which category.

Because proportions were plotted instead of frequencies, the two curves may be directly compared. When the n's of different categories are equal, proportions are not needed. Frequencies may be plotted opposite the midpoints and the resulting curves may be directly compared. When n's are not equal, frequencies must be converted to proportions.

• INTERPRETING THE RESULTS

The results of the experiment are much clearer now. As Fig. 1.6 shows, the subject was fairly consistent before the rest period. The graph of settings made before the rest period has only one mode, at

16.2 (the midpoint of the class interval 16.0–16.4), and the other settings cluster around this mode on both sides. It was after the rest period that the subject's responses became so variable. The line graph of settings made after the rest period has three modes, and the remaining settings cannot be said to cluster around any one of them. The bulk of the settings extend over seven class intervals, represented by the midpoints from 12.2 to 15.2. In short, settings made after the rest period account for the variability observed in the original histogram (Fig. 1.5).

Our earlier guesses about the results were wrong on some counts and right on others. We were wrong that observations in the interval 16.0–16.4 cm did not occur "at any particular time" during the experiment. Clearly, the great bulk of them occurred before the rest period. We were also wrong that settings made after the rest period were responsible for the mode at 15.0–15.4 cm in the original histogram. Settings in this class interval are found in exactly equal proportions before and after the rest period. But we were right that the subject made shorter settings after the rest period. Most of the settings made after the rest period are well below the subject's "typical" performance of 16.0–16.4 cm before the rest period. The highest peak on the graph of settings made after the rest period is at 13.0–13.4 cm, a very good match of the 13-cm standard. We conclude, therefore, that the subject probably did overcome the influence of the illusion after the rest period, but his variability after the rest period forces us to add that if he overcame it, he did so only temporarily.

• Discussing the Results

If the subject was able to overcome the influence of the illusion, as it appears, why was he so variable afterward? We already know from scanning the original data (given in Example 6 above) that the settings which came closest to matching the standard were made soon after the rest period and were followed by settings much farther away from the standard. Why did the subject not continue to make close settings? He was evidently able to do so. The data provide no answer to this question, just as they do not explain why the subject was able to make the close settings at all. If rest and practice produced the first event, perhaps fatigue and failing motivation produced the second. The data do not tell us in either case. After having reported the results of the experiment, the experimenter will add any informal observations or previous information from other studies that help to explain the results. If he has no further information, he will state in his report that he does not know the explanation.

Cumulative Graphs of Measures

Cumulative graphs of measures have many uses. One such use is illustrated in Example 8 below. Another is given in Chapter 2.

Example 8.   A rat has been conditioned to press a bar that releases a pellet of food. The experimenter decides to remove the food so that bar presses will no longer procure food pellets. He places the animal in the apparatus, which now releases no food. To be able to study the rat's behavior during extinction (as the process is called), he records the number of bar presses made by the rat during each successive minute in the apparatus over an interval of 20 minutes. He counts the following number of bar presses for each successive minute:

6, 10, 12, 6, 5, 3, 7, 5, 4, 0, 2, 1, 0, 5, 1, 0, 0, 0, 0, 0.

Number of responses per minute is a measure of the *rate* of responding. It is customary in Psychology to depict the rate of responding by a cumulative graph.

• • STEP 1. To construct a cumulative graph of the data, organize them first as shown in the first two columns of Table 1.8. The successive minutes of time are identified by the numbers from 1 to 20. Number of responses for each minute are given in the second column. To get the cumulative response column, the number of responses are cumulated downward beginning with the first minute. Thus, the first entry in the cumulative response column is 6 because six responses had been made by the *end* of the first minute. The second entry is 16 because 6 + 10 = 16 responses had been made by the end of the second minute. By the end of the third minute, 16 + 12 = 28 responses had been made, and so on for the rest of the column. The last entry in the cumulative response column is the total number of responses made during the 20 minutes.

• • STEP 2. To construct the cumulative response curve, lay out minutes of time along the horizontal axis, beginning with 0, and cumulative responses along the vertical axis, also beginning with 0. Fig. 1.7 shows how the axes should be numbered. Plot a point for each entry in the cumulative response column opposite minutes of time elapsed. Thus, a point is plotted on the graph for six responses opposite that point on the baseline which marks the end of the first minute. The next point, for 16 responses, is plotted opposite the end of the second minute, and so on as shown. When all the points have been plotted, they are connected by straight lines beginning at the origin (0,0).

Table 1.8
Number of Responses and Cumulative Responses for One Rat During the First 20 Minutes of Extinction

SUCCESSIVE MINUTES OF TIME	NUMBER OF RESPONSES	CUMULATIVE RESPONSES
1	6	6
2	10	16
3	12	28
4	6	34
5	5	39
6	3	42
7	7	49
8	5	54
9	4	58
10	0	58
11	2	60
12	1	61
13	0	61
14	5	66
15	1	67
16	0	67
17	0	67
18	0	67
19	0	67
20	0	67

$$n = 67$$

• INTERPRETING THE RESULTS

The cumulative response curve shown in Fig. 1.7 describes the rat's bar-pressing behavior during extinction better than do several paragraphs of words. To a practiced eye, the slope of the curve—its relative steepness or flatness—reveals instantly any changes in the rate of responding. Thus, in the beginning the slope rises—becomes steeper for a few minutes—indicating an increase in the animal's rate of responding. (If you check Table 1.8, you will see that the rate rose from 6 to 12 responses during the first three minutes.) Almost immediately after the increase, the curve bends over as the rate begins to fall off. The animal is slowing down. Then there is a recovery of responding, indicated by the second rise in the slope of the curve. Then the response rate drops abruptly to zero, as shown by complete flatness in the curve. For a few minutes, there is only occa-

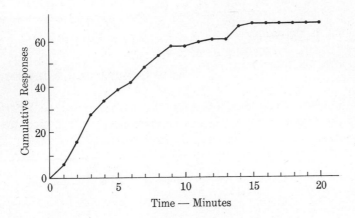

Figure 1.7

**Cumulative Response Curve for One Rat, Showing
Extinction of Bar-Pressing Response**

sional responding, indicated by an occasional "bump" in the curve. A last burst of responses occurs during the 14th minute, then the curve quickly becomes flat again and remains so, indicating that the animal made no further responses during the 20 minutes of testing. Clearly, removing the food considerably reduced bar-pressing behavior, although the effect was not immediate. All of this can be seen, of course, in Table 1.8, but it is difficult to compare several such tables at once, while several curves may be compared at the same time with ease.

- DISCUSSING THE RESULTS

In discussing his results, the experimenter will compare his curve with extinction curves obtained by other investigators in similar experiments. If there are marked differences or irregularities in his curve, he will discuss possible reasons for the irregularities in terms of his experimental procedure and the rat's previous training, both of which are usually reported in much greater detail than is given here.

In important experimental work, cumulative response curves like the one in Fig. 1.7 are obtained from a recording device. Instead of the experimenter counting the number of responses, the recorder cumulates the responses as they are made, and does so for every fraction of a second instead of only at the end of a minute. The resulting curve is a smoother version of the curve in Fig. 1.7, but the principle is the same.

Line Graphs and Functions

We shall refer to the graph of a function as a *line graph*. A function describes the change that occurs in one variable (say, reaction time) as some other variable is increased (say, stimulus intensity). The

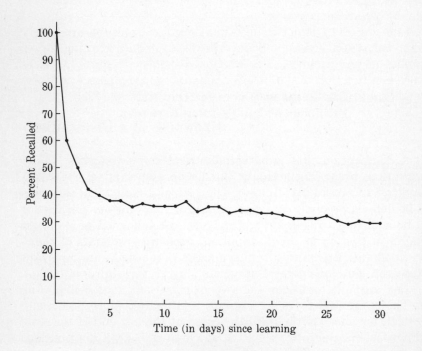

Figure 1.8

Retention Curve for One Subject, Showing Recall for Memorized Prose Material as a Function of Time

variable that is increased, often by the experimenter himself, is called the *independent variable*. The variable that "depends upon" and changes with such increases is called the *dependent variable*. Usually, in behavioral research, the subject's responses constitute the dependent variable.

For example, in studies of memory, the subject is typically required to memorize some material provided by the experimenter. Following this, the subject is tested at regular intervals to determine how much of the memorized material he can recall. A "retention curve" may then be plotted to show how recall changes as a function of time. A line graph of the data would probably look something like Fig. 1.8.

Note that in Fig. 1.8 the dependent variable, *Percent Recalled*, is plotted on the vertical axis and the independent variable, *Time*, is plotted on the horizontal axis. This is the conventional arrangement in depicting a functional relationship. The graph shows overall that recall decreases with time and that most of the loss occurs within the first few days after learning.

Line graphs to depict changes in a dependent variable are widely used in behavioral research. Some other examples are learning curves (changes in performance as a function of trials), changes in visual acuity as a function of illumination, changes in intelligence test performance as a function of age.

Skewness of a Distribution

A distribution that is not symmetrical about its center (more observations occur on one side of the distribution than on the other) is said to be a *skewed* distribution. This lack of symmetry or skewness can be defined precisely and mathematically, but for our purposes it will be sufficient to learn to recognize the phenomenon of skewness from an inspection of the distribution. Moderate amounts of skewness (moderate departures from symmetry) are usually unimportant in research, but considerable skewness may be very informative.

For example, consider the two distributions sketched in Fig. 1.9. The ranges of scores for normals and neurotics are practically identical, but most of the normals scored at the low end of the scale and most of the neurotics scored at the high end. Both distributions are severely skewed. The distribution for normals is said to be *positively skewed* or *skewed to the right*. The distribution for neurotics is *negatively skewed* or *skewed to the left*.

Locating the center of a distribution, observing its symmetry or

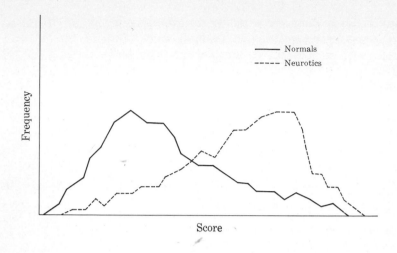

Figure 1.9

Scores Obtained by 1000 Normal Subjects and 1000 Neurotic Subjects on a Neuroticism Questionnaire

skewness, and determining its variability are the most important procedures of descriptive statistics. In the chapters immediately following, we will elaborate upon these concepts and consider additional methods for describing and interpreting the outcome of an experiment.

Practice Problems

For each of the problems below, organize the data and present it graphically (if a graph is appropriate) as you would in a formal report of the results. Describe briefly what the investigator has found in each case and comment upon any questions raised by the results or the experimental procedure.

1. An investigator is interested in the musical preferences of college students. He believes that in spite of their superior cultural opportunities and the current vogue of folk songs, most college students still prefer "popular" music over classical and folk music. To investigate his belief, he selects a random sample of 50 college students and asks them to name their five favorite songs or musical compositions. The students' lists are then classified according to whether they named predominantly popular music (P), predomi-

nantly classical music (C), or predominantly folk music (F). The results for the 50 students are as follows:

P, F, P, P, C, F, C, C, C, P, C, F, F, P, P, P, C, P, C, C, F, C, F,
F, C, C, C, P, C, F, P, F, C, C, P, P, P, C, F, C, C, C, P, P, F, P,
C, P, C, C.

2. A psychologist believes that the cognitive impairment of schizophrenics is reflected in their loss of a "sense of humor." To investigate whether schizophrenics do indeed have a lesser sense of humor than normal individuals, he prepares a series of simple cartoons which he shows to 28 normal subjects and to 21 schizophrenics. From the subjects' reactions and comments he determines whether they grasped the humorous aspects of the cartoons. The results are:

Normals: 25 saw the humor of the cartoons, 3 did not.
Schizophrenics: 10 saw the humor of the cartoons, 11 did not.

3. A researcher interested in attitudes toward TV conducts a questionnaire survey of 3000 TV owners chosen randomly from a large city. As part of the questionnaire, the subjects are asked to check one answer to the following question: "Most TV shows are _____ very good, _____ fair, _____ not good enough, _____ terrible." After the questionnaires are returned, the researcher counts the number of times each answer was checked and determines that of the 804 subjects who returned completed questionnaires, 86 checked "very good," 214 checked "fair," 320 checked "not good enough," and 184 checked "terrible."

4. On another part of the questionnaire described above, the subjects were asked to estimate the number of hours per week they spent watching TV. On the basis of their estimates, the researcher ordered the subjects from highest to lowest and divided them into three groups of equal size: Heavy Viewers (the upper third of all viewers), Average Viewers (the middle third), and Light Viewers (the lower third). He then examined how each group had answered the question given in (3) above as to their opinion of "most TV shows." He found the following:

Heavy Viewers: 28 subjects in this group checked "very good," 71 checked "fair," 107 checked "not good enough," and 62 checked "terrible."
Average Viewers: 29 subjects checked "very good," 71 checked "fair," 107 checked "not good enough," and 61 checked "terrible."
Light Viewers: 29 checked "very good," 72 checked "fair," 106 checked "not good enough," and 61 checked "terrible."

5. A football coach must choose from among his players the eleven men who will make up his first team. Considering their overall playing ability first, he puts Karsky at the top, then Jones and Marino together, then Harper, then Garvey; he feels that Fritz, Eiler, and Delancy are equally good players; then come Carlos and Brentano together, then Ashe. Assign ranks to the players.

6. The ten best trainees are desired from a group of 20 Peace Corps volunteers trained under two different instructors. The official in charge of choosing the ten trainees decides to base his selection on the performance ratings given by the two instructors. The ratings are as follows:

| | RATINGS GIVEN BY | |
TRAINEE	INSTRUCTOR 1	INSTRUCTOR 2
A	9	7
B	8	6
C	7	5
D	6	3
E	6	4
F	9	6
G	9	8
H	7	5
I	7	5
J	7	4
K	10	8
L	8	6
M	10	7
N	9	7
O	8	6
P	8	6
Q	8	5
R	10	8
S	7	5
T	6	4

7. Thirty subjects are to be divided into an Experimental group and a Control group for an experiment which will test the effect of a new drug on the learning of nonsense syllables. So that the two groups will be equal in their initial ability to learn such material, the experimenter plans to match the groups on the basis of how many trials they require to learn a preliminary list of nonsense syllables. The 30 subjects require the following number of trials to learn the preliminary list:

14, 18, 15, 12, 16, 11, 10, 15, 13, 16, 12, 12, 13, 13, 14, 10, 12, 15, 15, 16, 15, 12, 14, 15, 11, 11, 16, 17, 17, 14.

8. An investigator is interested in how well we are able to judge distance when deprived of visual cues. He chooses a subject who is good at judging small distances visually and asks him to try to draw a line exactly four inches long when blindfolded. The subject is given

50 trials and afterwards the experimenter measures the subject's 50 lines to the nearest tenth of an inch. Beginning with the first line, the lengths (in inches) are:

5.1, 5.3, 4.9, 5.4, 5.0, 5.2, 5.7, 5.6, 5.2, 5.0, 5.0, 5.1, 4.9, 5.2, 4.8, 5.5, 5.4, 5.0, 5.1, 4.9, 5.5, 5.7, 5.0, 6.2, 5.5, 5.1, 5.2, 5.1, 5.1, 4.9, 6.0, 4.8, 5.0, 4.8, 5.3, 5.3, 5.0, 5.2, 5.4, 5.2, 5.6, 5.8, 5.3, 4.9, 5.1, 4.8, 4.9, 5.0, 5.2, 5.1.

9. An experimenter has set up a discrimination problem for which he wants to measure reaction time. When the subject observes that two lights are equal in brightness, he presses a telegraph key in front of him. When one of the lights is dimmer than the other, he does not press the key. The subject is given 50 critical trials with the lights equal in brightness, interspersed with trials in which one of the lights is dimmed. On the 50 critical trials, the experimenter measures the time between the onset of the light and the subject's response to the nearest one-hundredth of a second. Beginning with the first critical trial, the subject's reaction times (in hundredths of a second) are:

49, 51, 46, 45, 48, 41, 42, 44, 39, 43, 38, 38, 45, 36, 42, 40, 37, 35, 41, 40, 39, 42, 35, 33, 36, 32, 30, 37, 30, 34, 33, 40, 29, 31, 31, 37, 35, 34, 30, 28, 28, 44, 20, 32, 31, 27, 26, 24, 27, 29.

In addition to presenting a graph of the distribution, plot a line graph showing how the subject's reaction time changes with successive critical trials.

10. A researcher has developed a new method for teaching children to read. Two first-grade teachers who are instructed in the new method agree to use it during the coming year, and their combined classes of 58 pupils become the "experimental group." Another three equally competent and successful teachers are found who are using standard methods to teach reading to children of the same general intelligence and background as are in the experimental group. The combined classes of these three teachers number 80 pupils, and constitute the "control group." At the end of the year, a reading achievement test is given to all the children. The results are:

Experimental group: 47, 52, 44, 41, 48, 50, 48, 46, 66, 53, 65, 48, 42, 73, 68, 58, 45, 51, 49, 38, 35, 72, 67, 32, 69, 45, 73, 78, 41, 56, 37, 36, 61, 75, 47, 40, 42, 66, 67, 57, 61, 64, 56, 36, 31, 65, 33, 52, 62, 71, 74, 55, 34, 72, 76, 53, 43, 62.

Control group: 61, 61, 53, 48, 59, 55, 67, 52, 50, 43, 54, 57, 38, 71, 42, 47, 51, 52, 52, 58, 63, 56, 36, 35, 54, 44, 44, 44, 53, 57, 55, 33, 64, 59, 51, 45, 52, 60, 50, 48, 47, 43, 65, 72, 63, 57, 34, 44, 39, 50, 56, 58, 43,

41, 46, 46, 49, 62, 60, 45, 47, 32, 52, 67, 37, 51, 54, 34, 42, 73, 69, 46, 57, 37, 62, 66, 61, 58, 47, 57.

11. A rat has been conditioned to press a bar which releases a pellet of food with every press. This schedule of food release is called "regular reinforcement." The experimenter records the number of responses per minute over a ten-minute interval. At the end of the tenth minute, he adjusts the apparatus so that a pellet is released only after five bar presses. This schedule of food release is called "fixed-ratio reinforcement." He continues to record the number of responses per minute over the next 20-minute interval. For each successive minute over the 30-minute total, the number of bar presses made by the rat are:

10, 11, 12, 10, 11, 9, 11, 10, 9, 12, 6, 6, 8, 14, 18, 16, 18, 18, 21, 20, 23, 24, 23, 25, 22, 28, 30, 28, 32, 30.

Answers

1. This problem is similar to Example 1. Because the investigator has predicted the outcome, the data should be organized and presented as in Table 1.1A and Fig. 1.1A—that is, with the predicted preference "popular music" first. The order of the other two categories is arbitrary. The results show that the investigator's prediction was mistaken; these students do not show a preference for popular music over classical and folk music.

This investigator has escaped the problem of a large "No Preference" category by accepting *predominance* as his criterion for showing a preference. Consistency in three out of five choices earns classification in one of the music categories, and so he was able to classify all his subjects. But he is on the other horn of the dilemma. Each of the categories includes subjects who listed that kind of music three times, together with subjects who listed it four times, and five times. For example, what if a subject listed two classical compositions, followed by three folk songs? He will be classified as showing a preference for folk music. Should he be? Is that the same as a list of five folk songs? Yet the two lists will be classified together in the same category. The result is some uncertainty about what the frequency in a given category really means. Thus, this investigator is no better off than the investigator in Example 1. They both have problems to consider in assessing their results.

Another problem for this investigator to consider is whether the students reported their preferences truthfully. Unlike the investigator of Example 1, who measured choices directly, this investigator measured the subjects' *reports* of their preferences. Some students may have been trying to impress the investigator by listing high-flown classical music instead of the popular songs they really prefer. Anonymous listings, and a generally informal and accepting atmosphere, may help to reduce the risk of subjects "faking" responses, but the risk cannot be totally eliminated.

2. This problem is similar to Example 2, and the data should be organized and presented as in Table 1.2 and Fig. 1.2, *except* that the frequencies should be converted to proportions or percentages for the graph, and the vertical axis labelled accordingly. (The procedure for converting frequencies to proportions is given in Step 2 of Example 7. For the present problem, n_1 and n_2 are, respectively, the number of normals and the number of schizophrenics.) The results support the investigator's belief insofar as these particular subjects are concerned, *if* the normals and schizophrenics were matched on variables which may affect one's sense of humor—such as cultural background, intelligence (the cartoons may not be "simple" for everyone), and present situation (being hospitalized, for instance).

3. These are *ordinal* categories. That is, the categories themselves are ordered along a continuum from "best" to "worst." This order should be maintained in the presentation of the data, regardless of which categories have the highest frequencies. In other respects, the results should be presented as in Table 1.1A and Fig. 1.1A. The results show that the majority of these subjects have negative attitudes toward "most TV shows." But no conclusions at all about the attitudes of TV owners in general can be drawn from the results. Questionnaires were sent to a random sample of 3000 TV owners and only 804 completed and returned them. Subjects who take the trouble to complete and return a questionnaire no longer constitute a "random sample of TV owners." They are, rather, a sample of subjects-who-fill-out-and-return-questionnaires. It may even be that negative attitudes predominate in the sample because it is chiefly disgruntled TV owners who are sufficiently aroused to fill out and return such questionnaires. The 2196 unknown opinions of those who failed to return the questionnaire could be distributed very differently (a large majority in positive categories, for example), and therefore could change the results completely.

4. The results should be presented as in Table 1.2, except that there will be three categories across the top (Viewers) and four categories listed in the column (Attitudes), or vice versa. The graph should appear as in Fig. 1.2, with Attitudes along the horizontal axis and three distinct bars used to represent the three different categories of Viewers. Both sets of categories are ordinal, so the order

from "most" to "least" should be preserved for both variables in the table and in the graph. The results show that the number of subjects who find most TV shows "very good" is just about the same among Heavy Viewers, Average Viewers, and Light Viewers. Similarly, the number of subjects who find most TV shows "terrible" is just about the same among the three different types of viewers. And this is also true for the attitudes in between. The subjects' attitudes toward TV apparently have nothing to do with how much time they spend watching TV. (As it is put by statisticians, attitude toward TV is not *related* to time spent watching TV, or time spent watching TV is *independent* of attitude toward TV.) These results are meaningful even though the subjects are not a random sample of TV owners. They *are* TV owners who watch TV relatively a great deal, a medium amount, or a little, and the sample may be redefined as three groups of viewers for whom the variable "filling-out-and-returning-questionnaires" is a constant. It is as though the investigator had controlled for this variable by matching his groups on it before the experiment. "Then" he asked them to check their attitudes toward most TV shows.

5. The correct ranks are 1, 2.5, 2.5, 4, 5, 7, 7, 7, 9.5, 9.5, 11, as determined by the procedure given in Example 3. No graph is necessary.

6. Ranks should be substituted for the ratings, as in Example 4. The ranks for Instructor 1's ratings, with the trainees in the order K, M, R, A, F, G, N, B, L, O, P, Q, C, H, I, J, S, D, E, T, are: 2, 2, 2, 5.5, 5.5, 5.5, 5.5, 10, 10, 10, 10, 10, 15, 15, 15, 15, 15, 19, 19, 19. For Instructor 2's ratings of the trainees *in the same order as above*, the ranks are: 2, 5, 2, 5, 9, 2, 5, 9, 9, 9, 9, 14, 14, 14, 14, 18, 14, 20, 18, 18. The ranks are in fairly good agreement. The ten trainees chosen include the six ranked at the top by both instructors (trainees K, M, R, A, G, N), and trainee F because he is ranked at the top by Instructor 1 and is among those ranked next by Instructor 2. The remaining three places are filled by drawing lots (or by some such chance procedure) among trainees B, L, O, and P, since these four were ranked next by both instructors. (Trainee Q is included in this group by Instructor 1, but is given a lower rank by Instructor 2, so Q would be omitted from the drawing.)

7. There are only nine classes altogether, so the data should be grouped into individual classes, as in Table 1.5, and presented graphically, as in Fig. 1.3 or Fig. 1.4. The graph is bimodal, identifying two groups of subjects: one group which "typically" required 12 trials to learn the list, and another group which "typically" required 15 trials. Apparently, some subjects find this task easier than others, since they memorize more quickly. To obtain Exper-

imental and Control groups matched in initial ability, the experimenter will assign half of the fast learners (10 to 13 trials) and half of the slow learners (14 to 18 trials) to the Experimental group, leaving similar halves for the Control group.

8. There are only 15 classes, so the data should be grouped into individual classes, as in Table 1.5, and presented graphically, as in Fig. 1.3 or Fig. 1.4. The mode is at 5.0–5.1 inches, at least an inch longer than the line the subject was trying to draw. (Try it, if you think you can do better!) The graph shows that the data are *skewed*— some of the observations trail out into a "tail" on one side of the graph but not on the other side—indicating that some responses were relatively far away from the mode. Again, this makes the mode less "typical" than it would be if all the observations were clustered around it. Since the observations in the tail of the graph are greater than the mode, the skewness is said to be *positive*. A few of the subject's lines were considerably longer than his "typical" line. Scanning the original data reveals that these longer lines occurred at various points in the beginning, middle, and end of the experiment. There is no obvious change in the subject's performance over time.

9. There are 32 classes but fewer than 100 observations, so the data should be organized into class intervals of five classes each and presented as in Table 1.6. A histogram as in Fig. 1.5 may be used, or a frequency polygon like one of those in Fig. 1.6. The graph is fairly symmetrical and reveals nothing unusual. Scanning the original data, however, reveals something not apparent from the frequency distribution. With few exceptions, the subject's reaction time became steadily less with successive trials. There seems to be a strong practice effect in this situation. This circumstance is apparent in the line graph, where the subject's reaction time (vertical axis) is plotted for each successive critical trial (horizontal axis). The line graph shows the subject's gradually lessening reaction time.

10. The data should be organized and presented as in Table 1.7 and Fig. 1.6. On the graph, the curve for the Experimental group is bimodal and shows greater variability than is evident in the Control group. The major mode (highest peak) of the Experimental group curve is somewhat below the mode for the Control group. This, and the way the curves overlap at the low end of the scale, indicate that many pupils taught by the new method performed less well than pupils taught by the standard method. On the other hand, the second mode of the Experimental group is considerably higher than the Control group's mode, indicating that *some* pupils taught by the new method did much better than pupils of the control group.

To arrive at a conclusion, the experimenter will have to determine whether the overall difference between the two groups is a reliable one. That is, is the difference sufficiently large, all things considered, to suggest that in repeated experiments of this kind one of the two groups will consistently perform better than the other? Only in this case can the experimenter conclude that one of the teaching methods is superior to the other. Otherwise, the difference observed in this experiment could reasonably be attributed to accidental inequities between the two groups—either in the individuals involved or in the experimental situations. A way of evaluating the difference between the performance of two groups is given in Chapter 10.

11. This problem is like Example 8, and the data should be organized and presented as in Table 1.8 and Fig. 1.7. The total number of responses (last entry in the cumulative column) is 515. The graph shows how the animal's behavior changed as the conditions of the experiment were changed. During the first ten minutes of regular reinforcement, the rate of responding was fairly steady (the curve is almost a straight line). When the experimenter changed the schedule of food release to fixed-ratio reinforcement, the response rate dropped briefly, shown by the bending over of the curve at this point. Then the response rate gradually increased, continuing to increase (the slope of the curve becomes steeper and steeper) throughout the remainder of the experiment. The rate of responding is much higher (the curve is steeper) at the end of the experiment than at the beginning, and the change in response rate is associated with the change in schedule of reinforcement. The experimenter may conclude that under these conditions, fixed-ratio reinforcement has the effect of increasing the animal's rate of responding.

chapter 2

The Median and Percentiles

Percentiles—or *centiles*, as they are often called—divide the range of a distribution into 100 parts such that 1% of the observations are included in each of the parts. Thus, the first centile of a distribution is the point on the scale of measure below which 1% of the observations fall. The second centile is the point on the scale below which 2% of the observations fall. The 30th centile is the point below which 30% of the observations fall. And the 100th centile is the point just above all the observations in the distribution—the upper exact limit of the highest class.

The best known and most widely used centile is the *median*. The median of a distribution is the 50th centile, the point on the scale of measure below which 50% of the observations fall. Hence, the median is the point that divides the distribution in half. The median is often taken as the representative value of a distribution, and is an acceptable representative of the data in many situations where the mode is not.

When the observations are a distribution of scores, there are occasions when it is useful to report the *centile ranks* of selected scores. "Rank" is a familiar term by now. The rank of an individual tells how many individuals are included at and below his position in the group; the centile rank tells the *percentage* included at and below his position. Thus if a score has a centile rank of 40, this means that 40% of the observations in the distribution are at and below that score. The score itself is the 40th centile.

The median and other centiles are computed most precisely from ungrouped data, that is, data that have not been grouped into class intervals. Sometimes this degree of precision is desirable in determining the median, but it is rarely necessary for other centiles. The examples which follow, therefore, illustrate how the median is found from ungrouped data, and how to find other centiles and centile ranks from data that have been grouped into class intervals.

THE MEDIAN

The Median As the
Representative Value

Example 1.   An experimenter interested in group behavior sets up a discussion group of seven subjects, all of whom are familiar with the problem to be discussed although they have not met before. During the discussion, the experimenter records the number of spontaneous questions and comments made by each subject. He would like to determine what is the typical number of such expressions made by subjects under these conditions. For the seven subjects, the number of spontaneous expressions, ordered from lowest to highest, are:

2, 2, 4, 6, 8, 11, 20

The distribution has a mode, 2, the only observation that occurs more than once; but 2 is obviously untypical of the group. For skewed data like these, where there are one or several extreme values—such as the 20 of this distribution—the median is often the best score with which to represent the group. We proceed, therefore, to find the median of the distribution.

• • STEP 1. When an odd number of observations are ordered from lowest to highest (or vice versa), the median has the value of the observation at the exact middle of the distribution, provided there is no other observation with this value. There are seven observations in this case, an odd number, and they are already ordered from lowest to highest. The observation at the middle of the array is 6, and since there is no other observation with this value, 6 is the median of these observations.

• RESULTS AND DISCUSSION

The representative number of spontaneous expressions among these subjects, as indicated by the median, is 6. This does not tell us very much. When the median of data is reported, the range is usually given also—and the combination of the two tells much more. Thus, the experimenter will report that the median number of spontaneous expressions is 6 and that the range extends from 2 to 20.

The fact that the median 6 is so much closer to one end of the range (2) than it is to the other end (20) indicates that the distribution is positively skewed. One, perhaps two, individuals initiated a lot more conversation than all the others. The skewness may be due to the particular subjects used—one was an especially aggressive fellow—or it may be that skewness is a stable characteristic of the results of such experiments. That is, it may turn out that when the experiment has been repeated many times with different subjects, the results are skewed every time. This could be of great interest. If the results were always positively skewed, there would be reason to think that perhaps this situation provided conditions for the emergence of dominance or leadership, since some one or two persons seem always to initiate much more conversation than do the others in the group.

The Median As a
Dividing Point

Example 2. An experimenter planning a stress experiment wishes to study the differential effects of stress on subjects who have relatively good and relatively poor muscular control. He measures the muscular control of 20 subjects by means of a steadiness test in which the subject is required to hold a stylus in a small hole for one minute without letting the stylus touch the metal sides of the hole. Each movement of the stylus which touches the metal side is recorded as an error. The experimenter wishes to divide the subjects into high and low steadiness groups on the basis of their performance on this test.

Example 2.1. The 20 subjects make the following errors: 8, 4, 11, 6, 6, 8, 9, 5, 5, 4, 7, 14, 19, 7, 7, 10, 8, 9, 7, 11

To determine "high" and "low" groups of subjects, distributions are frequently divided in half at the median. The division is referred to as a *median split*.

• • STEP 1. To find the median, begin by ordering the observations from lowest to highest (or vice versa). When there are not many observations, it may be easy simply to find the lowest one, count how many there are like it, and write down that amount. Thus, the lowest number of errors made was 4; there are two 4's, so two are written down in succession. Next come two 5's, then two 6's, four 7's, etc., as shown below:

4, 4, 5, 5, 6, 6, 7, 7, 7, 7, | 8, 8, 8, 9, 9, 10, 11, 11, 14, 19

Count them afterwards to be sure all have been written down. If you tend to make mistakes doing this, or if there are many observations, tally the observations as below:

Errors	Tally	f
4	//	2
5	//	2
6	//	2
7	////	4
8	///	3
9	//	2
10	/	1
11	//	2
14	/	1
19	/	1

• • STEP 2. There are 20 observations, an even number; therefore there is no "middle" score or value. The median in this case is the point halfway between the two middle observations. For 20 subjects, this will be the point between the 10th and 11th observations. Counting across the array of error scores until ten observations have been included, or counting down to the same point in the f column of the frequency distribution, the 10th and 11th observations are found to be 7 and 8. The median is the point halfway between them, so the median is 7.5. (If the 10th and 11th observations had been 7 and 9, the median would be 8 because 8 is the point halfway between 7 and 9.)

• RESULTS

The subjects will be divided at the median, 7.5, and the high and low steadiness groups will be made up of the ten subjects who made from 4 to 7 errors (High Steadiness) and the ten subjects who made from 8 to 19 errors (Low Steadiness).

Example 2.2. Suppose the results of the steadiness test had been as follows:

4, 4, 5, 5, 6, 6, 7, 7, 7, 8, | 8, 8, 8, 9, 9, 10, 11, 11, 14, 19

Now if we count across the array and collect ten observations, one of the 8's is included. How will the experimenter divide his subjects into two equal groups? He cannot sensibly put one of the four subjects who made 8 errors into one group and the other three subjects into a different group. When the median falls between two observations that have the same value, the median is somewhere within the exact limits of the class which includes this value. Since the observation 8 is included in the class 7.5–8.5, the median is somewhere between 7.5 and 8.5. The exact point is located in three steps.

First, determine how many of the observations having the same value are needed to reach the midpoint of the distribution. In this case, one of the 8's is needed to reach the midpoint of the distribution, so 1 is our number.

Second, divide this number by the total number of observations having the given value. Since there are four 8's, this gives $1 \div 4 = .25$.

Third, add this proportion to the lower exact limit of the class to get the median. The median is $7.5 + .25 = 7.75$. A median split of the subjects will result in a High Steadiness group of nine subjects (who made seven or fewer errors) and a Low Steadiness group of 11 subjects (who made eight or more errors). The groups are no longer equal in size, but a split at the median will always yield the most equal division possible.

Example 2.3. Suppose these were the results of the steadiness test:

4, 4, 5, 5, 6, 6, 6, 8, 8, 8, | 8, 8, 8, 9, 9, 10, 11, 11, 14, 19

The median is exactly 8, but how shall the experimenter divide his subjects into two groups? It is not sensible to put all of the 8's into either the low or the high group. He may omit the entire median group (all those who made eight errors), and settle for a Low Steadiness group composed of the seven subjects who made fewer than eight errors and a High Steadiness group of the seven subjects who made more than eight errors. Or, he may prolong his one-minute steadiness test to see if finer discriminations can be made over time; that is, to see if fewer subjects will get the same score when the stylus must be held for longer than one minute. Or, he may go out and get more subjects so that the extreme groups in the distribution will become larger. But since one-third of the present subjects fall at the median, the experimenter should not be surprised if about one-third of the new subjects he tests will also fall at the median. He may have to test a lot of people to find the additional "high" and "low" subjects he needs!

CENTILES AND CENTILE RANKS FROM GROUPED DATA

There are two ways of determining the centiles and centile ranks of data grouped into class intervals. When many centiles or centile ranks are desired, the easiest method is to construct a cumulative percentage graph and read the desired centiles or centile ranks directly from the graph. This method is illustrated in Example 3 below. If the graph is constructed carefully, this method will be accurate enough for most purposes. If only the median or some two or three centiles are desired, or if greater accuracy is necessary, the desired centiles or centile ranks should be computed directly from the frequency distribution. This method is outlined in Example 4.

Cumulative Percentage Graph

Example 3. A vocational interest inventory includes a scale designed to measure interest in a career as a musician. The test constructor wishes to establish "norms" for the scale so that users of the test will have a standard against which they may compare any individual score. To do this, he will collect the scores of large groups of subjects and publish the scores with their centile ranks. A user of the test will then be able to determine the rank of any individual score he obtains among the group provided as a standard. The test constructor begins by giving his test to a representative sample of 224 high school students. He makes a frequency distribution of the scores they obtain on the Musical Career scale, as shown in the first two columns of Table 2.1. The centile ranks will be determined from a cumulative percentage graph of the frequency distribution.

• • STEP 1. To construct a cumulative percentage graph, three columns must be added to the table of the frequency distribution. First, convert the frequencies to percentages by means of the formula: $(f/n) \times 100$. That is, divide each entry in the frequency column by n and multiply the result by 100. (Alternatively, determine the value of $1/n$ and multiply each frequency by this number.) Round off the answer to one decimal place and enter it in a separate "Percentage" column, as shown in Table 2.1. Sum the percentages afterwards to be sure they add up to 100.0—plus or minus .1, since rounding the percentages to one decimal place may result in a total which is not exactly 100. If the total does not fall between 99.9 and 100.1, an error has been made in computing the percentages. (Try to compute them carefully the first time!)

• • STEP 2. Cumulate the percentages and enter them in a Cumulative Percentage column. Begin at the bottom of the column with the percentage for the lowest class interval and cumulate *upward* to the highest class interval, adding each successive percentage to the sum of those below it. Thus, as shown in Table 2.1, .9 + 2.2 = 3.1. Above this, 3.1 + 4.5 = 7.6; and so on. The last entry, at the top of the column, should be equal to the sum of the Percentage column. If it does not equal that total, a mistake has been made in cumulating.

• • STEP 3. Determine the *upper exact limit* of each class interval. For the class interval 5–9, this is 9.5. For the interval 10–14, the upper exact limit is 14.5. Enter the upper exact limits of each class interval in a column, as in Table 2.1.

Table 2.1
Distribution of Musical Career Interest Scores
Obtained by 224 High School Students

Scores	f	Percentage	Cumulative Percentage	Upper Exact Limits
75–79	3	1.3	100.0	79.5
70–74	7	3.1	98.7	74.5
65–69	15	6.7	95.6	69.5
60–64	24	10.7	88.9	64.5
55–59	18	8.0	78.2	59.5
50–54	14	6.3	70.2	54.5
45–49	14	6.3	63.9	49.5
40–44	22	9.8	57.6	44.5
35–39	33	14.7	47.8	39.5
30–34	25	11.2	33.1	34.5
25–29	20	8.9	21.9	29.5
20–24	12	5.4	13.0	24.5
15–19	10	4.5	7.6	19.5
10–14	5	2.2	3.1	14.5
5–9	2	.9	.9	9.5
	$n = 224$	100.0		

•• STEP 4. To construct the cumulative percentage graph, use the column of Upper Exact Limits and the column of Cumulative Percentages. Lay out scores along the horizontal axis and cumulative percentages along the vertical axis of the graph, as in Fig. 2.1. Plot a point for each upper exact limit of score opposite its cumu-

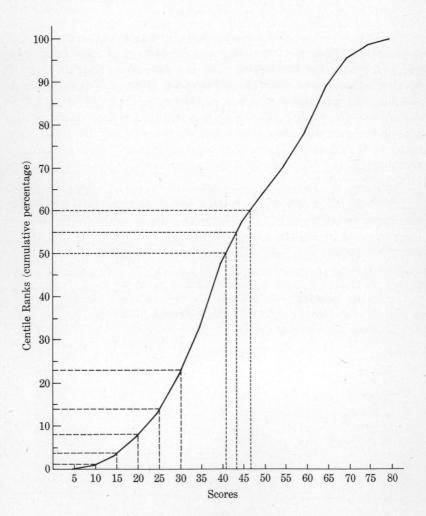

Figure 2.1

Centile Ranks of Musical Career Interest Scores Obtained by 224 High School Students

lative percentage. Also plot a point on the baseline, at the upper exact limits of the class interval *below* the lowest one in the distribution. For this distribution, the point on the baseline is at 4.5, the upper exact limit of the interval 0–4 which is just below 5–9. Connect all the points with straight lines.

• • STEP 5. The centile ranks may be read directly from the vertical axis of the cumulative percentage graph. The dashed lines that appear on Fig. 2.1 illustrate the procedure. Thus, the score 10 intersects the curve at a point opposite a centile rank of 1 on the vertical axis. Therefore, 1 is the centile rank of the score 10. The score 15 intersects the curve at a point opposite a centile rank of about 4. Since the nearest whole number is accurate enough for our purposes, we say the centile rank of the score 15 is 4. It is not, of course, necessary actually to draw the dashed lines. Simply lay a ruler parallel with the baseline of the graph and move it up for each desired score, reading the centile ranks on the vertical axis as you go. Centile ranks for every fifth score from 10 through 75 are shown in Table 2.2.

Another procedure is to decide ahead of time the centile ranks that are desired, and then find on the horizontal axis of the graph

Table 2.2 Musical Career Interest Scores: Norms for High School Students (n = 224)		Table 2.3 Musical Career Interest Scores: Norms for High School Students (n = 224)	
SCORE	CENTILE RANK	SCORE	CENTILE RANK
75	99	69	95
70	96	65	90
65	90	63	85
60	80	60	80
55	71	58	75
50	65	54	70
45	58	50	65
40	49	47	60
35	35	43	55
30	23	41	50
25	14	39	45
20	8	37	40
15	4	35	35
10	1	33	30
		31	25
		28	20
		26	15
		22	10
		17	5

which scores have these centile ranks. This was done for Table 2.3, which gives the scores having every fifth centile rank from 5 through 95. The procedure is illustrated by the dotted lines on Fig. 2.1. Thus, to find the score which has a centile rank of 50 (the median of the distribution), locate 50 on the vertical axis. The centile rank 50 intersects the curve at a point opposite the score 41; the score 41 therefore has a centile rank of 50 (and 41 is the median). Another way of expressing the same thing is to say that 41 is the 50th centile. Also from the graph, the 55th centile is the score 43, or, the score 43 has a centile rank of 55. The 60th centile is 47, or, the score 47 has a centile rank of 60. "Centiles" are scores and are read from the horizontal axis of the graph; "centile ranks" are cumulative percentages and are read from the vertical axis.

• RESULTS

The test constructor will publish a list of centiles or centile ranks, such as in Table 2.2 or Table 2.3, with a description of the standardization group whose scores furnished the basis for the list. A standardization group is a sample of subjects (usually much larger than our 224) who are like the subjects for whom the test is intended, and hence may be said to represent such subjects in general. The list of centile ranks derived from their scores constitutes *norms* for the test, a standard of comparison for the individual test user.

For example, let us suppose a test user gives the test to three high school boys—Jim, David, and Arthur—who play in the school band. Jim receives a score of 43. On Table 2.3, we find that a score of 43 has a centile rank of 55. This means that Jim's score of 43 surpasses the scores of 55% of the subjects in the standardization group. Jim may be a fine musician, but his interest in a musical career, as measured by this test, is no greater than the interest of about half of high school students in general. David received a score of 70. From Table 2.2, a score of 70 has a centile rank of 96. David's score surpasses 96% of the scores in the standardization group. His interest in a musical career is relatively very high, higher than that of most high school students. If he is also a fine musician, we might be willing to bet he could be successful in a musical career. Arthur's score is 31, and from Table 2.3 we find that his score surpasses only 25% of the scores in the standardization group. Some three-quarters of high school students in general are more interested in a musical career than Arthur is. We may wonder what he's doing in the school band at all. Perhaps it was his mother's idea!

• DISCUSSION

Note that centile ranks have all the properties of other ranks. Like any set of ranks, they represent the relative position of an individual (or score) within the particular group ranked. If we were to add to the standardization group 100 subjects with scores below 31, Arthur's score of 31 would have a centile rank of 48 instead of 25, since 31 would now surpass 48% of the scores. All the centile ranks of scores above 31 would also be higher.

The test constructor mitigates this slippery situation by deriving his norms from a large sample of subjects who represent as nearly as possible the total group of subjects, or *population*, as it is called, for whom the test is intended. Thus, if the test is intended for high school students, the test constructor will seek for his norms a sample of high school students as representative as possible of the population of high school students, *i.e.*, of all high school students. If he has managed to select such a representative sample for his norms, then the centile ranks of the scores will not be very different from what they would be for the whole population of such subjects. When the sample is truly representative, then the norms are representative also, and a given centile rank may be referred to the population represented, *e.g.*, all high school students, or high school students "in general." If the centile ranks are not derived from a representative sample of subjects from some clearly identifiable population, the centile ranks will still show the relative position of the subjects in that group, but they will not be useful as norms. That is, the centile ranks cannot be used as a standard of comparison because the "standard" cannot be identified in such a case.

Note another property of ranks which is also true for centile ranks. The "distances" between ranks are not necessarily equal. Look at Table 2.3. The score distance between the centile ranks 5 and 10 is $22 - 17 = 5$ units of score. The scoring distance between the centile ranks 35 and 40 is $37 - 35 = 2$ units of score. Sometimes an increase of five centile ranks means an increase of 5 in score and other times an increase in five centile ranks means an increase of only 2 in score. The "times" when the distances between ranks change is evident in Fig. 2.1. When the slope of the curve is steep, centile ranks are increasing faster than scores are; hence many centile ranks cover relatively few scores. When the slope is low, as at the beginning of the curve or where it bends over at the top, scores are increasing faster than centile ranks; hence many scores are covered by relatively few centile ranks.

Computation of Centiles
from Grouped Data

Example 4.   A test of English Usage has been given to all the entering freshmen at Ergo College. The chairman of the English Department has decided that those who score in the upper 25% of the group will be assigned to advanced sections of the English I course, the middle 50% to regular sections, and the lower 25% to slower sections in which additional work will be given. A frequency distribution of the scores is constructed (Table 2.4). The chairman needs to determine only two centiles: the 25th centile, which will separate the lower 25% of the group; and the 75th centile, which will separate the upper 25%. The freshmen who received scores between these two points will automatically constitute the middle 50% of the group.

It would be possible, of course, to draw a cumulative percentage graph and locate the 25th and 75th centiles on it, but it is hardly worth the trouble for only two centiles. Instead, these two scores will be located by another method. We will begin by locating the 25th centile of the distribution.

• • STEP 1. To locate the 25th centile, the first step is to determine how many subjects constitute the lower 25% of the group. Since there are 192 freshmen in all ($n = 192$), 25% of them is $.25 \times 192 = 48$ freshmen. We wish, then, the score which separates the lowest-scoring 48 freshmen from the rest of the group.

• • STEP 2. Turning to the frequency distribution of the scores, begin at the bottom of the frequency column and cumulate upward until you reach a frequency which, if added to the sum you already have, would give more than the desired number of subjects (more than 48, in this case). This frequency which would add too much identifies the class interval in which the desired centile falls, and the interval may immediately be marked as such. Thus, in Table 2.4, cumulating from the bottom of the f column, the sum of the first four frequencies is 37. If the next frequency, 19, is added, the sum will be 56 and we wish only 48 subjects. The frequency 19 then identifies the class interval 62–64 as containing the 25th centile, and it is marked as such in Table 2.4. A line is drawn across the frequency distribution below 19, and is labelled to represent the *lower exact limit* of the class interval which contains the desired centile. The lower exact limit of the interval 62–64 is 61.5, so the line is labelled 61.5.

• • STEP 3. Write down the sum of the frequencies below the line which has been drawn and determine how many more are needed to reach the desired total. In Table 2.4, 37 frequencies are included up to the line drawn, and since 48 is the desired total, 11 more are needed (48 − 37 = 11). We wish, then, 11 of the 19 frequencies that fall in the class interval 62–64.

• • STEP 4. In computing centiles from a frequency distribution, it is assumed that the frequencies are evenly divided over the class intervals into which they fall. Thus, it is assumed that the 19 frequencies in the interval 62–64 are evenly spread out over the distance 61.5 to 64.5 (the exact limits of the interval). Since we want 11 of the 19 frequencies, we want to traverse 11/19 of the distance 61.5–64.5. Since the total distance is 3 units of score (64.5 − 61.5 = 3, the size of the class interval), we want 11/19 of 3. This gives us 11/19 × 3 = 1.7 units of score. This is the point within the interval where the 25th centile lies.

• • STEP 5. The 25th centile has been found to lie 1.7 score units above the lower exact limit of the class interval 62–64. This lower exact limit is 61.5; therefore the 25th centile is 61.5 + 1.7 = 63.2.

Table 2.4
Distribution of English Usage Scores Obtained by Entering Freshmen at Ergo College ($n = 192$)

	SCORES	f	
	83–85	4	
	80–82	10	
	77–79	18	
CONTAINS 75TH CENTILE	74–76	22	
73.5			
	71–73	26	138, NEED 6 MORE
	68–70	32	
	65–67	24	
CONTAINS 25TH CENTILE	62–64	19	
61.5			
	59–61	10	37, NEED 11 MORE
	56–58	12	
	53–55	9	
	50–52	6	
		$n = 192$	

Formulas for Finding
Centiles and Centile Ranks

The five steps outlined above may be summarized by the formula:

$$C_{25} = L + \frac{i\,(.25n - f_b)}{f_i} \qquad (2.1)$$

where C_{25} is the 25th centile, and n is the total number of subjects; L is the lower exact limit of the class interval found to contain the 25th centile;
i is the size of the class interval;
f_b is the sum of the frequencies below L;
f_i is the frequency for the interval which contains the 25th centile.

Thus, for the distribution given in Table 2.4,

$$C_{25} = 61.5 + \frac{3\,[.25\,(192) - 37]}{19} = 61.5 + 1.7 = 63.2$$

The formula may be used to find any desired centile by substituting for .25 the desired proportion of subjects. For example, using the formula to find the 75th centile of the distribution in Table 2.4, we first find $.75n$. Thus, $1.75 \times 192 = 144$. Cumulating upward from the bottom of the frequency column, we find that the interval 74–76 contains the 75th centile. Substituting in the formula, we have

$$C_{75} = 73.5 + \frac{3\,(144 - 138)}{22} = 73.5 + .8 = 74.3$$

The reverse procedure, finding the centile rank of a given score, may be accomplished by the formula

$$CR = \frac{100}{n}\left[\frac{f_i\,(X - L)}{i} + f_b\right] \qquad (2.2)$$

where X is the score, L is the lower exact limit of the class interval that includes the given score, and CR is its centile rank. For example, if we wished to know the centile rank of a student who obtained a score of 56 on the English Usage test, we would find

$$CR = \frac{100}{192}\left[\frac{12\,(56 - 55.5)}{3} + 15\right] = 8.86$$

A score of 56 has a centile rank of 8.86, indicating that this score surpasses about nine per cent of the scores in the distribution.

• Results

The 25th centile is 63.2. This means that 25% of the freshmen obtained scores below 63.2 on the English Usage test. There are, of course, no scores of 63.2. The chairman will assign students with scores of 63 and below to the slower sections of the English I course. The 75th centile is 74.3. Freshmen receiving scores above this point, which means scores of 75 and higher, will be assigned to advanced sections of the course. And the "middle 50%," students with scores ranging from 64 to 74, inclusive, will attend regular sections of English I.

• Discussion

We saw how the computation of centiles from a frequency distribution assumes that the frequencies in each class interval are evenly divided over the interval. What if this assumption isn't true? What does that mean for centiles computed from the frequency distribution? For the centiles that have been computed, it may mean that the "lower 25%" of the group does not contain exactly 48 students at all. The same is true, of course, for the "upper 25%"—there may be more, or less, than 48 freshmen in it. The discrepancy can sometimes be corrected by determining the centiles from the ungrouped scores ordered into an array from lowest to highest, as in Example 2. But this will not always work either. Whenever several or many subjects have the same score, it is often not possible to separate out some predetermined number, like 48, who will all have scores below a given point. In such a case, the centiles tell us what the best possible dividing points are—the division that will yield a group closest in size to the desired one. For example, there may be only 45 freshmen with scores below 64, and 11 with scores at 64. Therefore, the "lower 25%" of the group will include only 45 students, but this is closer to the desired number 48 than is the 56 we would get by including the 11 students with scores at 64.

The 25th and 75th centiles that we have computed define what is called the *interquartile range* of the distribution. The 25th centile is the first quartile, Q_1, and the 75th centile is the third quartile, or Q_3. (The second quartile is the median.) The interquartile range, then, is $Q_3 - Q_1$. For this distribution, the interquartile range is $74.3 - 63.2 = 11.1$. The interquartile range, as we have seen, includes the middle 50% of the distribution. In this example, it tells us that the middle 50% of the scores extend from 63.2 to 74.3, or over about 11 units of score. The interquartile range is thus an index of the variability of the middle 50% of the observations in a distribution. With an interquartile range of 11 scoring units, and a range for the entire distribution of about 35 scoring units, we can conclude that the middle 50% of our scorers are a fairly homogeneous group.

The interquartile range and the *semi-interquartile range*, which is half of the interquartile range or $(Q_3 - Q_1)/2$, are often recommended as preferred alternatives to the range in indicating the variability of a distribution. The range is radically affected by one very high or very low score, while many scores are required to produce a sizeable change in the interquartile range. Hence, the interquartile range is said to be a more *stable* measure of variability than is the range. However, the two measures provide quite different kinds of information and one cannot really substitute for the other. Which is used will depend largely upon the investigator's purpose.

Practice Problems

1. In a class investigation of differences between the sexes, each student keeps track of the number of hours spent in study during one week. At the end of the week, every student turns in to the instructor a slip of paper giving his sex and the number of hours he spent in study during that week.

For the fifteen boys in the class, the number of hours reported are:

10, 8, 5, 12, 18, 16, 10, 7, 9, 13, 11, 2, 5, 10, 11

For the fourteen girls in the class, the hours reported are:

8, 14, 8, 10, 9, 12, 9, 9, 16, 11, 12, 15, 8, 10

Give the median and the range for each of the distributions. Comment upon the results and upon any questions relating to the procedure which occur to you.

For Nos. 2, 3, and 4 below, divide the subjects into high and low groups by means of a median split. (Tell in each case what the median is.)

2. On a neuroticism test, twelve new Army recruits receive the following scores:

48, 37, 42, 29, 40, 28, 35, 43, 21, 34, 55, 48

3. Sixteen nursery school children are ranked for the amount of dependency shown during their first day at nursery school. The ranks are:

1, 2, 3.5, 3.5, 5, 6, 7, 8.5, 8.5, 10, 13, 13, 13, 13, 16

4. A psychologist is curious about memory differences among people. He decides to study individual differences in the ability to recall verbal material. Thirty subjects memorize the same list of words, and three days later they are asked to recall as many words as they can from the list. The number of words correctly recalled by the 30 subjects is:

18, 14, 16, 9, 20, 15, 17, 7, 10, 16, 13, 14, 22, 12, 12, 11, 13, 16, 8, 14, 10, 11, 15, 17, 14, 13, 15, 18, 17, 16

5. Hupnick and Alzeo are competing for a prize in marksmanship. Each fires in turn 50 shots at a round target which has a small bulls-eye at the center. The distance of each shot from the bulls-eye is measured to the nearest centimeter. The results for the two men are:

CM FROM BULLS-EYE	ALZEO f	HUPNICK f
8	1	2
7	0	2
6	2	4
5	3	4
4	4	5
3	7	7
2	16	10
1	12	8
0	5	8
	$n_1 = 50$	$n_2 = 50$

Who should get the prize? Use the median as a criterion.

6. A test of mathematical reasoning is given to 158 applicants to an engineering school. The applicants' scores are tabulated into a frequency distribution, as shown below:

SCORES	f
70–74	5
65–69	3
60–64	12
55–59	17
50–54	21
45–49	28
40–44	25
35–39	20
30–34	15
25–29	8
20–24	4
	$n = 158$

Make a cumulative percentage graph of the distribution.
(a) Prepare a table showing the centile ranks for every fourth

score in the distribution beginning with a score of 24. (b) Prepare a table showing the scores which are at each tenth centile from 10 through 90. (c) Compute the median directly from the frequency distribution, and compare it with the median as found from the cumulative percentage graph.

7. An attitude test which measures prejudice towards minority groups is given to 132 department store sales clerks. Their scores are tabulated into a frequency distribution, as shown below:

Scores	f
50–5 !	2
45–49	8
40–44	12
35–39	10
30–34	9
25–29	17
20–24	22
15–19	19
10–14	12
5–9	11
0–4	10

$n = 132$

(a) The salesclerks are to be divided into four groups on the basis of their prejudice scores. The lowest quarter of the distribution (those who have the least prejudice on the test) will be assigned to work on the main floor, the second quarter to other busy departments, the third quarter to less busy departments, and clerks who scored in the top quarter of the group will be transferred to the mailroom. What scores divide the subjects into these groups? (b) Compare the range and the interquartile range of the distribution.

Answers

1. The median for both boys and girls is 10. The range for the boys is from 2 to 18; for the girls, 8 to 16. The boys' distribution is not noticeably skewed. The median is at the middle of the range and coincides with the mode, which is also 10. The girls' distribution is markedly skewed, with the median very near the low end of the range. The girls' mode is below their median, at 8 and 9. What of the large difference in the extent of the ranges? There is more variability among the boys, who report from two to 18 hours of study. The girls are a more homogeneous group, reporting only from eight to 16 hours of study. What are some reasons which might account for this difference in variability? Regarding the procedure: Do you

think all the students were telling the truth? Could some be trying to impress the instructor? (There isn't a single 0!) Might some students be influenced by a desire to see their sex come out better (or worse) than the opposite sex?

2. The median is 38.5. The high neuroticism group will include recruits with scores of 40 and higher; the low group, recruits with scores of 37 and below.

3. The median is 8.5. Two children are at the median. The best procedure would be to omit them from the study altogether, and make up high and low groups, respectively, of the children with ranks of 10 and above, and 7 and below.

4. The median is 14.25. All the subjects who recalled 14 words should be assigned to the low group (which includes a total of sixteen subjects). The fourteen subjects who recalled 15 or more words comprise the high group.

5. Use of the median as a criterion provides one way to compare the two men. The median distance from the bulls-eye of Alzeo's shots is 2.0 cm; for Hupnick, the median distance is 2.4 cm. Alzeo should get the prize because our best estimate from his median is that *no more* than 50% of his shots were farther away from the bulls-eye than 2.0 cm. From Hupnick's median of 2.4 cm, our best estimate is that *more* than 50% of his shots were farther away from the bulls-eye than 2.0 cm. We could be wrong. Measures were only made to the nearest centimeter and perhaps all of Hupnick's shots were on the "near" edge and all of Alzeo's shots on the "far" edge of the 2 cm interval. Lacking such information, we have made an impartial decision on the basis of the data at hand.

The range for the two men is the same, from 0 cm to 8 cm, and both distributions are positively skewed (in both cases, the median is much closer to 0 than it is to 8). Identical ranges do not indicate the same variability, however. Very different ranges usually indicate different variability, but the converse is not true. Look again at the frequency distributions of the two marksmen's shots. Hupnick's shots are more "spread out" than Alzeo's shots, which are clustered relatively close together. Hupnick's shooting is more variable; Alzeo's more consistent. If you were to make the same bet on each man—that his next shot would be 2 cm away from the bulls-eye—which bet would you feel more sure of?

6. (a) The centile ranks of every fourth score, beginning with the score 24, are:

2, 6, 12, 21, 31, 44, 58, 70, 80, 88, 94, 96, 98.

(b) The scores at each tenth centile, beginning with the 10th centile are:

31, 36, 40, 43, 45, 49, 52, 56, 61.

(c) By computation (as illustrated in Example 4), the median is 45.75. If your graph was drawn carefully, the reading of the median should not differ by more than a decimal fraction from 45.75.

7. (a) The 25th centile is 14.5, the 50th centile is 22.7, and the 75th centile is 33.9. The lowest quarter of the group includes all those salesclerks with scores of 14 and below; the second quarter includes all those with scores 15 through 22; the third quarter, those with scores 23 through 33; and the top quarter, those with scores 34 and above. (b) The range is 0 to 54; the interquartile range is 14.5 to 33.9. The range tells us only that the entire distribution extends over 54 units of score. The interquartile range tells us something about how the observations are distributed within that scoring distance of 54. Thus, the "middle 50%" of scores are concentrated at about the middle of the overall range, and they only extend over approximately 19 units of score, a much smaller distance than 54.

chapter 3

Populations and Samples

Statistical procedures are divided into two categories—*descriptive statistics* and *inferential statistics*. In any given case, the investigator's purpose determines which of the two types of procedure he uses. When his purpose is simply to describe the observations he has collected, he uses the procedures of descriptive statistics. The graphic methods of Chapter 1, the median, centiles, the mode, the range, are all examples of descriptive statistics. When it is possible to collect all of the observations pertinent to a research question, only descriptive statistics are needed for the analysis of the data. When *all* of the observations have been collected, the data are referred to as a *population*.

When, as usually happens, an investigator has only a *part* of the observations pertinent to his research question, the data are referred to as a *sample*. The investigator may, and often will, use descriptive statistics to describe his sample data, but if his purpose is to make inferences about the population from which his sample came, he will make use of inferential statistics as well.

In previous chapters, we considered some of the procedures of descriptive statistics. Before going on to consider some inferential statistics, we pause in this chapter to examine more closely the concepts of *population* and *sample*.

POPULATIONS

In the behavioral sciences, researchers sometimes ask a question about a particular group of subjects all of whom can be classified or measured in some way in order to answer the researcher's question. For example: What are the College Boards scores of applicants for admission to the State University this year? What is the average IQ of this group of 12 foster mothers? How many people voted for Kennedy in 1960? How do these four Negro children rank scholastically among their white classmates? In all of these cases, the investigator can readily collect the population of observations needed to answer his question.

Since his data constitute a population, the researcher will use the statistical procedures and formulas that are appropriate for populations. When such procedures are applied to populations, the resulting descriptions of the data are called *parameters*. Thus, the average IQ of the 12 foster mothers is a parameter of this population of IQ's. The proportion of people who voted for Kennedy in 1960 is a parameter of the voting behavior in that election. And the ranks of the four Negro children are parameters of their scholastic standing in that particular class.

More often, it is not possible to collect all of the observations and compute directly the parameters of the population. Most populations of interest to science are infinite, or else they are so large that for all practical purposes they are treated as infinite. By *infinite* we mean that however many measures are made, or however many subjects are studied, or however many groups are collected, it would still be possible to make more measures or study more subjects or collect more groups. Thus, a population is said to be infinite when it is *not possible even in theory* to collect all of the observations of that population. For example, consider the population of error scores made by white rats running through a maze. However many rats were tested, it would be possible to test more. Or, consider the population of responses to a word-association list. However many responses are collected, more *could* be collected. An infinite population is an *inexhaustible* population.

Even populations that are finite may be so large that it is not feasible to study the whole population. For example, it is not feasible to study the present population of hospitalized schizophrenics, or determine the IQ's of students currently majoring in Physics, or measure the attitudes of this year's automobile buyers. For all practical purposes, these populations are treated as though they were infinite.

Most of the time in the behavioral sciences, researchers are interested in populations that are too large to be studied in their entirety. The researcher must do his best to answer his question with only a part of the population. When the observations collected are only part of the population of interest, the data are referred to as a *sample*.

SAMPLES AND

SAMPLING

When an investigator collects a group of observations *in order to answer questions about some larger population which that group is intended to represent*, he has collected a sample of observations. When this is his purpose, and a statistical procedure of any kind is applied to the sample, the resulting value is called a *statistic* rather than a parameter. Thus, the median and range of a sample are referred to as *statistics*, while the median and range of a population are referred to as *parameters*.

It should be evident that the sample selected to represent a population should represent the population as closely as possible. This problem was discussed briefly in Example 3 of Chapter 2, where the researcher's purpose was to establish centile ranks for high school students "in general." To do so, obviously he must have a sample that is typical of high school students in general. Similarly, if the research question relates to neurotics, the neurotics of the sample should be as typical as possible of neurotics in general. If the sample is to represent all the people who will vote in the next election, the sample should include prospective voters from all the different regional, economic, and occupational strata of voters.

Since it is not possible to identify all the relevant strata of a population or know in advance what the "typical" is, investigators have recourse to what is called *random sampling*. That is, they select subjects or observations from a population by a predetermined scheme that will avoid any bias in the selection. For example, numbers may be assigned to all the available subjects (usually many more than will actually be studied). Suppose a sample of 20 subjects is desired from this larger group. A selection is then made from among the numbers by some procedure which gives every possible sample of 20 numbers, hence every possible sample of 20 subjects, an equal chance of being chosen. The numbers might be written on separate slips of paper which are then shaken up in a box; slips are selected one at a time until the investigator has 20 slips. The numbers written on the slips selected would identify the subjects to be used in the investigation. *The subjects chosen in this way are a random sample because every possible sample of 20 subjects had an equal chance of being chosen, and therefore every individual subject had an equal chance of being included in the sample.* These are the properties that define a random sample.

There are tables of random numbers which make it unnecessary to actually write out slips of paper and shake them in a box. Table G in the Appendix is such a table. In this table, the numbers themselves are in a random order. The reading of successive numbers from the table, either down columns or across rows, will give a random sample of numbers. This random sample of numbers may then be used to identify which members of a population will be chosen for study (assuming that numbers were previously assigned to the members of the population). The result is a random sample of subjects.

For example, suppose a sample of 60 subjects is desired from a population of 500 students. Assume the students have already been assigned numbers from 1 to 500. The table of random numbers is entered at some point that is itself chosen randomly. That is, the particular page, row, and column where one will begin to read numbers is chosen by a chance procedure. Assume that by making successive draws from a deck of cards prepared for this purpose,* the point of entry is determined as Row 00, Column 2–5 of the *2nd thousand* set of numbers. Beginning at this point and reading successive three-digit numbers down the column, we select as subjects those members of the population having the numbers 156, 490, 028, 128, 493, and so on until 60 subjects have been chosen. (The numbers 901 and 547 are skipped because we have no subjects numbered above 500.) The result is a random sample of 60 subjects from the population of 500 students.

When it is possible to identify at least some of the factors that are related to the variability of the observations, a procedure called *stratified random sampling* is often used. For example, if it is known (or anticipated) that answers to an attitude questionnaire will vary depending upon the subject's income level, the investigator will often divide the population into several different income strata, and take a random sample from each stratum. Such procedures as this insure that each of the levels or strata of the population is adequately represented in the sample. Note, however, that the principle of randomness is still employed. As will be seen, randomness of sampling is a basic assumption of inferential statistics, where the purpose is to generalize from a sample to the population from which it came.

* See Practice Problem 28 at the end of this chapter for a way of preparing such a deck of cards.

Randomness and
Representativeness

When large random samples are chosen, random sampling is very likely to produce a sample which is representative of the population sampled. This becomes progressively less true as sample size decreases, but for the purposes of statistical inference, a small random sample is still better than a small nonrandom one. However, *randomness does not guarantee representativeness*. The two concepts should not be confused. Random sampling is a procedure; representativeness is a result, and this result may or may not be achieved by random sampling. In fact, it can be demonstrated that some percentage (usually small) of the random samples drawn from any given population will actually misrepresent that population. For large random samples, the percentage of samples that will grossly misrepresent the population is exceedingly small, and it is this fact that gives us our confidence in the representativeness of a large random sample. But even for large random samples, representativeness is not a certainty.

It may seem that in some cases, deliberately choosing a "representative" group of subjects is preferable to random sampling. This depends upon whether the investigator is planning to make statistical inferences about the population from which his subjects were chosen. *Statistical inference from a sample to a population requires that the sample be randomly selected from that population.* Only when this condition is fulfilled is it appropriate to make a statistical inference about the population. Representativeness, known or assumed, does not fulfill this condition and cannot substitute for the procedure of random sampling.

If, as occurs in some instances, a group of subjects is clearly representative with regard to the variable under investigation, then of course there is no need to make statistical inferences at all. The results of the investigation will be generalized to the relevant population by common consent and the procedures of statistical inference are entirely superfluous. Such is the case, for example, when an investigator selects five subjects with normal hearing in order to study auditory thresholds for pure tones. If the experiment was carefully performed, the results will very likely be generalized to the population of people with normal hearing simply because the characteristic under investigation is pretty much the same for all people with normal hearing. The investigator need present only descriptive statistics. Generalizing to the population in this case is intuitive, not statistical.

Intuitive inferences may be valid but they are very different from statistical inferences and should not be confused with them. Intuitive inferences about a population derive from one's personal conviction about the representativeness of a sample. Statistical inferences, as will be seen, are essentially mathematical in nature and depend upon the condition of randomness.

Practice Problems

Tell for each of the following whether the researcher's question permits him to collect the population of observations, or whether his question must be answered from sample data.

1. What is the average class size at this school?

2. What is the average class size at private schools?

3. What proportion of the women employees at Company X are married?

4. What proportion of working women are married?

5. What is the extent of the Müller-Lyer Illusion for Bill Brown?

6. What is the extent of the Müller-Lyer Illusion for unpracticed subjects with normal vision?

7. What is the average hearing threshold of humans for a tone of 500 cycles per second?

8. What is the hearing threshold of Mary Jones for a tone of 500 cycles per second?

9. What is this rat's average response rate per minute during the first 20 minutes of extinction?

10. What is the average rate of response for rats with similar training during the first 20 minutes of extinction?

11. How do salesmen compare with machinists in emotional stability?

12. Are Republicans more conservative socially than Democrats?

13. Are the best pilots in this squadron more intelligent than the other pilots in the squadron?

14. Is success as a pilot related to intelligence?

15. Will Jane Miller's reaction time become longer after a dose of Drug X?

Answer the following:

16. A researcher desires a sample of five subjects for an experiment. Twenty subjects are available to him. He writes the 20 names on identical cards and shuffles them until they are thoroughly mixed. He takes the top card, then shuffles the cards again. He takes the top card again, then reshuffles the remaining cards, continuing with the procedure until he has five cards. Why are the five cards selected in this way a random sample from the deck of 20?

17. The researcher of (16) above wishes to select one subject from his sample of five for special treatment. He spreads out the five cards with the names of the subjects in alphabetical order on a table and gets his two-year-old daughter to pick one card. Why is the card chosen in this way not a random selection?

18. A researcher needs ten subjects. One hundred subjects are available to him, and the typist is preparing a list of their names. Before seeing the list, the researcher writes down the first ten numbers which come into his head. They are:

8, 30, 56, 92, 73, 12, 62, 44, 51, 58.

When the typist brings in the list, the researcher selects the 8th name, the 30th name, the 56th name, etc., until he has the ten names from the list which correspond to the numbers he wrote down. Why are the ten names not a random selection?

19. Instead of writing down numbers out of his head, the researcher of (18) above chooses every tenth name on the list. Are these names a random sample from the list? Why?

20. A researcher carefully selects a random sample of 500 property owners from his town. He sends them all a brief questionnaire asking about their attitudes toward the local school tax. Two hundred ten subjects fill out and return the questionnaire. Are their answers a random sample of the attitudes of the town's property owners? Why?

21. A cigarette company wishes to sample the public's reaction to a new package design. An employee is sent to stand on a downtown street corner with one of the new packages and one of the former packages to ask passers-by which of the two packages they prefer. Over several weeks, the employee collects 1000 observations. Are these observations a random sample of the public's reactions? Why?

22. An experimenter has 30 subjects who are to be assigned

randomly to an Experimental group and a Control group of 15 subjects each. Each subject's name has been written on a card. The experimenter arranges the 30 cards into a stack in alphabetical order. Beginning with the name on the top card, he assigns every alternate name in the stack to the Experimental group. The remaining 15 subjects are assigned to the Control group. Was the assignment of subjects to the two groups random? Why?

23. The experimenter of (22) above assigns a number to each of his 30 subjects. He writes the numbers on 30 white chips and shakes them up in a box. He draws one chip, shakes up the remaining chips, draws another chip, shakes them up again, draws a third chip, and so on until he has 15 chips. The subjects whose numbers appear on these chips are assigned to the Experimental group. The subjects identified by the chips still in the box make up the Control group. Is this a random assignment? Why?

24. A test constructor wishes to standardize his test on high school students. He gives the test to all the students in the city's three high schools. Is this a representative sample of high school students in general?

25. An experimenter wishes to study how rumors are transmitted in a group. He chooses as subjects a random sample of students who have not studied Sociology or Psychology. Will the results of his experiment be applicable to people in general?

26. A psychologist wishes to study the sensory adaptation of humans to colored light. He chooses ten subjects who have normal color vision from his class in Physiological Psychology. Will the results of his experiment be applicable to humans in general?

27. A psychologist wishes to study basic learning processes. Six rats are trained to run down a runway for a small food reward. The food reward is then increased by a large amount, and the rats soon begin to run faster. Are the results of this experiment applicable to humans?

28. Make a deck of cards that can be used to determine the point of entry in Table G, the table of random numbers in the Appendix. A set of 25 ordinary playing cards will do. Mark the faces of the cards with numbers from 0 through 24, corresponding to the row numbers of the table. To determine a point of entry in the table, first draw from among the cards numbered 1 through 5 to find which set of 5000 numbers will be entered. Draw from among cards 0 through 3 to determine the bank of columns, then from among cards 0 through 9 to determine the particular column. Finally, shuffle all the cards together and draw one to determine the row that will be

entered. *Be sure in each case that the cards are thoroughly mixed and previous draws have been replaced before the next draw is made.* Use this procedure to determine four independent points of entry in Table G. Use these points of entry to answer the following:

(a) Ten subjects, previously numbered from 0 through 9, are to be randomly divided into an Experimental group and a Control group. Note your point of entry and read across rows in Table G to choose a random sample of five subjects for the Experimental group.

(b) Ten subjects are to be randomly chosen from a class of 100, the members of the class having been previously numbered from 00 through 99. Note your point of entry and read across rows to determine the numbers of the ten subjects.

(c) Ten subjects are to be randomly chosen from among 750 applicants who have previously been numbered from 1 through 750. Note your point of entry and read down columns to determine the numbers of the ten subjects.

(d) Twenty subjects are to be randomly divided into an Experimental group and a Control group. Note your point of entry and read down columns to choose a random sample of ten subjects for the Experimental group.

(e) Four different intensities of light are to be presented to a subject in random order, each of the four intensities to be presented five times in a series of 20 trials. Make up a list of 20 trials in which the four intensities appear in random order, with the restriction that each intensity appear five times.

Answers

1. Population

2. Sample

3. Population

4. Sample

5. Sample. Since, in theory, an infinite number of trials could be given to Bill Brown, the population of possible measures is infinite.

6. Sample

7. Sample

8. Sample. Again, an infinite number of measures are theoretically possible.

9. Population. *This* rat's response rate can easily be measured over the entire 20-minute interval.

10. Sample

11. Sample. In fact, two samples will be needed: measures of the emotional stability of a group of salesmen, and similar measures for machinists.

12. Sample. Two samples are also required here, one of Republicans and one of Democrats.

13. Population. Two observations are required for each pilot in the squadron: his IQ, and a measure of his performance as a pilot.

14. Sample. The same two measures are needed as in (13) above, but now the measures are a sample. The researcher may even use as his subjects the pilots of that same squadron—hence the same data—but the data will now constitute a sample rather than a population because the researcher's question is about pilots in general, not about this particular group of pilots.

15. Sample. Two samples will be needed: a sample of Jane's reaction times before Drug X, and a sample after Drug X.

16. Because each card's chance of being on top was the same as every other card's, and this was true every time a card was drawn. Hence, every subject in the initial group of 20 had an equal chance of being chosen.

17. Because individuals—even presumably naïve individuals—cannot be assumed to operate in a random manner. The child may have a tendency to choose things always on the left, or on the right, or closest to her, or at a particular angle, etc. Any such tendency at all would mean that each card did not have an equal chance of being chosen. (The winner of a raffle is not randomly selected because a child is asked to draw the winning ticket, but because the box or barrel of tickets is thoroughly shaken up before one is drawn. Then it does not matter who draws the ticket.)

18. For the same reason given above—namely, individuals cannot be assumed to operate in a random manner. This researcher may have written down the first ten numbers that came into his head all right, but if you look at the numbers again you will see that eight of the ten are even numbers. The numbers that come into this researcher's head may tend to be even. Therefore, subjects whose names are at odd-numbered intervals on the list would have less chance of being selected than subjects at even-numbered intervals.

19. No. This procedure would yield a random sample if the names were typed in a random order, but we can hardly assume the typist to have done this.

20. No. A situation like this one was discussed in Chapter 1, in the answer to Practice Problem 6, where it was pointed out that persons who complete and return questionnaires can only be identified with certainty as a sample of persons-who-fill-out-and-return-questionnaires. Since the 210 subjects cannot be regarded as a random sample of property owners, their answers to the questionnaire are not a random sample of attitudes.

21. No. The subjects on whom the observations were made may be representative of persons who pass that street corner, but since the population of persons who constitute "the public" are not equally likely to pass any given street corner, the observations are not a random sample of the public's reactions.

22. No. This is like the researcher who chose every tenth name on the list. Subjects whose names appear at even-numbered intervals in the stack of cards have no chance at all of being assigned to the Experimental group, and the cards were not stacked randomly.

23. Yes, because every chip has an equal chance of being among the 15 which are drawn. Hence, every subject has an equal chance of being assigned to the Experimental group.

24. The sample is representative of high school students in general *only* insofar as the high school students of this city are representative of the population of high school students. Usually, the only way to find out whether such a sample is representative of the population is to give the test to many other samples drawn from the population. The test constructor will undoubtedly have to do this if he wishes to establish norms for high school students in general.

25. No. There is no reason to believe that the social behavior of college students is representative of the social behavior of "people in general." The process of rumor transmission *may* be the same for college students as for people in general; but without some evidence to this effect, any generalization of the results to the population at large is unwarranted.

26. Very probably, yes. Purely sensory functions are no different among college students than among any other healthy group of persons, so results of studies of sensory processes can usually be generalized to humans in general, even when the studies were carried out on a very small group of subjects chosen only on the basis of having normal senses. For the same reason, of course, college students would be quite representative of the population of healthy humans in many

physiological processes, in some physiological drives, in certain basic aspects of perception, and possibly in some very basic aspects of learning. Just as the chemist need not look far for a "representative sample" of oxygen, all samples being the same, so psychologists have found that a certain limited number of basic perceptual and behavioral processes are very nearly the same among all healthy people, and thus almost any small sample of healthy subjects is very likely to be representative of the population.

There is, of course, no reason to believe that college students (or any other social group) are representative of the population at large in temperament, attitudes, neuroticism, "personality," or any other trait which derives from a particular upbringing, environment, or heredity.

27. No. Samples of animal behavior cannot be assumed to represent the population of human behavior, or even the population of other animal species. To generalize the results to humans, there must be evidence that humans behave the same way when placed in similar situations.

chapter 4

The
Mean and
the Standard
Deviation

The *mean*, the *standard deviation*, and the *variance* are important both as descriptive statistics and in statistical inference. They are the statistics most often used when the data that have been collected are in the form of measures. The *mean* is an average of the measures and is therefore a central value of the distribution. As such, the mean is often taken as the representative value of a distribution. The *standard deviation* describes the variability of the distribution, the scatter of the observations about their mean. The standard deviation is the square root of the *variance*, itself a measure of variability. The variance is little used as a descriptive statistic but is very important in statistical inference. We shall make much use of it in later chapters.

In this chapter we shall be primarily concerned with the computation of the mean and standard deviation and their usefulness as descriptive statistics. We will also try to get some insight into the use of these two statistics in statistical inference, although the greater part of this discussion is necessarily reserved for later chapters.

Notation

In statistical formulas, the variable is designated by the letter X. The first observation may be designated X_1, the second X_2, the third X_3, and so on. When all the observations are to be added together, this operation is symbolized by ΣX, which means "the sum of" all the X's, or $X_1 + X_2 + X_3 + \ldots + X_n$.

The symbol ΣX^2 means that each X (each observation in the distribution) is to be squared first, then the squares are to be summed.

The symbol $(\Sigma X)^2$ means that the X's are to be summed first (as shown by the fact that ΣX is within parentheses), then this single sum is to be squared.

The symbol $\Sigma f X$ indicates that the variable X is being represented by the midpoints of the classes of the distribution (or the midpoints of the class intervals when the classes are grouped into intervals). $\Sigma f X$ means that each midpoint is to be multiplied by its frequency first, then the products are to be summed.

$\Sigma f X^2$ means that each midpoint is to be squared and multiplied by its frequency first, then the results are to be summed.

$(\Sigma f X)^2$ means that $\Sigma f X$ is to be determined first, then this single sum is to be squared.

DEFINITION OF THE MEAN AND STANDARD DEVIATION

The mean is more commonly known as the average of a set of measures. It is obtained by adding together all the measures and dividing their sum by n, the number of observations. Thus,

$$\text{Mean} = \frac{\Sigma X}{n} \qquad (4.1)$$

The mean of a set of measures is designated by the symbol $\overline{X}$. When these measures constitute a population, it is common practice to indicate that the mean in this case is a parameter by using the Greek letter μ (mu) in place of $\overline{X}$.

The standard deviation is also based on an average, but it is not a familiar one. The standard deviation is defined by the formula

$$\text{Standard Deviation} = \sqrt{\frac{\Sigma(X - \overline{X})^2}{n}} \qquad (4.2)$$

The term $(X - \overline{X})$ gives the distance of a score X from the mean of the distribution, $\overline{X}$. This distance is obtained for every score, then each of the distances is squared. What is averaged by the formula are these squared distances. The standard deviation, then, is a measure of variability reflecting how far the measures are from the mean of the distribution. When the measures are spread out far from the mean, the standard deviation will be large; when the measures are clustered close to the mean, the standard deviation will be small.

The standard deviation obtained by formula (4.2) is a descriptive statistic and describes the variability of a set of measures about their mean. When these measures constitute a population, their standard deviation is a parameter and is designated by the Greek letter σ (sigma). Formula (4.2) may also be used to *describe* the variability of a sample, but this formula should *not* be used when interest centers upon using the sample to estimate the variability of the population from which the sample came.

When the purpose of computing the standard deviation of a sample is to obtain an *estimate* of the standard deviation of the population from which the sample came, the following formula should be used:

$$s = \sqrt{\frac{\Sigma(X - \bar{X})^2}{n - 1}} \qquad (4.3)$$

where s is an estimate of the parameter σ, the standard deviation of the population from which the sample was drawn.

Other, equivalent formulas are more convenient for actually computing the mean and standard deviation. Some of these are given, and their use illustrated, in the examples that follow.

Computing the Mean and Standard Deviation from Ungrouped Data

When the mean and standard deviation are to be computed from data that have *not* been grouped into a frequency distribution, formula (4.1) is used to obtain the mean, and one of the following formulas (whichever is appropriate) may be used in place of the definition formulas to obtain the standard deviation:

$$\sigma = \sqrt{\frac{\Sigma X^2}{n} - (\bar{X})^2} \qquad (4.4)$$

$$s = \sqrt{\frac{\Sigma X^2 - \frac{(\Sigma X)^2}{n}}{n - 1}} \qquad (4.5)$$

The formula for σ is equivalent to formula (4.2) and should be used for descriptive purposes—*e.g.*, when the measures constitute a population. The formula for s is equivalent to formula (4.3) and should be used when the purpose is to estimate the population standard deviation from sample data.

Example 1. A camp director is concerned because only 74 campers have enrolled for the coming summer and his usual enrollment is near 100. He checks with his five competitors in the area, who also usually enroll close to 100 campers, and learns that their enrollments this year are:

88, 65, 76, 92, 69

(a) What is the mean enrollment of the other five camps?
(b) To what extent does the director's enrollment differ from the mean of his competitors?
(c) To what extent do the enrollments of his competitors differ from the mean enrollment?

• THE MEAN

The mean is computed from formula (4.1):

$$\overline{X} = \frac{\Sigma X}{n} = \frac{(88 + 65 + 76 + 92 + 69)}{5} = 78.00$$

The mean could have been designated μ instead of $\overline{X}$ in this case because the five enrollments constitute a population of observations (the present enrollments of all of our camp director's present competitors).

• THE STANDARD DEVIATION

To describe the variability of the five observations, σ is computed from formula (4.4).

• • STEP 1. To get the first term in the formula, each observation is squared first, then summed, and the sum is divided by n. Thus,

$$\frac{\Sigma X^2}{n} = \frac{(88)^2 + (65)^2 + (76)^2 + (92)^2 + (69)^2}{5} = 6194.00$$

• • STEP 2. To get the second term in the formula, square the mean of the observations.

$$\overline{X}^2 = (78.00)^2 = 6084.00$$

• • STEP 3. Subtract the result of Step 2 from the result of Step 1, and find the square root of the remainder:

$$6194.00 - 6084.00 = 110.00$$

$$\sigma = \sqrt{110.00} = 10.49 = 10.5$$

The mean enrollment at the other five camps is 78.0. Since the other camps also have an expected enrollment of 100, the mean of 78.0 indicates that, as a group, enrollments are down for them also.

Our director's enrollment is 74, which is four campers less than the mean of his competitors. Four campers does not seem like much of a difference. But how does this difference compare with his competitors? How "different" are their enrollments from the mean?

One camp has an enrollment of 92, 14 campers more than the mean, and another camp has 88, 10 more than the mean. We could indicate the situation for these two camps by assigning a value +14 to the first camp and +10 to the second. For the other three camps, enrollments are below the mean. These camps have enrollments of only 76, 69, and 65, or 2, 9, and 13 campers less than the mean of 78.0. The situation for these three camps can be indicated by assigning them, respectively, the values −2, −9, and −13.

Now we have the rudiments of an answer to the question originally asked—*viz.*, to what extent do the competitors' enrollments differ from the mean enrollment? They differ by +14, +10, −2, −9, −13. *On the average*, they differ by the average of these values. The only trouble is that if we sum the values in order to take their average, we get + 24 and −24, which adds up to zero. So we square the values first, which gets rid of the minus signs. Then we can find the average of the squares. Afterwards, we will "undo" or compensate for our squaring operation by taking the square root of this average:

$X - \overline{X}$	$(X - \overline{X})^2$
+14	196
+10	100
− 2	4
− 9	81
−13	169
$\Sigma = 0$	$\Sigma = 550$

$$\text{Average} = \frac{\Sigma(X - \overline{X})^2}{n} = \frac{550}{5} = 110$$

The square root of the average = σ

$$= \sqrt{\frac{\Sigma(X - \overline{X})^2}{n}} = \sqrt{110} = 10.49$$

$$= 10.5$$

All we have done, of course, is to use the definition formula (4.2) for computing σ, and the result is the same as when σ was found by the computational formula (4.4). (It was easy to use the definition formula in this case because the mean was a whole number, and therefore no decimals were involved in the subtractions from the mean. That is the *only* time the definition formula is easy to use!)

The standard deviation tells us, then, to what extent the observations of a distribution differ from their mean, "on the average." This is not an average in the usual sense, of course. A simple average of distances from the mean could be obtained by summing the differences $(X - \overline{X})$ irrespective of sign, and dividing the sum by n. This procedure gives a little-used statistic called the *mean deviation*, which is a simple average of differences from the mean. The standard deviation, as we have seen, is derived from the average of the squared differences. For the same set of data, the value of the standard deviation will usually be a little larger than the value of the mean deviation. So long as these distinctions are kept in mind, we shall not be led astray by regarding the standard deviation as a measure of average distance from the mean.

Our standard deviation of 10.5 tells us, then, that "on the average," the enrollments at the five competitor camps differ from the mean enrollment by 10.5 campers. Some camps differ by more than this and some by less, but on the average, they differ by 10.5 from the mean. Since our director's enrollment differs by only four from the mean, his difference is relatively small compared to 10.5. Even though his enrollment is below the mean of his competitors, we can now say that, relatively, it is not much below their mean.

Computing the Mean and Standard Deviation from a Frequency Distribution

When measures have been grouped into a frequency distribution, the mean and standard deviation may be computed directly from the frequency distribution by the formulas given below.

$$\overline{X} = \frac{\Sigma fX}{n} \tag{4.6}$$

$$\sigma = \sqrt{\frac{\Sigma fX^2}{n} - (\overline{X})^2} \tag{4.7}$$

$$s = \sqrt{\frac{\Sigma fX^2 - \frac{(\Sigma fX)^2}{n}}{n - 1}} \tag{4.8}$$

Example 2. An experimenter wishes to determine the number of trials required to learn a particular list of nonsense syllables. He selects a random sample of 34 students from several large classes, and they all agree to take part in the experiment. The 34 subjects learn the list, and the experimenter constructs a frequency distribution showing the number of trials required by the different subjects. The frequency distribution is shown in the first two columns of Table 4.1.

The experimenter has 34 answers to his question: What is the number of trials required to learn this list of nonsense syllables? To reduce the 34 answers to one answer, he will find the mean of the observations. Because his subjects were randomly selected, the sample mean will provide him with a good estimate of the population mean. He will also estimate the standard deviation of the population and this, as we shall see, will help him to know how much confidence he can have in his estimate of the mean.

• THE MEAN

Since the observations are grouped into a frequency distribution, the mean is computed from formula (4.6). The computation is illustrated in Table 4.1 and explained below.

• • STEP 1. The X in the formula represents the midpoints of the class intervals. In this example of individual classes, the midpoints have the values used to designate the classes themselves, so X stands for the different values of the classes. The formula instructs us to multiply each X by the frequency for that class. Thus, beginning with the highest class, $12 \times 1 = 12$, $11 \times 0 = 0$, $10 \times 3 = 30$, and so on as shown in Table 4.1. Each product is entered in a column headed fX.

• • STEP 2. When the products have all been entered in the fX column, add up the column to get ΣfX. For these data $\Sigma fX = 269$.

• • STEP 3. To get the mean, divide ΣfX by n, the number of observations (*not* the number of classes). Thus, the mean is $269/34 = 7.91$.

• THE STANDARD DEVIATION

Our interest is in *estimating* the population standard deviation, so formula (4.8) for s is used.

• • STEP 1. To get the first term in the formula, a column fX^2 is added to the table. The entries in the fX^2 column are obtained by multiplying each fX value by X. Thus, $12 \times 12 = 144$, $11 \times 0 = 0$, $10 \times 30 = 300$, and so on as shown in Table 4.1. When all the

Table 4.1
Computing the Mean and Standard Deviation from a Frequency Distribution

(Example 2: Number of Trials Required to Learn List of Nonsense Syllables)

No. of Trials X	f	fX	fX^2
12	1	12	144
11	0	0	0
10	3	30	300
9	8	72	648
8	9	72	576
7	7	49	343
6	4	24	144
5	2	10	50
	$n = 34$	$\Sigma fX = 269$	$\Sigma fX^2 = 2205$

$$\bar{X} = \frac{\Sigma fX}{n} = \frac{269}{34} = 7.91$$

$$s = \sqrt{\frac{\Sigma fX^2 - \frac{(\Sigma fX)^2}{n}}{n-1}} = \sqrt{\frac{2205 - \frac{(269)^2}{34}}{34-1}} = \sqrt{\frac{2205 - 2128.26}{33}}$$

$$= \sqrt{\frac{76.74}{33}} = \sqrt{2.33} = 1.53$$

entries have been made, sum the column to get ΣfX^2. For these data, ΣfX^2 is found to be 2205.

• • STEP 2. The second term in the formula is $(\Sigma fX)^2/n$. $(\Sigma fX)^2$ is $(269)^2 = 72361$. Dividing by n, we get $72361/34 = 2128.26$, the value of the second term in the formula.

• • STEP 3. The numerator of the formula can now be obtained by subtracting the result of Step 2 from the result of Step 1. Thus, $2205.00 - 2128.26 = 76.74$.

• • STEP 4. The numerator found in Step 3 is divided by $n - 1$. Thus, $76.74/33 = 2.33$. s is the square root of this value, or 1.53.

• RESULTS AND DISCUSSION

The mean number of trials required by the 34 subjects is about 7.9.

This mean is also an estimate of the population mean, μ. The experimenter's best guess about the population of students like these is that they would learn the list of nonsense syllables in a mean number of 7.9 trials.

How sure can the experimenter be of this number? If he takes another random sample of 34 subjects from the same population, will they also require a mean number of 7.9 trials to learn the list? Probably not. Even if the population mean really is exactly 7.9 trials, we would expect the means of random samples drawn from the population to vary both above and below 7.9. Since such departures are more the rule than the exception, we are virtually led to expect that our sample mean of 7.9 represents some sort of deviation from the population mean, though we cannot determine precisely how deviate it is or whether it is above or below the population mean. Interestingly, we can use the standard deviation of our sample to help us in conjecturing how far the population mean is from 7.9.

The standard deviation of the population was estimated by s to be about 1.5. According to this estimate, the number of trials required by students like these are clustered pretty close together. If 1.5 is representative of the amount by which students differ from the mean, a student who differed from the mean by as much as four trials (more than twice 1.5) would be unusual, and a student who differed from the mean by ten trials is practically unthinkable. *If, in the population, the individual observations differ little from the population mean, then there cannot be very great differences among the means of samples drawn from the population.* That is, where observations are clustered close together, the sample means of such observations must also cluster close together. If the sample means are clustered close together, their values cannot differ by much. Hence, the sample means in general will tend to be close to the population mean. Therefore, because his estimate of the population standard deviation is relatively small, the experimenter can conclude that the sample mean he obtained is likely to be close to the population mean. He can have some confidence that his sample mean of 7.9 trials is a reliable estimate of μ—where *reliable* signifies that most such sample means will differ little from μ.

The statistic s, then, serves as an indicator of how sure we can be of the sample mean as an estimate of the population mean. When s suggests that in the population, the observations have a small variability, tending to differ little from their mean, $\overline{X}$ can usually be taken as a reliable estimate of μ. When s is relatively large, suggesting great variability in the population, we are relatively *unsure* that $\overline{X}$

is a reliable estimate of μ. Other information must be taken into account. This topic is considered further in Chapter 5.

Computing the Mean and Standard Deviation from Coded Scores

When measures have been grouped into a frequency distribution and numbers are large, computations are greatly simplified by the "coding" procedure illustrated in Example 3 below. The mean and standard deviation are then computed from the coded measures.

Example 3. A personnel psychologist has been receiving an increased number of complaints about the competence of the clerical workers hired under his program of selection. As a first check on his selection procedure, the psychologist decides to compare the company's present clerical workers with the workers hired when the selection program was first established some years previously. This original group of clerical workers had a mean score of 50 with a standard deviation of 8 points on the clerical aptitude test used in the selection program. The psychologist wishes to determine whether the company's present clerical employees have a lower mean score on this test than the original group of clerical workers. The test scores of the company's present clerical employees are tabulated in a frequency distribution, as shown in the first two columns of Table 4.2.

• CODING SCORES

To code the scores of a frequency distribution, first list the midpoints of the class intervals, as shown in the third column of Table 4.2. To simplify later computations as much as possible, choose that midpoint around the middle of the column which has the largest frequency. For this distribution, the midpoint 52 has the largest frequency (56 cases), so 52 is chosen. This midpoint will be designated M_o and is assigned a coded score of 0. Midpoints above M_o are assigned coded scores of 1, 2, 3, etc., in ascending order. Midpoints below M_o are assigned coded scores of -1, -2, -3, etc., in descending order. This has been done in the fourth column of Table 4.2. The scores are now coded, and the column is labelled X' to indicate that these are coded measures.

This is all that need be done to code the scores of any frequency distribution. The coded scores provide a simplified scale which is comparable to the original scale. The large numbers of the original scale, represented by the midpoints of the class intervals, are equidistant from each other, as they usually will be in a frequency distribution. To construct a comparable scale, it is only necessary to substitute for the large numbers small ones that are also equidistant from each other. The distances between the values of the two scales will then be comparable, in which case the scales are said to be comparable. This will remain true regardless of which midpoint is chosen as M_o and assigned a coded score of 0. When there are ten or fewer class intervals and numbers are not so large, it is often easier to choose the lowest midpoint as M_o and put the 0 at the bottom of the scale so that all the coded scores will have plus values.

• THE MEAN

To compute the mean of a distribution from coded scores, first compute the coded mean, then transform the coded mean into the units used in the original measures.

• • STEP 1. To compute the coded mean $\overline{X}'$ use the formula

$$\overline{X}' = \frac{\Sigma f X'}{n} \tag{4.9}$$

As the formula instructs, multiply each coded score by the frequency for that class interval, as shown in the fX' column of Table 4.2. Sum the plus and minus entries separately, then add the sums algebraically to get $\Sigma f X'$. Divide $\Sigma f X'$ by n to get $\overline{X}'$, as shown in Table 4.2.

• • STEP 2. To "uncode" $\overline{X}'$ and find the mean of the distribution in the same units as the original measures, $\overline{X}'$ is put in the formula below, which reverses the operations implicit in the original coding:*

$$\overline{X} = (\overline{X}')i + M_o \tag{4.10}$$

Multiply $\overline{X}'$ by the size of the class interval (i), and add M_o to the result. These operations are applied to the present data in Table 4.2. The mean is found to be 50.2.

---

* Our coding procedure, in effect, subtracts the value of M_o from each midpoint and divides the result in each case by i. Any such operations carried out on the scores are automatically carried out on the mean of the scores. The standard deviation is unchanged by the subtraction or addition of a constant to the scores, hence is unaffected by the subtraction of M_o. But multiplying or dividing the scores by a constant, such as i, is automatically carried out on the standard deviation. So the standard deviation of coded scores must be multiplied by i in order to return to the original unit of measure.

Table 4.2
Computing the Mean and Standard Deviation from Coded Scores

(Example 3: Clerical Aptitude Scores of Present Employees)

Score Interval	f	Midpoint X	Coded Score X'	fX'		fX'^2
85–89	1	87	7	7		49
80–84	3	82	6	18		108
75–79	10	77	5	50		250
70–74	19	72	4	76		304
65–69	18	67	3	54		162
60–64	27	62	2	54		108
55–59	40	57	1	40		40
50–54	56	52	0	0	+299	0
45–49	46	47	−1	−46		46
40–44	35	42	−2	−70		140
35–39	20	37	−3	−60		180
30–34	28	32	−4	−112		448
25–29	16	27	−5	−80		400
20–24	8	22	−6	−48		288
	$n = 327$				−416	
						$\Sigma fX'^2 = 2523$

$$\Sigma fX' = 299 - 416 = -117$$

$$\bar{X}' = \frac{\Sigma fX'}{n} = \frac{-117}{327} = -.36$$

$$\bar{X} = (\bar{X}')i + M_o = (-.36)5 + 52 = 50.20$$

$$\sigma = i\sqrt{\frac{\Sigma fX'^2}{n} - (\bar{X}')^2}$$

$$= 5\sqrt{\frac{2523}{327} - (-.36)^2}$$

$$= 13.80$$

- ### The Standard Deviation

The standard deviation may be computed directly from coded scores. Formulas for σ and s are given below.

$$\sigma = i\sqrt{\frac{\Sigma fX'^2}{n} - (\bar{X}')^2} \qquad (4.11)$$

$$s = i \sqrt{\frac{\Sigma f X'^2 - \frac{(\Sigma f X')^2}{n}}{n - 1}} \qquad (4.12)$$

Since interest in this case centers upon the test scores as a population of observations, formula (4.11) for σ is used to describe their variability.

● ● STEP 1. Construct an fX'^2 column by multiplying each fX' entry by its corresponding X' value. Thus, $7 \times 7 = 49$, and so on as in Table 4.2. The sum of this column, which has no minus signs, is $\Sigma f X'^2$. Divide $\Sigma f X'^2$ by n to get the first term of the formula.

● ● STEP 2. The second term of the formula is $(\overline{X}')^2$. Since $\overline{X}'$ has already been computed, it is simply squared and entered in the formula.

● ● STEP 3. The result of Step 2 is subtracted from the result of Step 1, and the square root of the remainder is taken. This result is then multiplied by i, the size of the class interval, as shown in Table 4.2.

● RESULTS AND DISCUSSION

The mean score of the company's present clerical employees on the clerical aptitude test is 50.2. The original group of clerical workers had a mean score of 50. The two means differ by very little—.2 points—and hence the present clerical workers, as a group, cannot be considered to perform less well on this test. If the test was originally a good predictor of clerical competence, and we assume that it was since it was included in the selection program, why, now, the increased number of complaints about the competence of clerical employees?

The reasons, of course, may have nothing to do with competence as shown by performance on the clerical aptitude test. The motivation or morale of present employees may be different. Or perhaps job requirements have changed subtly over time, and now more is required of clerical workers than was the case when the original group was hired. These, and other possibilities, would have to be investigated. One possibility, however, is suggested by the difference in the standard deviations found for the present employees and the original group of clerical workers.

The standard deviation of scores obtained by the original

group was 8 points, while the standard deviation of the scores obtained by present employees is 13.8. The scores of present employees are more variable, spread out much farther from the mean. There are more employees now with high scores on the test, but there are also more with low scores. Possibly, therefore, the increased number of complaints is due to an increased number of workers of relatively low competence, whose low aptitude scores are balanced in the overall selection process by a parallel increase in workers who receive high aptitude scores. Thus, the mean score obtained by clerical job applicants remains the same over time; but among present employees the mean is the balance point or average of relatively high and relatively low scores, whereas for the original group the mean was the average of scores clustered much closer together. A comparison of the means alone does not give us this information.

We find, then, that in order to interpret correctly a difference (or lack of difference) between two means, it is necessary to compare the standard deviations as well as the means of the two distributions. The standard deviations tell us something about the particular combination of scores that produced the mean in each case. When the standard deviations of two distributions are nearly the same, it is likely, though not necessary, that a similar combination of scores produced the mean in both cases. But when the standard deviations of two distributions are very different, it is safe to conclude that a very different combination of scores produced the mean in each case.

DESCRIPTIVE STATISTICS AND THE SHAPE OF A DISTRIBUTION

The mean, the median, and the mode are often referred to as *measures of central tendency*. Measures of central tendency are so called because they are useful in locating various centers or central values of a distribution. The mode is a center of concentration, the point where the largest number of observations are found; the median is the midpoint of the distribution; and the mean is the average of all the observations.

Measures of variability, sometimes called *measures of dispersion*, provide information about the spread of the distribution. The range, the interquartile and the semi-interquartile ranges, the mean deviation, the standard deviation, and the variance (yet to be considered) are all measures of variability. The various ranges describe extent of spread. The mean deviation, the standard deviation, and the variance are averages based upon the distance of each observation from the mean of the distribution.

When an investigator reports his results, he will give both a measure of central tendency and a measure of variability. Sometimes, several such measures are needed in order to describe accurately the distribution. This is especially true in the case of skewed distributions and highly variable distributions.

For a fairly symmetrical distribution that has only one mode, the mean and standard deviation alone usually provide a good picture of the distribution. Even when the distribution is not symmetrical, the mean and standard deviation are useful descriptive statistics. For example, it can be shown that at least 75% of the observations of any distribution must fall within two standard deviations of the mean, and at least 89% must fall within three standard deviations of the mean. These are minimum values. More often, all of the observations are within three standard deviations of the mean and more than 90% are within two standard deviations of the mean. Thus, a quick way to get a rough estimate of the extent of the bulk of a distribution is to add and subtract two standard deviations from its mean.

Skewed Distributions

When the possible values that a variable can take are limited at one or both ends of the scale, the mean and standard deviation often provide important information about the shape of the distribution. Consider the following situation:

Example 4. In a study of drug effects, the mean number of speech errors made by subjects after an injection of the drug is 8.5 with standard deviation of 10.

The distribution is certain to be skewed. The lower limit of the scale of errors is fixed at 0 (no one can make fewer than zero errors). The standard deviation, as we have seen, is a kind of average of how far observations are from their mean. To get a standard deviation of 10, some of the observations must be closer to the mean than 10 and *some must be farther away from the mean than 10*. These more "distant" observations must be high error scores since, with a mean of 8.5 and a lower limit of 0, scores even ten units below the mean are not possible. Therefore, the distribution must be positively skewed, having a "tail" of high error scores, something like this:

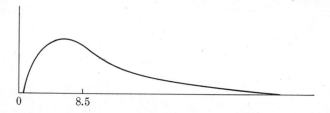

Figure 4.1
Positively Skewed Distribution

When the standard deviation of a distribution is equal to or larger than the mean, and there can be no observations below 0, the distribution is positively skewed.

In many cases of skewness, the shape of the distribution is not apparent from the mean and standard deviation, and more information than this is needed. Consider the following:

Example 5. On a test of physical endurance, the scores obtained by a large group of Marines are described by the following statistics:

Mean = 31, Standard deviation = 7
Median = 35, Range = 10 to 43

The mean and standard deviation alone do not suggest that the distribution is skewed. But from a consideration of the median and range, it is clear that there is a heavy concentration of scores at the upper end of the distribution. Fifty percent of the men obtained scores between 35 and 43, a scoring distance of only eight units, while the remaining 50% are spread over a much larger scoring distance of 25 units (from 10 to 35) at the low end of the distribution. The distribution must be negatively skewed, something like Fig. 4.2.

Whenever a distribution is skewed, the mean and the median will have different values. Extreme scores "pull" the mean in their direction, away from the median of the distribution. Hence, *when the mean is larger than the median, the distribution is positively skewed.*

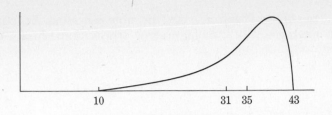

10   31 35   43

Figure 4.2
Negatively Skewed Distribution

When the mean is smaller than the median, the distribution is negatively skewed. It follows that skewness can always be indicated by giving both the mean and the median of a distribution.

Highly Variable
Distributions

Great variability is, of course, reflected in a large standard deviation, but the standard deviation alone will not make clear the shape of the distribution. A large standard deviation may indicate a "flat" or rectangular distribution—great variability within a relatively narrow scoring range. In this case, the range as well as the standard deviation should be given. In other cases, there may be a decided peak near the middle of the distribution, but remaining scores are sparsely scattered over a very wide range. Here, the median and the interquartile range will often serve to locate the central concentration of scores. Or, a large standard deviation may reflect a distribution that has more than one mode. Any time a sizeable distribution has more than one mode, the modes should be reported.

The possible shapes of distributions are more than can be enumerated. Suffice it to say that the researcher should report the values of whatever measures are necessary to convey best the shape of the distribution he has obtained.

Practice Problems

Compute the mean and standard deviation (s or σ, depending upon which is appropriate) of each of the following distributions:

97   PRACTICE PROBLEMS

1. Two baseball teams, A and B, have played against the same ten opponents in the course of a season. The number of runs made by each team against each of the ten opponents is given below:

RUNS MADE BY

TEAM A	TEAM B
3	1
3	2
6	11
2	0
4	8
4	3
3	6
0	0
2	1
5	5

Compare the overall performance of the two teams, in terms of runs scored.

2. At a private school which caters to children of superior intelligence, the children in the third grade have the following IQ's:

125	122	127	110
133	118	117	140
115	129	115	118
112	116	136	113
110	123	122	123

Mrs. C. is considering transferring her daughter, who is in the third grade, to this school. Mrs. C. is concerned, though, lest her daughter feel inferior if the other children in the class are much brighter than she is. Mrs. C.'s daughter has an IQ of 118. How does this compare with the IQ's of the other children?

3. An experimenter has devised a new maze and he wishes to know the number of errors untrained rats can be expected to make on their first run through this maze. A random sample of 30 animals from the lab's rat colony are tested in the maze and the number of errors made by each rat is recorded. The results are:

ERRORS	f
15	1
14	2
13	6
12	9
11	7
10	4
9	0
8	1

Is the mean of this sample a reliable estimate of μ?

4. In an attempt to measure the extent to which delinquents

have an underlying need for recognition, an investigator studies a random sample of 50 teen-age delinquents from the state reform school. He prepares a series of picture cards that depict teen-age boys and girls in a variety of ambiguous situations, and the subjects are asked to tell a story about each situation. Afterwards, the investigator counts for each subject the instances of seeking or gaining recognition which appeared in that subject's stories. The results for the 50 subjects are:

INSTANCES OF RECOGNITION	f
12	2
11	4
10	3
9	1
8	0
7	0
6	0
5	1
4	4
3	5
2	8
1	12
0	10

(a) How good is the mean in this case as an indicator of the "typical" performance of these delinquents?

(b) What do the results suggest about how the population of measures would be distributed if all the delinquents like these could be tested?

5. A vocational interest test includes a Social Service scale that measures interest in rendering service to others. The test has been given to all the nurses on the staff of a large hospital. They obtained a mean score of 60 on the Social Service scale of the test, with a standard deviation of 8.2 points. The 100 student nurses who begin their training at the hospital that year are also given the test. Their Social Service scores are distributed as follows:

SCORE	f
95–99	1
90–94	3
85–89	5
80–84	10
75–79	16
70–74	20
65–69	17
60–64	12
55–59	7
50–54	4
45–49	3
40–44	2

How do the scores of the student nurses compare with those of the staff nurses?

6. In a test of visual positioning for gunners, a subject is required to move a knob to a target position as soon as a signal is given. On 161 trials, the subject's reaction time is distributed as follows:

REACTION TIME IN MILLISECONDS	f
279–281	2
276–278	0
273–275	3
270–272	4
267–269	7
264–266	7
261–263	11
258–260	17
255–257	24
252–254	31
249–251	28
246–248	14
243–245	8
240–242	5

How reliable is $\overline{X}$ as an estimate of μ, the subject's theoretical mean reaction time, if the experiment were to be repeated indefinitely?

7. On a Mathematical Reasoning test, the seventh-graders of School X obtain a mean score of 81 with standard deviation of 10. What range must include at least 75% of the scores? Suppose that norms for this test give a mean for seventh-graders of 60. How do the seventh-graders of School X compare with this norm?

8. Children living in a city slum area are found to have a mean IQ of 94 with standard deviation of 12. Children living nearby in a middle-class neighborhood are found to have a mean IQ of 102 with a standard deviation of 12. Compare the two distributions.

9. A group of subjects are randomly divided into an Experimental group and a Control group. Control group subjects perform a task under normal conditions. They achieve a mean performance rating of 23 with standard deviation of 3. The Experimental group performs the same task under stress conditions, and obtains a mean rating of 22 with standard deviation of 9. Compare the two distributions.

10. On a test of sentence memory, normals obtain a mean score of 50 with standard deviation of 10. A large group of schizophrenics obtain a mean score of 38 with standard deviation of 4. Compare the two distributions.

11. Differences between the IQ's of identical twins are found in

MEAN; STANDARD DEVIATION   100

one study to range from 0 to 24. The median difference is 8. Describe the general shape of the distribution. Is the *mean* difference below 8 or above 8?

12. The mean number of trials required to learn an experimental task is found to be 5.1, with standard deviation of 4.8. Describe the general shape of the distribution. Is the *median* number of trials above 5.1 or below 5.1?

13. A test constructor is trying to develop an intelligence test for young children that will depend as little as possible upon vocabulary and language skills. He tries out a preliminary form of his test on a large group of five-year-olds. They obtain a mean score of 32. The median is 25. Describe the general shape of the distribution. What does this shape imply about the difficulty of the test for this group?

14. An art school is getting many more applicants than it is able to accept. The school decides to screen the applicants by giving them a standard Artistic Aptitude test. The first year's applicants obtain a mean score of 72 on the test. The median is 80. What is the general shape of the distribution? It may be difficult to select the best applicants from a distribution like this one. Why?

15. In a survey of attitudes toward government policy, subjects are presented with a list of 100 items describing present and proposed policies and are asked to check those with which they agree. The median number of items checked is 55. The interquartile range is 45 to 65, and the overall range is from 10 to 95. What can be concluded about this distribution?

16. Scores on a certain neuroticism test may range from 0 to 30. A large group of clinic patients are found to have a mean score of 14 on the test with a standard deviation of 10. What can be concluded about this distribution?

Answers

1. For Team A, $\overline{X} = 3.2$ with $\sigma = 1.6$. For Team B, $\overline{X} = 3.7$ with $\sigma = 3.5$. Team B obviously made more runs over the course of the season, but Team B's performance is highly variable compared to the consistent performance of Team A. Team B's standard deviation is almost equal to their mean. When there cannot be observations below 0, as in this case, a standard deviation approximately equal to the mean indicates the presence of one or more relatively high observations, hence a positively skewed distribution. Thus,

Team B often makes few runs, but sometimes many runs. A bet on their performance against an unknown opponent is a very uncertain bet. For Team A, such a bet carries much less risk of being greatly in error because Team A's performance is much more consistent.

2. The third-grade children have a mean IQ of 121.2 with $\sigma = 8.3$. Mrs. C.'s daughter has an IQ of 118, which is 3.2 points below this mean. But the children of the class themselves differ from the mean by 8.3 points "on the average," and compared to this, Mrs. C.'s daughter does not differ greatly in IQ from the mean of the class. There will almost surely be a number of pupils in the class with IQ's lower than that of Mrs. C.'s daughter.

3. The mean number of errors is 11.8 with $s = 1.4$. According to the estimate of σ provided by s, the population of all such error scores would be clustered close together, differing "on the average" by only 1.4 from the true mean μ. If the observations of the population are clustered close together, the means of random samples drawn from the population must of necessity be close to one another also. Hence, it is highly unlikely that the sample mean of 11.8 differs much from μ. Since this is the case, $\overline{X}$ may be regarded as a reliable estimate of μ.

4. (a) The mean for the 50 delinquents is 3.4 with $s = 3.9$. Looking back at the distribution of scores, it is plain that only a handful of subjects have scores in the 3 to 4 range. The bulk of the scores lie below the mean, and these are balanced by a few scores relatively far above the mean. The mean, therefore, is not a good indicator in this case of the "typical" performance. (The median, which is 1.9, is a better indicator.)

(b) With $\overline{X} = 3.4$ as the best estimate of μ, and $s = 3.9$ as the best estimate of σ that can be made from the data, the results suggest that the population of measures would be positively skewed for the same reasons as in Problem 1: namely, a standard deviation about equal to the mean. Thus, some delinquents would be expected to get very high scores compared to the rest of the group. If the test is independently shown to provide valid measures of the need for recognition among such subjects, then the findings suggest that there are two types of delinquents—some for whom the need for recognition is strong, and many for whom it is relatively unimportant.

5. For the student nurses, $\mu = 70.2$ with $\sigma = 11.2$. The mean for the student nurses is 10.2 points higher than the mean of 60 obtained by the staff nurses. Perhaps the student nurses are more eager to render service to others than are the staff nurses who have been doing it for some time already. The staff nurses have a lower standard deviation (8.2), indicating they are a more homogeneous

group with respect to scores on this test. The student nurses are a less homogeneous group.

6. The subject's mean reaction time is 255.2 milliseconds. s is 7.8, which is large enough to suggest quite a bit of variation in the population of measures. From a consideration of s alone, we cannot determine the reliability of $\overline{X}$. In the next chapter, we will learn how to take both s and n into account in order to judge the reliability of a sample mean.

7. At least 75% of the scores must fall within two standard deviations of the mean, or between 61 and 101. Thus, *at least* 75% of these pupils are above the norm of 60. The seventh-graders of School X are clearly a superior group so far as performance on this test is concerned.

8. Although the means of the two groups differ by eight IQ points, there is considerable overlapping of the two distributions. Each of the means is well within a distance of one standard deviation from the other. If we add and subtract two standard deviations from each mean, we obtain a range for the slum children of 70 to 118, and a range for the middle-class children of from 78 to 126. Thus, while the two groups differ in mean IQ, it is clear that many individual slum children have higher IQ's than their middle-class neighbors.

9. The difference between means is only one point. The striking difference between the two distributions is in their variability. The ratings obtained by Control group subjects are clustered very close together, while the ratings of the Experimental group are spread out, extending both above and below the Control group distribution. Apparently, the stress conditions employed affected these subjects differently. Some subjects responded to the stress by performing even better than Control group subjects, and some responded with a much worse performance than that of the Control group. Thus, the larger standard deviation of the Experimental group reflects a marked difference in individual reactions to this stress condition.

10. There is not much overlap between these two distributions. Few, if any, schizophrenics obtained a score as high as the normal mean of 50, which is three standard deviations above the schizophrenic mean of 38. Some normals scored as low as the schizophrenics, but it would be safe to conclude that the large majority had higher scores. As a group, the performance of schizophrenics on this test is decidedly inferior to that of normals. In addition, the much smaller standard deviation of the schizophrenics reveals that they are a relatively homogeneous group with respect to the function being measured. Among the normals, with a standard deviation of 10, there are considerable individual differences in performance. As far

as this particular memory function is concerned, the effect of schizophrenia seems to be to "wipe away" individual differences, reducing performance to very nearly the same low level in most of the individuals affected

11. The distribution is positively skewed. The median is much closer to the low end of the range (0) than it is to the high end (24), indicating that scores are "bunched" at the low end. The mean will be pulled away from the median toward the "tail" of large differences, and therefore the mean difference will be above 8.

12. The distribution is positively skewed. With a standard deviation almost equal to the mean, and no observations as low as zero possible, some subjects must have required a very large number of trials. The mean will be increased by these extreme values, but the median will be unaffected by them. Therefore, the median will be below 5.1.

13. Because the median is lower than the mean, the distribution must be positively skewed, with scores bunched at the low end of the scale and a tail of high scores to the right. This distribution implies that the test is difficult for these children. Scores are crowded at the low end of the scale; relatively few of the five-year-olds are able to obtain a high score on this test. If the test is intended for children about this age, the test constructor will want to add more "easy" items to his test in order to spread the low scorers over a wider range, thus achieving better discrimination among them.

14. This distribution is negatively skewed, with scores bunched at the high end of the scale and a tail of low scores to the left. This test is "easy" for most of the applicants; relatively few fail to obtain a high score. It may be difficult to choose the best applicants because so many applicants have high scores. The test does not discriminate well at the high end of the distribution. To achieve a better separation of high scorers, a more difficult test will have to be used.

15. The interquartile range is symmetrical about the median, suggesting a symmetrical distribution for the middle 50% of scores. The very large difference between the interquartile range and the overall range suggests a wide scatter of the remaining scores, both above 65 and below 45. We would conclude that the distribution is probably highly variable, in spite of a concentration of scores close to the median. We could be wrong. There could be only one score at 10 and one at 95, and all the remaining scores close to 45 and 65. This is not likely but it is possible, and in that case the distribution would not be characterized as "highly variable."

16. This distribution is unquestionably highly variable. The standard deviation, as we have seen, is a type of average. To obtain

an average of 10, either there must be a considerable number of observations farther away from the mean than 10, or there must be at least one observation that is extremely distant from the mean. Since scores on this test can only range from 0 to 30, it is not possible to have even one observation that is "extremely distant" from the mean. Therefore, there must be many observations farther away from the mean than 10. To be farther away from the mean than 10, the observations must be crowded into the scoring spaces 0 to 4 and 24 to 30. Thus, the distribution is highly variable over a narrow range of possible scores. The shape of the distribution may be rectangular, or it may be bimodal or multimodal. In any case, it is clear that the patients tested are by no means a homogeneous group with respect to the neuroticism factor measured by this test.

chapter 5

The Normal
Curve

The normal curve shown in Fig. 5.1 is the graph of a theoretical frequency distribution. A frequency distribution is called *theoretical* if it was derived mathematically rather than empirically. Our interest in theoretical frequency distributions is that they serve as models, ideals of a sort, of what we believe would occur under certain circumstances if we could obtain all the observations of a specified population. When we can and do obtain all the observations in a population, then of course we do not need a theoretical frequency distribution. When we cannot obtain all the observations it is especially useful to have a theoretical distribution that can reasonably be taken as a model of the population. The normal distribution is such a theoretical distribution and, as will be seen, may be taken as a model of the population in many different situations.

The normal curve is best defined by its equation, which describes how the height of the curve varies with changes along the baseline of the graph. But for our purposes it will be more useful to describe how *proportions of area* under the curve vary with changes along the baseline. It will be recalled that a given proportion of the observations in a frequency distribution is represented by a corresponding and equal proportion of the area enclosed by a histogram or frequency polygon of the distribution. If we wished to know, for example, what proportion of the observations falls between two points in a frequency distribution, it would be possible to find out by applying a ruler to the histogram of the distribution and determining the proportion of the area that falls between verticals erected at these two points. Thus, "proportion of cases" and "proportion of area" have equivalent meanings. The normal curve represents an infinite population of cases distributed in proportions corresponding to the distribution of areas under the curve shown in Fig. 5.1.

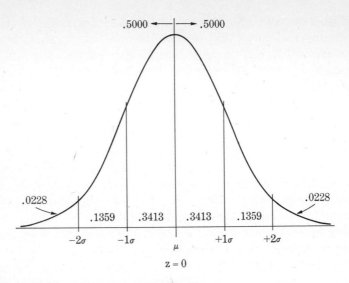

Figure 5.1

Distribution of Area Under the Normal Curve

How the area under the normal curve is distributed (hence how the scores of a normal distribution are distributed) is given in Table B of the Appendix. The column at the left of this table gives the z values of the scores. The z value of a score is its distance from the mean of the distribution measured in units of standard deviation. Thus, if a score has a z value of $+1.00$, this indicates that the score is one standard deviation (1σ) *above* the mean of the distribution. If a score has a z value of $-.50$, this indicates that the score is half a standard deviation ($.5\sigma$) *below* the mean of the distribution. Given the mean and σ of a distribution, the z value of any score X in the distribution may be obtained by substituting in the formula,

$$z = \frac{X - \bar{X}}{\sigma} \qquad (5.1)$$

If all the scores in a distribution are replaced by their z values, the distribution of z values will be identical in shape to the original distribution. Thus, where the original scores are normally distributed, the z values of those scores are also normally distributed. Table B shows the distribution of z values for the normal curve. Were we to start with any particular normal distribution and convert its scores to z values, the distribution of those z values would be given by Table B.

In the body of Table B may be read the proportion of the area under the normal curve that lies between the mean, which is at the exact center of the distribution, and given z values. The first entry in the table, $z = .00$, indicates the mean itself and, of course, there is zero area between the mean and itself. A vertical erected at the mean of the distribution divides the area under the normal curve in half, as may be seen in Fig. 5.1. Table B tells us that .3413 of the area under the curve lies between the mean and $z = 1.00$. Thus, about 34% of the cases in a normal distribution fall between the mean and a point one standard deviation above the mean. Since the normal distribution is perfectly symmetrical, it follows that .3413 of the area lies between the mean and $z = -1.00$, or one standard deviation below the mean. Some of the relationships between z and the distribution of area under the normal curve are illustrated in Fig. 5.1.

We shall illustrate first the use of the normal curve as the model for an empirical distribution that is approximately normally distributed. Following this, we will consider normal sampling distributions and the role of the normal curve in estimating parameters from sample values.

NORMAL EMPIRICAL DISTRIBUTIONS

Empirical distributions are never perfectly normal, but they may approximate the normal distribution. When they do, it is usually assumed that the population of measures, if they were obtainable, would be normally distributed. A normal curve, *with the same mean and standard deviation as those of the empirical distribution,* is taken as the model of the population. Centiles and centile ranks may then be computed directly from the normal curve table. The procedure is illustrated below.

Centiles and Centile Ranks of the Normal Curve

Example 1. Scores on an intelligence test are approximately normally distributed among the large group of subjects on whom the test was standardized. The mean score is 100 with $\sigma = 15$.

(a) Assuming a normal population, what is the centile rank of a score of 118? 106? 94? 82?

• • STEP 1. Find the z values of the scores by substituting in formula (5.1). Thus, for the score 118, $z = (118 - 100)/15 = +1.2$. The scores and their z values are shown in the first two columns of Table 5.1.

Table 5.1
Centile Ranks of Normally Distributed Scores (Mean = 100, σ = 15)

SCORE	z VALUE	AREA FROM MEAN TO z	CENTILE RANK
118	+1.2	.3849	88.49
106	+ .4	.1554	65.54
94	− .4	.1554	34.46
82	−1.2	.3849	11.51

• • STEP 2. Each z value is referred to Table B of the Appendix in order to determine the proportion of cases (the proportion of the total area) falling between the mean and this z value. Thus, .3849 of the area under the curve lies between the mean and $z = +1.2$. This value is entered in the third column of Table 5.1. Between the mean and $z = +.4$ is .1554 of the area. For minus values of z, the proportions are the same as for the corresponding plus values of z, except of course that these proportions lie below the mean.

• • STEP 3. When first learning to locate areas under the normal curve, it is helpful to make a rough sketch of the normal curve and shade in the portion(s) of interest. For example, to find the centile rank of $z = +1.2$, we wish the proportion of the area below this value.

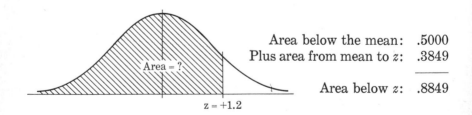

Area below the mean: .5000
Plus area from mean to z: .3849
_____
Area below z: .8849

z = +1.2

Figure 5.2
Finding the Centile Rank

The picture makes it clear that the proportion read from Table B must be *added to* the proportion below the mean (.5000). The same procedure is followed to determine the centile rank of $z = +.4$.

For minus values of z, we are led to a slightly different procedure. Thus, for $z = -.4$, we have

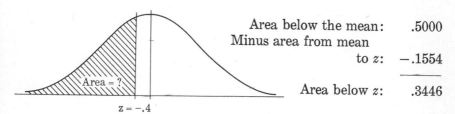

Area below the mean:	.5000
Minus area from mean to z:	$-.1554$
Area below z:	.3446

Figure 5.3

Finding the Centile Rank

Here it is clear that the proportion read from Table B must be *subtracted from* .5000 in order to determine the centile rank of z. This must also be done in the case of $z = -1.2$.

The proportions determined in this way are each multiplied by 100 to give the centile ranks shown in the last column of Table 5.1.

(b) What is the 90th centile of the distribution? the 10th centile?

• • STEP 1. To find the centiles of a normal distribution, the above procedures are carried out in reverse order. The 90th centile is the point on the scale of scores below which 90% of the observations fall. Thus we are given the area below z, .90. The problem is to determine the value of z. The desired z can be found from Table B if we know the area that lies between this z value and the mean. Accordingly, the first step is to determine the area from the mean to the desired z, as shown below.

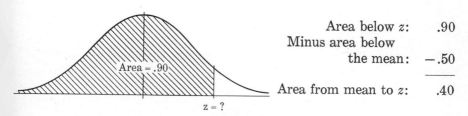

Area below z:	.90
Minus area below the mean:	$-.50$
Area from mean to z:	.40

Figure 5.4

Finding the Centile

Using the area column of Table B, the closest value we find to .40 is .3997. The corresponding z value is 1.28. Since, as our sketch shows, z is above the mean, the value read from the table is a plus value. Thus, $z = +1.28$ is the 90th centile, the point below which 90% of the observations fall.

The 10th centile will be of the same z distance below the mean, since .40 of the area also falls between the mean and the 10th centile of the distribution.

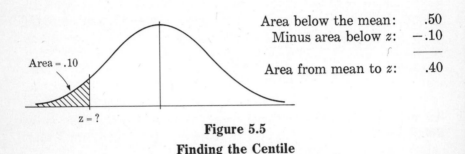

Area below the mean: .50
Minus area below z: −.10
_____
Area from mean to z: .40

Area = .10

z = ?

Figure 5.5
Finding the Centile

Since z is below the mean in this case, the value read from the table is a minus value. Thus, $z = -1.28$ is the 10th centile, the point below which 10% of the observations fall.

• • STEP 2. The obtained z values are converted to the original units of measure by solving formula (5.1) for X. Thus,

$$X = \bar{X} + z\sigma \qquad (5.2)$$

For the 90th centile, we have

$$X = 100 + (+1.28)(15) = 100 + 19.20 = 119.2$$

For the 10th centile, we have

$$X = 100 + (-1.28)(15) = 100 - 19.20 = 80.8$$

The 90th centile of this distribution is 119.2 and the 10th centile is 80.8. These are the values that cut off the upper and lower 10% of the distribution.

• DISCUSSION

In this problem, we used the normal curve as a model to determine centiles and centile ranks for an unavailable population of scores.

These centiles and centile ranks are not the same ones we would obtain by computation from the available, empirical distribution, but if the unseen population is normal, they are likely to indicate relationships in that population quite accurately. In fact, the normal curve approximations may provide a more accurate estimate of population relationships than centiles and centile ranks computed from the obtained empirical distribution.

When the obtained empirical distribution closely approximates the normal, then of course differences between the empirical centiles and normal-curve centiles will be small. One way to judge the normality of an obtained distribution is to compare, say, every fifth centile of the distribution with the corresponding centiles of a normal curve having the same mean and standard deviation. If the differences are not great—and they should not be if the sample is very large—the obtained distribution is regarded as "approximately normal" and the sample is assumed to come from a normal population. Obviously, if an empirical distribution is not approximately normal, it would be inappropriate to use the normal curve as a model of the population.

NORMAL SAMPLING DISTRIBUTIONS

Suppose a vast number of random samples of the same size are drawn from a population and the mean of each sample is computed. The resulting means may then be organized into a frequency distribution, plotted as a frequency polygon, and in general treated like any other distribution of values. Such a distribution is called a *sampling distribution*, in recognition of the fact that its values—means, in this case—are attributes of *samples* rather than attributes of individuals.

Statistics other than the mean may be treated in the same manner. We could compute the median of each of our samples and make a sampling distribution of the medians. Similarly, we could make a sampling distribution of the standard deviations of the samples, or their ranges, or any other sample characteristic of interest to us. Suppose instead of scores or measures, our samples consisted of data classified into categories. We could determine for each sample the proportion of observations falling in a given category, such as the proportion of Republicans in each sample, and make a sampling distribution of these proportions. Thus, a sampling distribution may be made for any statistic (sample characteristic) by collecting a multitude of random samples of the same size, computing the statistic of interest for each sample, and organizing the resulting values into a frequency distribution.

Mathematicians have determined what particular sampling distributions would look like if an infinite number of sample values were obtained. That is, for particular sample attributes like the mean, they have described the distribution of an infinite population of random sample values—the distribution we would approach more and more closely if random samples of a given size were continually drawn from an inexhaustible supply. A number of such sampling distributions are known to be normal or to approach closely the normal curve in form. When this is so, the normal curve is taken as the model of that sampling distribution.

We shall consider here two sampling distributions for which, under appropriate circumstances, the normal curve may be taken as a model: the distribution of sample means, and the distribution of sample proportions.

Sampling Distribution of Means ($n \geq 30$)

We consider now the *sampling distribution of the mean*—that is, the distribution of sample means that would result if we drew from a given population an infinite number of random samples (all of the same size n), determined the mean $\overline{X}$ of each sample, and organized the $\overline{X}$'s into a frequency distribution. When the sample size n is 30 or more, the distribution of random sample means closely approaches the form of the normal curve. The mean of the sampling distribution, $\mu_{\overline{x}}$, will be equal to the mean μ of the population from which the samples came. The standard deviation $\sigma_{\overline{x}}$ of the sampling distribution is equal to $\sigma/\sqrt{n}$, where σ is the standard deviation of the population and n is the size of the sample. These relationships between the parameters of the sampling distribution and the parameters of the population from which the samples came may be stated:

$$\mu_{\overline{x}} = \mu$$

$$\sigma_{\overline{x}} = \frac{\sigma}{\sqrt{n}}$$

The population values μ and σ will not ordinarily be known, but they can be estimated from the sample. Thus, the sample mean $\overline{X}$

is an estimate of μ, and s is an estimate of σ. The standard deviation of the sampling distribution may then be estimated by $s/\sqrt{n}$. We shall call this estimate $s_{\bar{x}}$. Thus,

$$s_{\bar{x}} = \frac{s}{\sqrt{n}} \tag{5.3}$$

We shall use this relationship in the example that follows to judge the reliability of a sample mean, and to determine a range of values that is likely to contain the parameter μ.

Example 2.   In a survey to study the amount of use of home telephones, it is determined that a random sample of 400 evening calls made from different points in a large residential area had a mean duration $\bar{X} = 6.3$ minutes with standard deviation $s = 2.4$ minutes.
    (a) Is this mean a reliable estimate of μ?

• • STEP 1. The sample mean $\bar{X}$ is regarded as one of a multitude of sample means that are normally distributed about $\mu_{\bar{x}}$, the mean of the sampling distribution. To estimate the variability of the $\bar{X}$'s, we compute $s_{\bar{x}}$. Thus, by formula (5.3),

$$s_{\bar{x}} = \frac{2.4}{\sqrt{400}} = .12$$

The value .12 estimates the standard deviation of the sampling distribution.

• Discussion

The value .12 is very small, suggesting that the $\bar{X}$'s of this sampling distribution are clustered very close together. According to our estimate, they differ from $\mu_{\bar{x}}$ by only .12 "on the average." In that case, it is likely that our particular sample mean, which is one of these $\bar{X}$'s, does not differ much from $\mu_{\bar{x}}$ either. Because $\mu_{\bar{x}} = \mu$, it follows that our sample mean is also likely to be close to μ, the value of the population mean. Therefore, the value 6.3 may be regarded as a reliable estimate of μ.

In general, if $s_{\bar{x}}$ is small, then it is likely that $\bar{X}$ differs little from μ. In this case, $\bar{X}$ is said to be a *reliable estimate* of μ. If $s_{\bar{x}}$ is large, then it is not possible to conclude *either* that $\bar{X}$ differs little from μ *or* that $\bar{X}$ differs much from μ. It is in this latter case that $\bar{X}$ is said to be an *unreliable estimate* of μ.

(b) Estimate a range of values that is likely to contain μ.

Our best single estimate of μ is given by $\overline{X}$. Although the computations of part (a) suggest that $\overline{X}$ differs little from μ, only vague information is conveyed by the statement, "μ is probably close to 6.3 minutes." How close? Would five minutes be a good guess? Seven minutes? Within what range of values is μ likely to be? We cannot directly determine a likely range for μ, the population mean, but we can estimate such a range for $\mu_{\bar{x}}$, the mean of the sampling distribution. Since $\mu_{\bar{x}} = \mu$, our range will hold for μ also.

We turn again to the sampling distribution of $\overline{X}$'s, seeking a range of values that is likely to include the unknown $\mu_{\bar{x}}$. For the moment, let us assume that the estimate of $\sigma_{\bar{x}}$ obtained in part (a) is exactly correct. That is, assume it is known that $\sigma_{\bar{x}} = .12$. Because the sampling distribution is normal, we know from Table B that about 68% of the sample means fall within the range bounded by one $\sigma_{\bar{x}}$ below and one $\sigma_{\bar{x}}$ above the mean, or within $\mu_{\bar{x}} \pm .12$. It seems likely enough that our sample mean should be one of these 68%. We may say the chances are about 68 in 100 that $\overline{X}$ is within a distance of .12 from $\mu_{\bar{x}}$. From Table B, about 95% of all sample means are within two $\sigma_{\bar{x}}$ of the mean, or within $\mu_{\bar{x}} \pm .24$. It is very likely that our sample mean is one of these 95%. The chances are thus about 95 in 100 that our sample mean is within a distance of .24 from $\mu_{\bar{x}}$. If $\overline{X}$ is within a distance .24 of $\mu_{\bar{x}}$, then of course $\mu_{\bar{x}}$ must be some value within the range $\overline{X} \pm .24$. We do not know, of course, how far $\overline{X}$ is from $\mu_{\bar{x}}$, but the chances are 95 in 100 that the distance is no more than .24. Therefore we claim, with a 95% chance of being correct, that $\mu_{\bar{x}}$ (hence μ) is some value within the range $\overline{X} \pm .24$.

A range such as the one we obtained is called a **confidence interval**. For this example, with $\overline{X} = 6.3$, the confidence interval for μ is $6.3 \pm .24$, or 6.06 to 6.54. The values 6.06 and 6.54 are called *95% confidence limits*.* We write: $6.06 < \mu < 6.54$, with 95% confidence. And from a consideration of this range of values, we can now say that five minutes and seven minutes are not good guesses about the population mean μ; these guesses are far outside the range of "likely" values.

The foregoing is based on the assumption that $\sigma_{\bar{x}}$ is *known* to be .12. Actually, .12 is the estimate $s_{\bar{x}}$ and not the parameter $\sigma_{\bar{x}}$, so the confidence interval we obtained must be regarded as an approximation. When the sample size is as large as 30, s is a reliable estimate

* Conventionally, in obtaining 95% confidence limits, the more precise value $1.96\sigma_{\bar{x}}$ is used in the calculations rather than $2\sigma_{\bar{x}}$, used here to simplify the illustration.

of σ and the approximation will usually be a good one. The larger the sample, the more certain we can be of a good approximation. (For $n < 30$, see Chapter 10).

To summarize: Using s as an estimate of σ, approximate confidence limits for μ may be obtained from the formula

$$\bar{X} \pm z_o \frac{s}{\sqrt{n}} \qquad (5.4)$$

where z_o is determined by the investigator's choice of a confidence level. Typical confidence levels are .90, .95, .99, .997. To illustrate, we compute a 99% confidence interval for this example.

• • STEP 1. Determine the value of z_o. A confidence level of .99 implies a range that includes the middle 99% of sample means. Therefore, we wish the z values that include the middle 99% of the normal distribution. From Table B, we find the z value for which the area between the mean and z is .495 (half of .99). This value, $z = 2.58$, is z_o.

• • STEP 2. Compute $s/\sqrt{n}$, the estimate of $\sigma_{\bar{x}}$. From part (a), $s/\sqrt{n} = .12$.

• • STEP 3. Substituting in formula (5.4), we have

$$6.3 \pm 2.58(.12) = 6.3 \pm .31$$

This gives 5.99 to 6.61 as the 99% confidence interval. We write,

$$5.99 < \mu < 6.61, \text{ with 99% confidence.}$$

• DISCUSSION

Obviously, the range of values "likely to contain μ" varies with the confidence level that is chosen. The range depends upon how likely we want it to be that our statement about μ is correct. With a 95% chance of being correct, a narrower interval could be given (6.06 to 6.54) than when we chose a 99% chance of being correct (and obtained the interval 5.99 to 6.61). In either case, we would reject five minutes and seven minutes as unreasonable guesses about μ. But what about six minutes? It is excluded as a likely value by the 95% confidence interval but included by the 99% confidence interval. One cannot state with great confidence that μ is not six minutes, while such statements can be made about five minutes and seven minutes.

Sampling Distribution of a Proportion (nP and nQ Greater than 5)

When a population is divided into two mutually exclusive categories—male and female, voters and non-voters—it is called a *binomial population*. The proportion of the population in one category is designated P and the proportion in the other category is designated Q. The corresponding proportions in a sample drawn from the population are designated p and q.

If random samples of the same size n are drawn from a binomial population, the sampling distribution of p approaches the normal distribution for larger and larger n. How fast the sampling distribution of p approaches the normal distribution depends upon both the sample size n and the population proportions P and Q. When both nP and nQ are greater than 5, the normal curve provides a model of the sampling distribution that is satisfactory for most purposes. When P and Q are unknown and the sample estimates p and q are used in their place, a safer guide is to require that both np and nq are at least 10 before using the normal curve as a model of the sampling distribution. We shall adopt this as our rule.

A confidence interval may be determined for the population proportion P by applying the same logic used to obtain a confidence interval for μ. That is, using the normal curve as a model of the sampling distribution of p, we compute a confidence interval for the mean μ_p of the sampling distribution. Since $\mu_p = P$, the obtained confidence interval holds for P also. The relationships between the parameters of the sampling distribution and the population parameters P and Q are:

$$\mu_p = P$$

$$\sigma_p = \sqrt{\frac{PQ}{n}}$$

The standard deviation σ_p of the sampling distribution is estimated by substituting the sample values p and q for the parameters P and Q. This results in an approximation which, again, we can have confidence in only when n is large. Confidence limits for P are then given by

$$p \pm z_o \sqrt{\frac{pq}{n}} \tag{5.5}$$

Example 3. An investigator is interested in the development of form perception in young children. He tests a random sample of 80 children of the same age to determine how many of them can discriminate between a six-sided figure and an eight-sided figure. He finds that only 24 of the children tested are able to make this discrimination. What is the 95% confidence interval for P, the proportion able to make this discrimination in the population from which the sample came?

• • STEP 1. Check that the normal curve will give an acceptable approximation of the sampling distribution. The frequency 24 is the value of np, and since $nq = 80 - 24 = 56$, both np and nq are well over 10. We conclude that the normal curve may be taken as the model of the sampling distribution.

• • STEP 2. Determine the sample proportions p and q. Thus,

$$p = \frac{f}{n} = \frac{24}{80} = .30$$

$$q = 1 - p = .70$$

The proportion of children *in the sample* who are able to make the discrimination is .30, and the proportion who are not able is .70.

• • STEP 3. Determine the value of z_o. Since the 95% confidence interval is desired, we wish the z values that include the middle 95% of the normal distribution. From Table B, we find the z value such that the area between the mean and z is .4750 (half of .95). This value, $z = 1.96$, is z_o.

• • STEP 4. Substituting in formula (5.5), we obtain

$$.30 \pm 1.96 \sqrt{\frac{(.30)(.70)}{80}} = .30 \pm 1.96(.0512) = .30 \pm .10$$

The limits .20 and .40 give us an approximate confidence interval for μ_p, the mean of the sampling distribution. Since $\mu_p = P$, we claim

$$.20 < P < .40, \text{ with 95\% confidence.}$$

• DISCUSSION

According to our confidence interval for P, somewhere between 20 and 40% of these young children are able to discriminate between a six-sided and an eight-sided figure. The proportion unable to make the discrimination is given by the corresponding interval for Q. (Since $P + Q = 1$, if P is between .20 and .40, Q must be between .80 and .60.) Thus,

$$.60 < Q < .80, \text{ with 95\% confidence.}$$

It seems safe to conclude that a majority of the children in the population sampled are not able to make this discrimination.

Note that these conclusions could refer only to the population of children from which the sample was drawn. No investigator has the means to draw a random sample from the population of all three-year-olds or all four-year-olds, or all of any age group. Nor can any statistical procedure lead to inferences about a population that was not sampled. *Statistical inferences are necessarily limited to the population from which the sample came.* It is for this reason that investigators in the behavioral sciences, when reporting their research, take great care to describe their subjects and how they were selected. If the population sampled seems fairly representative of some larger population (*e.g.*, much like all middle-class three-year-olds), the reader himself may generalize to this larger population. But he does so on the basis of his own accumulated experience and perceptions, not because relevance to this larger population has been demonstrated.

SAMPLING DISTRIBUTIONS AND EXPECTATION

The mean of a sampling distribution is called the *expected value* or the *expectation* of the statistic. And the standard deviation of a sampling distribution is called the *standard error* of the statistic. For example, $\mu_{\bar{x}}$ is the expected value or expectation of the statistic $\bar{X}$ because $\mu_{\bar{x}}$ is the mean of the sampling distribution of $\bar{X}$. $\sigma_{\bar{x}}$ is called the standard error of $\bar{X}$ (more commonly, "the standard error of the mean") because $\sigma_{\bar{x}}$ is the standard deviation of the sampling distribution of $\bar{X}$. Similarly, μ_p is the expectation of the sample value p, and σ_p is the standard error of p.

Because $\mu_{\bar{x}} = \mu$, the population mean, and $\mu_p = P$, the population proportion, the expected values of $\bar{X}$ and p are commonly written

$$E(\bar{X}) = \mu$$
$$E(p) = P$$

When it is true of a statistic that the mean of its sampling distribution is equal to a population parameter, as in these cases, the statistic is called an *unbiased estimate* of that parameter. Thus, $\bar{X}$ is said to be an unbiased estimate of μ, and p an unbiased estimate of P.

A statistic is said to be a *biased estimate* of a parameter when the mean of its sampling distribution is either smaller or larger than, rather than equal to, the parameter. For example, the variance of a sample computed from the formula $\sigma^2 = \Sigma(X - \overline{X})^2/n$ gives a biased estimate of the population variance σ^2 because such sample variances tend, when averaged, to have a mean smaller than the parameter σ^2. It is for this reason that when sample data are used to estimate the population variance, the variance $s^2 = \Sigma(X - \overline{X})^2/(n - 1)$ is computed from the sample. The mean of the sampling distribution of s^2 is equal to the population variance σ^2, so s^2 is an unbiased estimate of the parameter σ^2. (While it is not true that s, the standard deviation, provides an unbiased estimate of the parameter σ, s remains the best estimate we can make of σ.)

The procedures of this chapter are representative of that branch of statistical inference called *parameter estimation*. Actually, as we have seen, population parameters are not estimated directly. It is the parameters of the sampling distribution that are estimated. We began with one random sample value and asked, in effect, what is the mean of its sampling distribution? We were able to translate the answer to this question into a statement about the population parameter *because the mean of the sampling distribution was equal to the population parameter*. Thus, the procedure requires an unbiased estimate of the parameter; it requires a statistic whose sampling distribution has a mean that is equal to the parameter.

To summarize: In order to estimate the value of a parameter from sample data, it is necessary to have a statistic that is an unbiased estimate of the parameter. The sample yielding this statistic must, of course, be a random sample. It is the sampling distributions of *random* sample values that are known to us; we know nothing at all about how nonrandom sample values are distributed. And, to repeat, the sample must come from the population about which inferences will be made. Statistical inferences cannot be made about populations other than the one actually sampled.

Practice Problems

1. A student applies to a counselling center for vocational guidance. He is given a series of tests, with results as shown below. The tests were previously standardized on large groups of comparable students, and the scores in each case were found to be approximately normally distributed. The standardization group mean and standard

deviation is shown for each test. What is the centile rank of each of the student's scores, with reference to the group on which the test was standardized?

Test	Student's Score	Standardization Group	
		Mean	σ
General Intelligence	130	100	15
Emotional Stability	40	50	10
Extraversion	49	64	12
Science Aptitude	127	100	20
Artistic Aptitude	70	70	13
Vocational Interest:			
Science	50	57	10
Art	71	54	8
Business	38	52	7
Social Service	59	55	9

2. Scores on a graduate-school admissions test are normally distributed with mean $= 500$ and $\sigma = 100$. (a) Frank obtained a grade of 540 and his friend Al a grade of 510. What is the difference between their centile ranks? (b) Joe obtained a grade of 730 and his friend Bill a grade of 700. What is the difference between their centile ranks? (c) Explain why the answers to parts (a) and (b) are not the same. (d) If a graduate school decides to consider only those applicants who score among the upper one-third on this test, what is the minimum score an applicant must obtain in order to be considered by this school?

3. Repeated measurements of a subject's auditory threshold for a stimulus tone are found to be approximately normally distributed with mean intensity $= 15$ decibels and $\sigma = 3$ decibels. (a) What is the interquartile range of the distribution (25th to 75th centiles)? (b) What is the median of the distribution? (c) On 90% of trials, the subject's threshold is *below what value?* (d) On 95% of trials? (e) On 99% of trials? (f) On 90% of trials, the subject's threshold is *above what value?* (g) On 95% of trials? (h) On 99% of trials?

4. A theoretical distribution of sample means is normal in form with $\mu_{\bar{x}} = 50$ and $\sigma_{\bar{x}} = 2.0$. (a) What proportion of the sample means differs from $\mu_{\bar{x}}$ by as much as 1.0? (Both in the direction of being larger *and* in the direction of being smaller than $\mu_{\bar{x}}$.) (b) What proportion differs by as much as 2.0? (c) By as much as 3.0? (d) By as much as 4.0? (e) 5.0? (f) 6.0? (g) Ten percent of the sample means differ from $\mu_{\bar{x}}$ by as much as ___?___ (h) Five percent of the sample means differ from $\mu_{\bar{x}}$ by as much as ___?___ (i) One percent of the sample means differ from $\mu_{\bar{x}}$ by as much as ___?___

5. Is the distribution of scores given below approximately normal? ($\bar{X} = 25.0$, $\sigma = 5.0$)

Scores	f
36–38	2
33–35	5
30–32	11
27–29	19
24–26	26
21–23	19
18–20	11
15–17	5
12–14	2

$$n = 100$$

There are several ways of determining whether an empirical distribution is approximately normal. One way is to proceed as follows: Convert the frequencies to proportions and make a cumulative proportion column. The entries in this column give the proportion of cases that fall below the *upper exact limit* of each scoring interval. Using formula (5.1), find the z values of the upper exact limits. From the normal curve table, determine the proportion of cases in a normal distribution that falls below these z values. If the distribution of scores is approximately normal, the entries in the cumulative proportion column should be close to the proportions found from the normal curve table.

6. Is this distribution approximately normal? ($\bar{X} = 40$, $\sigma = 6.0$)

Scores	f
51–53	4
48–50	8
45–47	12
42–44	16
39–41	20
36–38	16
33–35	12
30–32	8
27–29	4

$$n = 100$$

7. The mean number of parts turned out per day by 36 machine operators randomly drawn from a large number of workers is found to be 42.3 with $s = 12$. (a) Is this mean a reliable estimate of μ? (b) Is it likely that the population mean is as low as 30? (c) Compute a 95% confidence interval for μ.

8. A subject's mean reaction time for 161 trials was found to be 255.2 milliseconds with $s = 7.8$. (a) Is this mean a reliable estimate of μ? (b) Compute a 99% confidence interval for μ.

9. The mean number of Rorschach responses given by a random

sample of 49 clinic patients is 22.9 with $s = 16.1$. (a) Compute a 95% confidence interval for μ. (b) A group of normals drawn from the same community gave a mean of 25.0 Rorschach responses. Is it likely that the population mean for clinic patients is as high as 25?

10. High school seniors in a certain county are all given the same academic achievement examination before graduating. A random sample of 144 seniors from School A obtained a mean of 78 on the exam with $s = 12$. A random sample of 169 seniors from School B obtained a mean of 83 with $s = 13$. Does this difference in sample means indicate that the population means of Schools A and B are different? Or should the difference be attributed to the accidents of random sampling? (Compute 95% and 99% confidence intervals for each mean.)

11. In a survey of attitudes toward foreign aid, 79 out of 100 subjects interviewed were in favor of withholding all aid from Communist-supported nations. What statement can be made about the proportion of subjects in the population who favor this policy?

12. A random sample of 300 automobile owners are asked which of two automobile designs they prefer, A or B. Design A is preferred by 180 of the subjects. (a) Compute a 99% confidence interval for P, the proportion in the population who prefer Design A, and a similar interval for Q, the proportion who prefer Design B. (b) Is it likely that the designs are equally preferred in the population?

13. In a weight discrimination experiment, a subject is asked to judge which of two weights presented to him is the heavier. When the difference between the two weights was three grams, the subject judged correctly on ten out of the 20 trials given. (a) Compute a 95% confidence interval for P. (b) Is it likely that the subject is able to make this discrimination as often as 65% of the time? (Is it likely that P is as high as .65?) (c) Suppose the subject had judged the weights correctly on 50 out of 100 trials. Would the answer to parts (a) and (b) be the same?

14. In a study of the effectiveness of a new psychiatric drug, a group of 50 schizophrenic patients are randomly divided into an Experimental group and a Control group. All subjects are given psychiatric ratings by independent raters who have no knowledge of the experiment. The Experimental group subjects are then given the new drug daily over a two-week period, while Control group subjects receive daily placebos over the same period. Two weeks after the conclusion of the experiment, the patients are rated again by the same raters. Of the 25 Experimental group subjects, 14 are found to show improvement. Of the Control group, only ten of the 25 subjects are improved. Can it be concluded that the new drug is more effective

than a placebo in improving the condition of these patients? Compute a 95% confidence interval for each group.

Answers

1. In the order in which the tests are listed, the student's centile ranks are: 97.72, 15.87, 10.56, 91.15, 50.00, 24.20, 98.32, 2.28, 67.00. The test results suggest problems which the student and his counsellor will discuss together. For example, compared to the standardization groups, the student has a very strong interest in art but only an "average" aptitude for art, while his high aptitude for science is accompanied by a relatively low interest in science. What else do the test results suggest?

2. (a) Frank's centile rank is 65.54, Al's is 53.98. The difference is 11.56 centile ranks. (b) Joe's centile rank is 98.93, Bill's is 97.72. The difference is 1.21 centile ranks. (c) Although the scoring difference is the same between the two sets of friends, so many students obtain scores around the middle of the distribution that an increase of 30 points here is sufficient to surpass a large percentage of students, while so few students score at the extremes of the distribution that a similar score increase in these regions surpasses only a small additional percentage of students. Since this is always true when scores are normally distributed, centile ranks can often be misleading. For this reason, many tests report norms in the form of "standard scores" (transformed z values) as well as giving the centile ranks of the scores. For example, the z values of the friends' scores, .4 and .1, and 2.3 and 2.0, do reflect equal scoring differences. (d) 544.

3. (a) 13.0 db to 17.0 db. (b) 15.0 db. (c) 18.8 db. (d) 19.9 db. (e) 22.0 db. (f) 11.2 db. (g) 10.1 db. (h) 8.0 db.

4. (a) .3085 are above 51 and .3085 are below 49, so a total of .6170 of the sample means differ from $\mu_{\bar{x}}$ by as much as 1.0. (b) .3174 (c) .1336 (d) .0456 (e) .0124 (f) .0026 (g) 3.28. The extreme 10% of the sample means lie beyond $z = \pm 1.64$. These sample means differ from $\mu_{\bar{x}}$ by at least 1.64σ. Since σ is 2.0, they differ from $\mu_{\bar{x}}$ by as much as $1.64(2.0) = 3.28$. (h) 3.92. (i) 5.16.

5. The cumulative proportions found from the normal curve table, in order from highest to lowest, are: .9965, .9821, .9332, .8159, .6179, .3821, .1841, .0668, .0179. These proportions are very close to those given by a cumulative proportion column for the distribution. The form of the distribution is close to normal, although it is slightly more "peaked" at the center than a normal distribution.

6. The cumulative proportions found from the normal curve table, in order from highest to lowest, are: .9878, .9599, .8944, .7734, .5987, .4013, .2266, .1056, .0401. There are important (because systematic) discrepancies between these proportions and those given by the cumulative proportion column for the distribution. Observe that below the mean the cumulative proportions tend to increase faster than the normal curve proportions, while above the mean they tend to increase more slowly than the normal curve proportions. The distribution is more "spread out" than a normal distribution; there are more cases in the "tails" of the distribution than occur in a normal distribution. This distribution is not "approximately normal."

7. (a) The standard deviation of sample means is estimated by $s_{\bar{x}}$ to be 2.0. The sample mean of 42.3 may be regarded as a fairly reliable estimate of μ, since about two-thirds of such sample means are estimated to be within 2.0 of μ. (b) It is highly unlikely that μ is as low as 30. This value is at a distance of more than six standard errors (six standard deviations) from 42.3, and it is extremely rare to obtain a random sample value that is six standard errors from the mean of its sampling distribution. (c) $38.38 < \mu < 46.22$, with 95% confidence.

8. (a) $s_{\bar{x}} = .61$. This estimate suggests that the sample means are clustered close together about μ. Hence, the mean of this sample is likely to be close to μ and may be regarded as a reliable estimate of μ. (b) $253.63 < \mu < 256.77$, with 99% confidence.

9. (a) $18.39 < \mu < 27.41$, with 95% confidence. (b) Yes, in the sense that 25 is not an implausible value. $s_{\bar{x}} = 2.3$, which places our sample mean within one standard deviation of the value 25.

10. For School A, the 95% confidence limits are 76.04 and 79.96, while for School B the 95% limits are 81.04 and 84.96. There is no overlap at all between these two interval estimations of the population mean. The 99% confidence limits for the two school means are 75.42 and 80.58 (School A) and 80.42 and 85.58 (School B). Even at the 99% confidence level, there is only a very small overlap between the two confidence intervals. It seems highly unlikely that the population means of School A and School B are the same; the population mean of School B is almost certainly the higher.

11. If the 100 subjects interviewed are a random sample, a statement can be made *about the population that was sampled*. If the subjects are not a random sample, no statements can be made about some larger group. Assuming the former circumstance, we can assert with 90% confidence that $.723 < P < .857$, or with 95% confidence that $.710 < P < .870$, or with 99% confidence that $.685 < P < .895$.

That is, we can make a statement about the population proportion who favor this policy at any desired level of confidence.

12. (a) The 99% confidence intervals are: $.527 < P < .673$, and $.327 < Q < .473$. (b) No, it is very unlikely that P is as low as .5 (or that Q is as high as .5).

13. (a) $.281 < P < .719$, with 95% confidence. (b) Yes, in the sense that we cannot reject .65 as an implausible value for P. (c) No. In this case, the 95% confidence limits for P are .402 and .598. Since .65 lies well above this range, it is unlikely that P is as large as .65.

14. For the Experimental group, the 95% confidence limits for P are .366 and .754. For the Control group, the 95% confidence limits are .208 and .592. There is a substantial overlap between the two intervals, making it entirely plausible that P, the proportion who improve, is the same for the populations of Experimental and Control group subjects, and therefore that the drug is no more effective than a placebo for these patients. The drug *may* be more effective—this is also "plausible"—but its superiority has not been demonstrated by this experiment and no conclusions can be drawn.

chapter 6

Linear
Correlation

Correlation refers to the relationship between two variables. Is body type related to temperament? Is speed of learning related to the amount of reward? Do traffic accidents go down as the weather gets colder? Questions such as these inquire basically whether two variables *change together in some consistent way*. For example: The plumper the body type, the more jovial the temperament. Or, the greater the reward, the faster the learning; the colder the weather, the fewer the traffic accidents. When two variables tend to vary together in a consistent way, they are said to be *correlated*. When there is no consistent pattern or relationship between them the variables are said to be *uncorrelated*. This would be the case if, for example, it were found that some very plump people are jovial but just as many are not.

There are many types of measures of correlation, appropriate for different situations and for different kinds of data. We shall consider here what is called *linear correlation*. Linear correlation is typically computed for data that are in the form of measures, and then, as the name implies, only when the measures are linearly related. The degree of linear correlation between two sets of measures is designated by the letter r, which is called the *coefficient of linear correlation* or, more briefly, just the *correlation coefficient*.

LINEAR

CORRELATION

The Scatter Diagram and Linearity

Example 1.　　An army psychologist has the job of selecting men who are skillful in tracking a moving target. Because so much time is required to test the men individually by means of a realistic tracking test, the psychologist would like a simpler screening device that might be given to large groups of men at one time. He develops a pencil-and-paper maze-tracing test that seems to require a kind of skill similar to that required in tracking. If men who do well on this Maze Test also do well on an individual Tracking Test, then the Maze Test can be used with large groups to speed up the selection process. As a preliminary study, he gives the Maze Test and a Tracking Test to ten men who have had no previous tracking experience. Their scores are as follows:

SUBJECT	MAZE TEST (X)	TRACKING TEST (Y)
A	8	10
B	7	7
C	4	8
D	4	6
E	4	6
F	4	4
G	3	7
H	3	4
I	2	3
J	1	5

Do subjects who score high on the Maze Test also score high in tracking? From an inspection of the results, it would seem to be so. There is a tendency for tracking scores to change in a consistent way with maze scores. As maze scores increase, tracking scores increase; as maze scores become lower, tracking scores are lower. The trend is not perfectly consistent. There are exceptions—*e.g.*, Subject G, who received a low maze score and a relatively high tracking score— so the correlation is not perfect. Still, the trend is strong and we should like a measure of the correlation that is present.

• • STEP 1. Before computing r, we check to see that the relationship between the two variables is approximately linear. This is done by inspecting a *scatter diagram* of the scores. One of the variables is laid out along the Y axis and the other along the X axis, as shown in Fig. 6.1. A point is plotted for each pair of scores. Thus, there is a point on the graph for the first pair of scores, 8 and 10, another point for the second pair, 7 and 7, and so on.

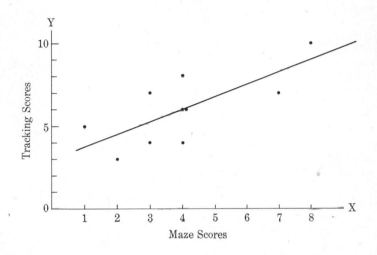

Figure 6.1

Scatter Diagram Showing the Relationship Between Scores on a Tracking Test and Scores on a Maze Test

• DISCUSSION

A relationship is said to be linear when the best-fitting line for the plotted points of the scatter diagram is a straight line. Roughly defined, the best-fitting line is the line that, over all, comes closest to all the points. A straight line has been added to the scatter diagram in Fig. 6.1, and, as may be seen, it "fits" the data rather well. When this is true, r will give a good description of the correlation between the two variables. When this is not true and the points of the scatter diagram are better fitted by a curved line, as in (c) of Fig. 6.2, then r will give an inaccurate description of the correlation. Some other correlational method should be used. For the data of

Fig. 6.1, we conclude that the relationship is linear and that r will accurately describe the correlation.

In our example, the slope of the best-fitting line is positive so the correlation is said to be *positive*. A positive slope occurs when an increase in one variable is accompanied by an increase in the other variable, as in Fig. 6.1. A negative slope occurs when an increase in one variable is accompanied by a *decrease* in the other variable. This would be the case, for example, if the higher the scores on the Maze

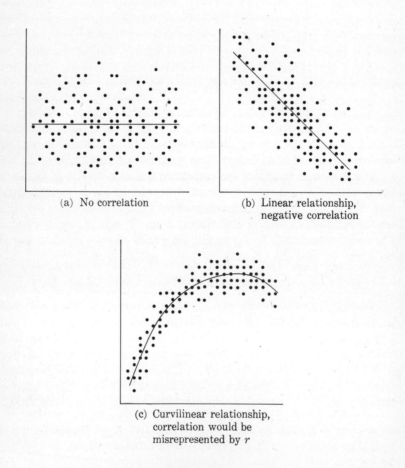

(a) No correlation

(b) Linear relationship, negative correlation

(c) Curvilinear relationship, correlation would be misrepresented by r

Figure 6.2

Scatter Diagrams Showing Linear and Curvilinear Relationships. r is Computed for (a) and (b), not for (c)

Test, the *lower* the score in tracking. When the slope of the best-fitting line is negative, the correlation is said to be *negative*. An example of negative correlation is shown in (b) of Fig. 6.2. When there is no correlation between the two variables, the best-fitting line is horizontal (slope zero), as in (a) of Fig. 6.2.

Computing r from z Scores

We are often interested in the correlation between two sets of measures that are expressed in different units, such as age in years and test performance in scores of some kind. The correlation coefficient r is independent of units of measurement, and all formulas for r transform the original measures into a standard scale that is the same for both variables. This is accomplished by replacing each of the original measures by its z value. In fact, r is easily computed from the two sets of z scores. The formula is

$$r = \frac{\Sigma z_x z_y}{n} \tag{6.1}$$

where $z_x z_y$ is the product of a pair of z scores. The products are summed algebraically over all pairs and divided by n, the number of pairs. We illustrate with the data of Example 1.

• • STEP 1. Find the mean and standard deviation (σ) of the X distribution and of the Y distribution. By formulas (4.1) and (4.2) of Chapter 4, these values are as given in Table 6.1 (p. 134).

• • STEP 2. Using the mean and standard deviation of a given distribution, convert each measure of that distribution to its z value by formula (5.1) of Chapter 5. Thus, the first z score of the X distribution is $(8 - 4)/2 = +2.00$. For the Y distribution, the first z score is $(10 - 6)/2 = +2.00$. The z scores are entered in separate columns as shown in Table 6.1. As a check that they have been correctly computed, sum each column. The sums should be zero.

• • STEP 3. The products $z_x z_y$ are obtained, as shown in the last column of Table 6.1. The algebraic sum of this column is $\Sigma z_x z_y$.

• • STEP 4. $\Sigma z_x z_y$ is substituted in formula (6.1) to obtain r. (Note that n is the number of products or pairs, 10, *not* the total number of scores.) As shown in Table 6.1, $r = +.725$.

Table 6.1

Computation of r from z Scores

(Example 1: Maze scores and Tracking scores of Ten Army Men)

MAZE TEST X	TRACKING TEST Y	z_x	z_y	$z_x z_y$
8	10	+2.00	+2.00	+4.00
7	7	+1.50	+ .50	+ .75
4	8	.00	+1.00	.00
4	6	.00	.00	.00
4	6	.00	.00	.00
4	4	.00	−1.00	.00
3	7	− .50	+ .50	− .25
3	4	− .50	−1.00	+ .50
2	3	−1.00	−1.50	+1.50
1	5	−1.50	− .50	+ .75
		0.00	0.00	+7.50
				− .25
			$\Sigma z_x z_y =$	+7.25

$\overline{X} = 4.0, \quad \sigma_x = 2.0$
$\overline{Y} = 6.0, \quad \sigma_y = 2.0$

$$r = \frac{\Sigma z_x z_y}{n} = \frac{+7.25}{10} = +.725$$

• DISCUSSION

The correlation between Maze Test scores and tracking scores is +.725. The "plus" indicates that the correlation is positive, *i.e.*, increases in one variable are accompanied by increases in the other variable, as we saw in the scatter diagram of the scores. The value .725 describes the magnitude of the correlation and indicates a substantial relationship. The psychologist will feel encouraged to continue his investigations. If the results of this study are confirmed on a much larger group of men, the Maze Test will probably become part of the standard selection procedure.

To understand why the value .725 was said to indicate a substantial relationship, look again at the last column of Table 6.1, the column of $z_x z_y$ products. Remember that whatever makes the sum of this column large will make r large, and anything that reduces the sum of this column will reduce the value of r. It is apparent that the sum of the column will be large (in absolute value) when there are many or large entries that have the same sign. And the sum will be correspondingly reduced by entries having an opposite sign.

It can be shown that the largest positive value r can take is $+1.00$. $r = +1.00$ indicates perfect positive correlation. The largest negative value r can take is -1.00, which indicates perfect negative correlation. Perfect correlation occurs only when the pair of z values that are multiplied to give a $z_x z_y$ product are numerically identical in every case (with like signs in the case of positive correlation and unlike signs in the case of negative correlation.) This makes sense because it is only then that a change in one variable is paralleled by an exactly equal change in the other variable. There are no exceptions to the pattern. Any time a change in one variable is *not* paralleled by an exactly equal change in the other variable—that is, if the pair of z_x and z_y values are not numerically identical—the correlation will be numerically smaller than 1.00. These pairs are "exceptions" to the pattern of perfect correlation and such exceptions act to reduce the numerical value of r. The more "exceptions" there are, the closer r approaches to 0.

Thus, differences in the absolute values of z_x and z_y pairs tend to lower the correlation. The effect of these differences may be quite small, however, if most of the $z_x z_y$ products nevertheless turn out to have the same sign. It is when the $z_x z_y$ products differ in sign that r is most sharply reduced. When $z_x z_y$ products have different signs, it means that sometimes X scores that are above the mean $(+z_x)$ are associated with Y scores that are above the mean $(+z_y)$, a positive trend, and sometimes X scores above the mean $(+z_x)$ are associated with Y scores that are below the mean $(-z_y)$, a negative trend. Inconsistencies of this kind are obviously an even greater departure from the pattern of perfect correlation than mere numerical discrepancies within pairs of z values. Differences in the signs of the $z_x z_y$ products constitute the really serious exceptions to whatever happens to be the prevailing trend of the correlation. Many or large differences of this kind finally reduce r to zero—the balance-point between individual positive and negative associations which is called "no correlation."

One way to interpret the magnitude of r, then, is in terms of "exceptions" to the prevailing trend or pattern of the correlation. When r is close to $+1.00$ or -1.00, there are only minor exceptions to the trend of the correlation. When r is closer to zero, there are serious exceptions to the trend. Our r of $+.725$ reflects the presence of some exceptions. A study of Table 6.1 reveals that these exceptions consist mostly of numerical discrepancies between the z_x and z_y scores of the subjects. In addition, there is one reversal of sign among the $z_x z_y$ products produced by a subject who scored below the mean on the X variable and above the mean on the Y variable. The total picture is not one of "serious" exceptions to the positive trend; the correlation may be described as "substantial."

Below are given, as a guide to usage, some conventional adjective descriptions of different r values.

r VALUE	ADJECTIVE DESCRIPTION
+.9 or −.9	High correlation
+.7 or −.7	Substantial correlation
+.5 or −.5	Moderate correlation
+.3 or −.3	Low correlation

These adjective descriptions will not always be applicable to particular situations. In many instances, a correlation of .5 is regarded as quite "high," as, for example, if such a correlation is found between two behavior traits that are logically independent. But if the correlation between two tests that are intended to measure the same trait is only .5, we would regard this as a very low correlation. The r value of .5 indicates equivalent "exceptions" in both cases. In the first case, however, we expected even more exceptions so we tend to regard the correlation of .5 as "high"; in the second case very few exceptions should occur, so the correlation of .5 looks "low."

Computing r from Raw Scores

It is not necessary to convert the X and Y distributions to z scores before computing r. Equivalent formulas are available for obtaining r directly from the raw data. One such formula is

$$r = \frac{n\Sigma XY - (\Sigma X)(\Sigma Y)}{\sqrt{[n\Sigma X^2 - (\Sigma X)^2][n\Sigma Y^2 - (\Sigma Y)^2]}} \tag{6.2}$$

In this formula, the conversion to a standard scale of z scores and the computation of r are accomplished at once.

Example 2. An investigator is curious about the relationship between intelligence and certain personality traits. He obtains test scores for a random sample of 20 college students. The students' IQ's and their scores on an Introversion Test are shown below. Is there a relationship between these two variables?

IQ	INTROVERSION	IQ	INTROVERSION
112	47	120	53
105	50	126	64
134	45	122	57
116	55	108	59
117	41	114	54
128	52	115	46
103	62	120	47
110	57	114	52
115	66	124	43
131	53	116	37

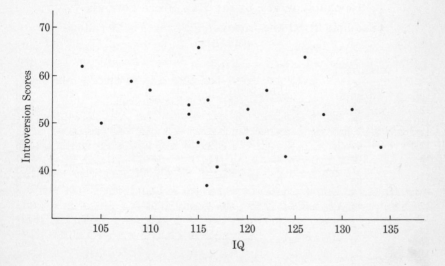

Figure 6.3

Scatter Diagram of IQ and Introversion Scores ($n = 20$)

• • STEP 1. The linearity of the relationship is checked by inspecting a scatter diagram of the scores. As may be seen in Fig. 6.3, the points are widely scattered. They do not seem to fall near a straight line, but neither do they fall near a curved line of some kind. There is no clearly discernible linear trend and no evidence of a curvilinear relationship. r may be computed. *Where a straight line fits the points about as well as any other line that could be drawn, the relationship will not be misrepresented by r.* The lack of a pattern simply indicates that the correlation is low.

•• STEP 2. To compute r by formula (6.2), five basic sums are required: ΣX, ΣX^2, ΣY, ΣY^2, and ΣXY. If an automatic calculator is available, these sums are easily obtained from the raw scores and are then simply inserted in the formula. If computations are to be done by hand, it is easier to "code" the scores first so that numbers will be small, and then to obtain the five sums.

Table 6.2
Computation of r by the Raw Score Formula
(Example 2: IQ and Introversion scores of 20 college students)

IQ	INTROVERSION	X	Y	X^2	Y^2	XY
112	47	-3	-3	9	9	$+9$
105	50	-10	0	100	0	0
134	45	$+19$	-5	361	25	-95
116	55	$+1$	$+5$	1	25	$+5$
117	41	$+2$	-9	4	81	-18
128	52	$+13$	$+2$	169	4	$+26$
103	62	-12	$+12$	144	144	-144
110	57	-5	$+7$	25	49	-35
115	66	0	$+16$	0	256	0
131	53	$+16$	$+3$	256	9	$+48$
120	53	$+5$	$+3$	25	9	$+15$
126	64	$+11$	$+14$	121	196	$+154$
122	57	$+7$	$+7$	49	49	$+49$
108	59	-7	$+9$	49	81	-63
114	54	-1	$+4$	1	16	-4
115	46	0	-4	0	16	0
120	47	$+5$	-3	25	9	-15
114	52	-1	$+2$	1	4	-2
124	43	$+9$	-7	81	49	-63
116	37	$+1$	-13	1	169	-13
				1422	1200	
		$+89$	$+84$			-452
		-39	-44			$+306$
		$+50$	$+40$			-146

$$r = \frac{n\Sigma XY - (\Sigma X)(\Sigma Y)}{\sqrt{[n\Sigma X^2 - (\Sigma X)^2][n\Sigma Y^2 - (\Sigma Y)^2]}} = \frac{20(-146) - (40)(50)}{\sqrt{[20(1422) - (50)^2][20(1200) - (40)^2]}}$$

$$= \frac{-2900 - 2000}{\sqrt{(28440 - 2500)(24000 - 1600)}}$$

$$= -.20$$

Transformations of Scores

Whatever scores we start with, the formula for r will transform them to a standard z scale. Any operations, therefore, that have no effect on the z values of the scores will have no effect on r. Operating with a constant upon every score in the distribution—*i.e.*, adding or subtracting a constant to every score, multiplying or dividing every score by a constant, or some combination of these operations carried out in the same order for every score—will have no effect on the z values of the scores. Any such operation that will result in conveniently small numbers may be carried out without affecting the value of r. In Table 6.2, the scores of this example have been reduced in size by subtracting a constant from each score. The constant 115 was subtracted from every IQ, with the result shown in column X. The constant 50 was subtracted from every Introversion score, with the result shown in column Y. These small values in the X and Y columns now take the place of the original scores in the computation of r. In Table 6.2, the five basic sums required for formula (6.2) are obtained from the values in the X and Y columns.

• • STEP 3. The five sums found in Step 2 are substituted in formula (6.2) to obtain r. As shown in Table 6.2, for these data $r = -.20$.

• DISCUSSION

The correlation is negative and very slight indeed. We may say there is a very small tendency *in this group of subjects* for high IQ's to be associated with low Introversion scores. At the same time, there are so many exceptions to the trend that we hesitate to assign any importance to it.

Since the investigator selected a random sample of students for his study, the question arises: Can the small correlation that was found be generalized to the population from which the sample came? Can we at least assume that the correlation is not zero in the population? The answer is not simple. To make inferences about the population correlation ρ (rho) on the basis of one sample r, we need to know how such sample r's are distributed, how they vary around the parameter ρ. More precisely, we want the standard deviation of the sampling distribution of r. This standard deviation is given by the following formula:

$$\sigma_r = \frac{1 - \rho^2}{\sqrt{n - 1}} \qquad (6.3)$$

As may be seen, the value of σ_r depends upon both ρ and n, the size of the sample. The trouble with using the formula is, of course, that we never know the value of ρ. We cannot logically put r in place of ρ in the formula, since this implies that we already know r to be a reliable estimate of ρ, whereas we want to use the formula to help us decide whether r is a reliable estimate of ρ. We cannot, therefore, use formula (6.3) to evaluate the reliability of r or obtain confidence limits for ρ the way analogous formulas were used in Chapter 5. The problem must be approached in another way.

One approach is to assume that ρ is zero, then ask the question: If ρ is zero, is it likely that random sampling would yield a sample r having the particular value that I obtained? In short, we can consider the plausibility of the hypothesis that ρ is 0. For example, let us examine the hypothesis that in the population sampled there is no correlation between IQ and Introversion scores. That is, we will assume a sampling distribution of r whose mean, ρ, is 0. By formula (6.3), the standard deviation of this sampling distribution is

$$\sigma_r = \frac{1 - 0^2}{\sqrt{20 - 1}} = .23$$

When the population correlation is 0 and the sample size is 20, the sampling distribution of r has a standard deviation of .23. It is evident that our sample r of $-.20$ is within one standard deviation of the parameter ρ of 0; hence $\rho = 0$ is a plausible hypothesis. In other words, if the population correlation is zero, many random samples of this size will yield correlations that differ from zero by as much as .20. Therefore, we have no basis for claiming that a correlation exists in the population between IQ and Introversion. Our obtained r of $-.20$ cannot be regarded as evidence against the hypothesis that the population correlation is zero.

In Chapter 10, a procedure is given for formally testing the hypothesis that a population correlation is zero. In this chapter, we will be satisfied to make an intuitive judgment based upon the extent of the sampling variation of r when $\rho = 0$. Later, we will draw more rigorous inferences. It should be pointed out that the sampling distribution of r is not normal, although it is approximately normal under the special circumstances of $\rho = 0$ and $n \geq 30$. Only under this combination of circumstances can we draw upon the known relationships of the normal distribution to tell us how sample r's are distributed. Under other circumstances, our "intuitive judgments" will be limited to clearcut cases like the one considered in this example.

Although any hypothesized value of ρ may be substituted in formula (6.3), the student should be cautioned against interpreting the resulting value of σ_r as representing some amount of *symmetrical* variation around ρ. The sampling distribution of r is symmetrical only when $\rho = 0$. The distribution becomes increasingly skewed for larger and larger values of ρ, and then, of course, there is much wider variation on one side of the sampling distribution than on the other. In general, unless the sample size is very large, symmetrical variation about ρ should only be assumed for $\rho = 0$.

Correlation, Causation, and Prediction

When two variables are found to be correlated, it does not follow that one of the variables is "caused" or determined by the other. Correlation is only a statement of association, not a statement of cause and effect. One variable *may* be the cause of the other, but if this is so, the fact is not demonstrated by showing only that the two variables are correlated. For example, much of the uncertainty in scientific minds about the early findings relating smoking to lung cancer arose from the fact that most of the studies reported were correlational in nature. The correlations did not and could not demonstrate that smoking *caused* lung cancer, only that the two were associated. Most people were ready to interpret the association as a cause-and-effect relationship because it seemed the intuitively obvious explanation. But the possibility remained that some unsuspected third variable, or complex of variables, caused both a tendency to heavy smoking and a tendency to develop cancer in the lungs. Correlations alone could not eliminate this possibility.

While correlation does not establish causation, one of the important uses of correlation is in *prediction*. If the correlation between two variables is high, knowledge of performance on one variable makes it possible to predict performance on the other variable with much greater accuracy than would be the case if little or no correlation existed between the variables. In Example 1 of this chapter, a correlation of about .72 was found between maze-tracing scores and tracking performance. The investigator cannot conclude that maze-tracing ability "causes" tracking skill, anymore than he can conclude that tracking skill "causes" maze-tracing ability. But the substantial correlation between the two will help him to predict the tracking scores of his subjects from a knowledge of their maze scores.

Technically, the prediction is accomplished by means of a *regression equation*. The regression equation is the equation of the best-fitting straight line for the points of the scatter diagram. Instead of locating the line by inspection, as we have done, its location is determined precisely by a procedure that minimizes the sum of the squared, *vertical* distances between obtained Y scores and corresponding Y values on the line.* This precisely located line, called the *regression line of Y on X*, then serves as the basis for predicting Y scores from given X scores. A given X value is found on the baseline of the scatter diagram and the Y value read above it *on the regression line* is the predicted Y score for a person obtaining the given score on X. Predictions made in this way will usually be in error for any one individual, but the overall error for many individuals is greatly reduced by proper use of the technique.

In order to predict X values from given Y scores, the *regression line of X on Y* is determined by minimizing the sum of the squared, *horizontal* distances between obtained X scores and corresponding X values on the line. Unless the correlation is perfect, the two regression lines, Y on X and X on Y, will be different. And a different regression equation will be used depending upon whether prediction is to be made from X to Y or from Y to X.

Detailed accounts of regression and prediction are available in more elaborate statistics texts and in texts devoted to psychometrics. The purpose here is only to suggest some of the further techniques that derive from correlation.

Practice Problems

1. In a "level of aspiration" study, a group of 11 subjects are told that average performance on an experimental task is 10. They are shown the task and each subject is asked to predict what his performance will be on the first trial. The predictions the subjects make, together with their actual performance on the first trial, are

---

* The mathematically advanced student will recognize this procedure as the *method of least squares*. By the method of least squares, the slope of the regression line of Y on X is found to be: $b_{yx} = \dfrac{n\Sigma XY - (\Sigma X)(\Sigma Y)}{n\Sigma X^2 - (\Sigma X)^2}$. Since one point on the regression line is also known—the point $(\overline{X}, \overline{Y})$—the equation of the line is readily determined.

shown below. (a) Plot a scatter diagram of the results. Is the relationship approximately linear? What kind of relationship is suggested by the scatter diagram? (b) Convert the scores of the two distributions to their respective z values and compute r by formula (6.1). Is there a relationship between the subjects' predictions and their actual performance?

SUBJECTS' PREDICTIONS	ACTUAL PERFORMANCE
14	7
12	10
11	9
11	6
10	8
10	8
10	8
9	12
9	7
8	4
6	9

2. Fifteen students in a typing class are given a test to determine their progress. The students all type the same material, and the time and number of errors is recorded for each student. Upon inspecting the results, the instructor notices a tendency for the faster students to make more errors than the slower students. Below are given the z values of the time scores and the error scores of the 15 students. (a) Plot a scatter diagram of the z scores. Is the relationship approximately linear? Does the scatter diagram seem to confirm the instructor's impression? What kind of relationship is suggested by the scatter diagram? (b) Compute r. What conclusions can be drawn from the value of r?

z SCORES TIME	z SCORES ERRORS	z SCORES TIME	z SCORES ERRORS
− .2	+ .4	+1.0	− .4
+ .7	0.0	− .9	−1.3
+1.6	0.0	− .5	− .8
−1.6	+1.7	− .5	+1.3
+ .2	− .8	− .9	− .4
− .2	+ .8	−1.1	+1.3
+ .3	+ .4	− .2	0.0
+2.2	−2.1		

3. Using the data of Example 1, compute r by the raw score formula (6.2).

Plot a scatter diagram for each of the following. If the relationship is approximately linear, compute r by formula (6.2) for raw data.

4. A test constructor working on a Word Recognition test has made up two forms of the test which he believes to be equivalent.

He tries out the two forms on a group of 12 subjects, six of whom take Form A first and then Form B, the other six subjects following the opposite procedure. The results for the 12 subjects are:

Form A	Form B
48	42
53	48
41	33
44	37
53	45
49	39
54	43
46	36
57	51
62	53
50	42
59	48

5. The investigator of No. 4 above intends his Word Recognition test to be a measure of vocabulary. To check on how well his intention is fulfilled by the test, he also administers a standard, individual vocabulary test to each of the 12 subjects. He then examines the relationship between the subjects' Vocabulary scores and the scores they achieved on the Word Recognition Test. The scores are:

Word Recognition Test	Vocabulary Test
48	24
53	27
41	22
44	20
53	28
49	29
54	33
46	25
57	27
62	36
50	31
59	32

6. In a study to investigate the relationship between neuroticism and suggestibility, a random sample of 20 clinic patients are given a series of tests. Among the tests are a Neuroticism questionnaire and a Body-Sway Suggestibility Test in which the maximum amount of body sway is measured during a three-minute interval while a recorded voice suggests to the standing subject that he is falling forward. The neuroticism score and the maximum amount of body sway under suggestion is given below for each of the 20 subjects. Do the results suggest a relationship between neuroticism and body-sway suggestibility?

Neuroticism	Body Sway (cm)	Neuroticism	Body Sway (cm)
8	4.0	21	4.3
10	5.2	21	7.5
13	5.7	22	6.5
14	5.0	23	5.5
16	2.4	23	3.6
17	4.8	24	6.7
17	4.7	25	5.6
19	4.5	27	5.2
20	3.0	31	5.8
20	5.2	32	6.1

(To simplify the measures of body sway, multiply each measure by 10 to eliminate the decimals, then subtract a convenient constant.)

7. A company is interested in cutting down the turnover among its machine operators. Twenty newly-hired operators are given an Intelligence Test as part of a study to determine the causes for the turnover rate. One year later, the Intelligence Test scores of the men are compared with the number of weeks they remained on the job, as shown below. Is there a relationship between Intelligence Test score and weeks on the job?

Intelligence Score	Weeks on Job	Intelligence Score	Weeks on Job
41	12	88	6
55	30	49	8
62	52	54	43
81	4	51	28
73	27	83	13
57	52	47	19
65	52	68	52
44	3	71	38
77	18	76	32
64	52	68	48

8. In a study of prejudice against minority groups, a random sample of 20 subjects from a new residential area are asked to fill out an attitude questionnaire that consists of two parts. One part of the questionnaire inquires as to the subject's beliefs about and feelings toward persons belonging to the given minority groups. The other part of the questionnaire asks how the subject would behave in hypothetical situations involving such persons. Separate scores are obtained for the two parts of the questionnaire so that the relationship between the feelings reported by the subjects and their projected behavior may be examined. The scores are given below. What is the relationship between scores obtained on the two parts of the questionnaire?

"Feelings"	"Behavior"	"Feelings"	"Behavior"
12	20	31	28
16	18	31	42
17	12	32	31
20	34	34	17
22	27	35	49
24	36	37	27
25	41	40	52
28	32	42	37
28	43	46	30
30	23	50	38

9. What is the value of σ_r when $\rho = 0$ and the sample size is (a) 10? (b) 26? (c) 37? (d) 50? (e) 100? (f) 200? (g) For which of these sample sizes is the sampling distribution of r symmetrical? For which is the sampling distribution approximately normal?

10. Suppose the investigator of Problem 6 above had obtained a correlation of .36 using a sample of 50 subjects. Could he then conclude that the population correlation is not zero?

11. Suppose the investigator of Problem 8 above had obtained a correlation of .46 using a sample of 37 subjects. Could it be reasonably concluded that the population correlation is not zero?

12. An investigator finds a correlation of .14 between two variables that are measured for a random sample of 200 subjects. Is it likely that the population correlation is zero?

13. In Example 1 of this chapter, the investigator found a correlation of .725 between the maze scores and the tracking scores of ten Army men. Given only this information, no conclusions can be drawn about the population of Army men. Why?

14. Suppose a random sample of ten Army men were selected from the population of interest and a correlation of .725 was obtained for this sample. What conclusions could be drawn about the population?

Answers

1. The relationship appears to be generally linear although there are wide discrepancies. At first glance, it may seem to be a positive relationship. A straight line with positive slope can be drawn through six of the eleven points. Actually, this is not the *best-fitting* straight line, as indicated by the fact that r is exactly zero for these data. The best-fitting line is a horizontal through the point $X = 8$ and $Y = 10$, the means of the two distributions. If you examine the

scatter diagram carefully, you will see that this horizontal comes closer to the points *overall* than does the aforementioned line with positive slope. Thus, there is no correlation between the subjects' predictions and their actual performance.

2. The relationship is generally linear and does seem to confirm the instructor's impression. That is, the relationship appears to be negative in that high time scores tend to be accompanied by low error scores, although there are exceptions to this trend. $r = -.54$, indicating a moderate negative correlation. We may conclude there is a definite tendency in this group for the faster students to make more errors than the students who took more time for the test. But there are also definite exceptions: Some fast students make few errors and some slow students make many.

3. You should get the same result, $r = +.725$, as was found by the z-score formula.

4. $r = +.95$, indicating a very high positive relationship. A high correlation is, of course, necessary if the two forms of the test are to substitute for one another. The investigator will feel reassured that both forms of the test are "measuring the same thing" at least in this group of subjects, and will no doubt extend his investigations to larger groups. Observe, however, that the high correlation found does *not* mean that subjects obtained the same scores on both forms of the test. Scores are generally higher on Form A (mean = 51.3) than on Form B (mean = 43.1). The high correlation means only that subjects who obtained relatively high scores on A obtained relatively high scores on B, and the same for low-scoring subjects. But the two forms of the test are not "equivalent" in the sense of yielding the same scores. In order to compare scores obtained by different subjects, the scores should all be obtained from the same Form of the test. (The investigator will probably shift test items to make the two forms of the test equivalent in this sense also.)

5. $r = +.83$, indicating a high positive relationship. Although this correlation is lower than the .95 found between the two forms of the Word Recognition Test, two different tests are involved now and the correlation is expected to be lower. The correlation of .83 indicates that the Word Recognition Test is a *valid* measure of vocabulary, at least insofar as the standard individual test is a valid measure of vocabulary, because scores on the two tests parallel each other closely.

6. $r = +.36$. There is some tendency for neuroticism scores and body sway to be related *among these subjects*, but the size of r indicates that there are many (or serious) exceptions to the trend even among these subjects. To consider whether some correlation may be

attributed to the population, we examine the hypothesis that $\rho = 0$. For a sample of 20 and $\rho = 0$, σ_r is .23. Our r of .36 is about 1.6 standard deviations (.36/.23) above the mean of the sampling distribution. Since we do not know how many r's are this far away from the mean of the distribution, we cannot tell whether our r should be regarded as unusual or not. *If we knew* that r's as large as ours were only rarely obtained when the population correlation is zero, we would then conclude that $\rho = 0$ is an implausible hypothesis. We are not in a position to make this decision and must suspend judgment now, although we shall be able to make this judgment in Chapter 10.

7. There is a definite relationship, but it is not linear. The relationship evident on the scatter diagram is shaped something like a hairpin. Men who received very low or very high intelligence test scores remained on the job only a short time, while men who scored in the middle range remained the longest (suggesting a very definite hiring policy to reduce turnover!). This curvilinear relationship is not measurable by r, so r should not be computed. (If it is computed, we find $r = -.013$, suggesting falsely that there is a near-zero relationship between the two variables. What this r tells us is only that the *linear* relationship between the two variables is practically zero. Since we already know that the relationship is not linear, we have no use for r). A measure called *eta* or the *correlation ratio*, which may be found in many standard statistics texts, is used to measure the strength of a curvilinear relationship.

8. $r = +.46$, indicating only a moderate positive relationship between these subjects' reports of how they feel and how they would behave. Apparently, the two parts of the test measure different aspects of prejudice, aspects that are not so highly correlated as one might suppose. Since this is only a sample of 20 subjects, the correlation may be higher in the population, or it may be lower. Could it be 0? If $\rho = 0$, $\sigma_r = .23$ and our sample r of $+.46$ is exactly two standard deviations above the mean of the sampling distribution. Again, we are not yet in a position to decide whether such an r is unusual or not. For the time being, we must suspend judgment about the hypothesis $\rho = 0$.

9. (a) .33. (b) .20. (c) .17. (d) .14. (e) .10. (f) .07. (g) The sampling distribution of r is symmetrical whenever $\rho = 0$, so it is symmetrical in all of these cases. The sampling distribution is approximately normal in form when the sample size is 30 or more; that is, for (c), (d), (e), and (f).

10. If $\rho = 0$ and $n = 50$, $\sigma_r = .14$. A sample r of $+.36$ is then

2.57 standard deviations (.36/.14) above the mean of the sampling distribution. Because the sampling distribution is approximately normal for a sample size of 50, we can use the normal curve table to determine about how many r's are this far from the mean. From Table B in the Appendix, we find that only .0051 of the cases in a normal distribution are 2.57 standard deviations above the mean, and of course only .0051 of the cases are 2.57 standard deviations below the mean. Adding these two values, we are able to say that only about .01, or 1%, of sample r's are as large as .36 when $n = 50$ and the population correlation is zero. Thus, it is *possible* that a random sample of 50 cases will yield an r as large as .36 when the population correlation is zero, but it is very unusual. If we drew samples of this size over and over again from a population where $\rho = 0$, only one time in a hundred would we find an r this large. Rather than believe that such a one-in-a-hundred event has occurred, most investigators would conclude that $\rho = 0$ is not a plausible hypothesis.

11. If $\rho = 0$ and $n = 37$, $\sigma_r = .17$. A sample r of $+.46$ is 2.71 standard deviations (.46/.17) above the mean of the sampling distribution. Because this sampling distribution is approximately normal, we may use the same procedure outlined above. From the normal curve table, we find that $.0034 + .0034 = .0068$, or less than 1% of the sample r's are as large as .46 when $n = 37$, and the population correlation is zero. Either we fell by chance upon a very unusual random sample (one that would occur less than one time in a hundred in the long run), or else the population correlation is not zero. Again, most investigators would agree that under these circumstances, $\rho = 0$ is not a plausible hypothesis.

12. If $\rho = 0$ and $n = 200$, $\sigma_r = .07$. A sample r of .14 is exactly two standard deviations from the mean of the sampling distribution. From the normal curve table, only $.0228 + .0228 = .0456$, or less than 5%, of sample r's are as large as .14. If $\rho = 0$, less than five times in a hundred in the long run would we find a sample of this size in which the correlation is as large as .14. The population correlation may be zero, but we would not regard this as a *likely* possibility.

13. The ten Army men are not a *random* sample from some specified population; therefore we know nothing whatever about the sampling distribution of r in this case. We cannot even determine σ_r because formula (6.3) for σ_r gives the standard deviation of *random sample r's* about ρ, and we do not have a random sample.

14. Even though the sample correlation is so high, we are still

not in a position to conclude that the population correlation is not zero. Our sample r is 2.2 standard deviations (.725/.33) above the mean, but the sampling distribution is not normal and we do not know how many sample r's are this far from the mean. We cannot draw any conclusions about the population correlation. (Again, we shall be able to make such a judgment in Chapter 10.)

chapter 7

Probability
and
Sampling
from
a Binomial
Population

Probability refers to the chances that some given event will occur under a specified set of conditions. For example, what is the probability that a child of divorced parents will become emotionally disturbed? The event is "becoming emotionally disturbed" and the condition specified is "divorced parents." If we knew just how likely this event was under these conditions, we would have a basis for taking action in such situations. Sometimes such a probability basis is extremely important in making decisions. For example, what is the probability that Drug X will have an adverse effect on intellectual functioning? However helpful Drug X may be for colds or insomnia, we still want to know just how likely it is to impair intellectual functioning before we venture to take it.

The *statistical probability* of an event is defined as the proportion of times the event occurs over the long run—that is, if the situation were to be repeated indefinitely. The statistical probability of an event is, thus, the proportion of times the event occurs among the population of occasions when it *could* occur. If among all the births of children 50.1% of the infants are boys, the statistical probability of this event—giving birth to a boy—is .501, or 501 chances out of 1000 in the long run. But such populations of occasions are never available for study. Scientists, therefore, must rely upon estimates of the statistical probability of an event. There are two ways of making such estimates—inductively and deductively—and both approaches have great usefulness for science.

INDUCTIVE

PROBABILITY

ESTIMATES

Inductive probability estimates are empirical. They are simply mathematical statements of what has happened in the past. If an event could have occurred on 100 different occasions in the past, and it occurred in fact only 20 times, then our empirical estimate of that event's probability is 20/100, or .20. If the event occurred 90 times out of a possible 100, then its estimated probability is 90/100, or .90. An inductive probability estimate, then, is an empirical proportion: the number of times an event occurred, divided by the number of times when it could have occurred. This statement may be written

$$p = \frac{f}{n}$$

where p is the proportion of times an event occurred,

f is the number of times the event occurred,

n is the total number of occasions when the event could have occurred.

The proportion, p, provides an inductive or empirical estimate of the statistical probability of the event for which p was computed. The sum of events which are possible alternatives to this event has an estimated probability q. Since $p + q = 1$, q is always equal to $1 - p$. Thus, if the probability of an event is estimated as .30, the estimated probability of the sum of alternative events is $1.00 - .30 = .70$. Some examples are given below.

Example 1. Among 80 hospitalized schizophrenics, 48 have shown some improvement after 15 sessions of group psychotherapy. What is the probability that Patient A, who is schizophrenic, will show improvement after 15 such sessions of therapy?

The event "improvement" has occurred 48 times out of 80 under the conditions specified. So $p = 48/80 = .60$. The best estimate that can be made on the basis of this information is that Patient A has a probability .60 of showing improvement after 15 sessions of group psychotherapy. In other words, his chances of showing improvement are estimated to be 60 out of 100. Alternative outcomes, such as getting worse or showing no change, have a combined probability of $q = 1.00 - .60 = .40$. So the chances are estimated to be 40 out of

100 that Patient A will be worse or just the same after 15 sessions of group psychotherapy.

It obviously makes a difference whether patients who do not improve under a treatment become worse or simply remain as they were and show no change. To estimate the likelihood of becoming worse, q can be broken down into its two component parts: the probability of becoming worse, and the probability of showing no change. If 9 patients out of the original 80 were judged worse after 15 sessions of group psychotherapy, the probability that a patient will be worse after such treatment is estimated to be $9/80 = .11$. Since $q = .40$, the estimated probability of showing no change is $.40 - .11 = .29$.

In summary, the chances are estimated as 60 out of 100 that a schizophrenic patient will show some improvement after 15 sessions of group psychotherapy, 29 out of 100 that he will show no change, and 11 out of 100 that he will become worse.

Example 2. In a test of visual acuity, a subject is required to report whether a cardboard square placed some distance from him has grid markings (black lines close together against a white background) or whether the card is solid gray in color. When the lines on a card are so close together that the card always appears gray to the subject, the distance separating the lines on this card is considered to be beyond the subject's capacity to discriminate. Several cards with lines varying in closeness are shown, interspersed with a solid gray card used as a check on the subject's tendency to give positive judgments even when he cannot see lines. Out of 50 presentations of the solid gray card, the subject makes a positive judgment that lines are present eight times. What is the probability that this subject will make positive judgments under these conditions, even when the lines on a card are so close together that he cannot see them?

Positive judgments were erroneously made on eight out of 50 trials, so $p = 8/50 = .16$. It is estimated that in the long run, this subject will make positive judgments 16 times out of 100 when in fact he is unable to discriminate the lines on a card.

In interpreting the results of the experiment, the best guess is that any card of lines for which the subject gives positive judgments about 16% of the time or less should be considered lines which the subject is unable to discriminate. We could be in error. Perhaps the subject did actually see the lines some number of those times, but our best guess on the basis of the evidence is that he did not.

DEDUCTIVE PROBABILITY ESTIMATES

Deductive probability estimates are theoretical in nature. They are arrived at by making logical deductions from a premise. For our purposes, this premise will always be that *every possible outcome in a given situation has an equal chance of occurring*. Each outcome is therefore considered to have a probability of occurrence of $1/N$, where N is the total number of possible outcomes.

Traditionally, this type of probability model has been illustrated by such games as the toss of a fair coin or the roll of a fair die. For the coin, there are two possible outcomes, heads or tails; under the premise, therefore, that each outcome is equally likely, the probability of heads is $1/N = 1/2$ or .5, and the probability of tails is also .5. There are six possible outcomes for the die. Given the premise that the six outcomes are equally likely, the probability of any one of them is $1/6$ or .17. The same principle holds if, for example, a random procedure is employed to select one subject from 15 which are available. In this case, there are 15 possible outcomes, and since the random procedure is designed to guarantee that each outcome is equally likely, the probability that any given subject will be chosen is $1/15$.

When some number m of the possible outcomes could each produce the Event A, then the probability of the Event A is given by:

$$P(A) = \frac{m}{N} \tag{7.1}$$

For example, let the Event A be the random selection of a subject with poor eyesight. If three of the 15 available subjects have poor eyesight, then the event could be produced by each of three outcomes, and m is 3. The probability of randomly selecting a subject with poor eyesight in this situation is $3/15$ or .20.

Obviously, our deductive probability model is not suitable for answering questions such as those posed in the previous examples of this chapter. We should not be interested in a prediction that schizophrenics have one chance in three of showing improvement after a given treatment, based on the unlikely notion that the three possible outcomes—improvement, getting worse, and no change—are equally probable. When there is no basis for making predictions in advance about the population which will be sampled, as in the previous examples, the proper procedure is to conduct an "exploratory" study and determine from this study an empirical probability estimate for the event of interest, as was done in Examples 1 and 2. The empirical estimate may then be put forth as a hypothesis and tested by the deductive probability model in a new experiment. The procedure is illustrated below.

Example 3.   On the basis of previous findings (see Example 1 of this chapter) an investigator hypothesizes that .60 of the population of schizophrenics will show improvement after 15 weeks of group psychotherapy. He wishes to conduct an experiment to test this hypothesis.

The hypothesis proposes, in effect, a picture in which .60 of the population of schizophrenics are of a type (not necessarily definable) such that they will improve with this treatment, while .40 of the population are not of this type and hence will not improve. Just to illustrate the situation, we will imagine that the population consists of a total of five schizophrenics, represented by the numbers 1 to 5 below. According to the hypothesis, .60 or three of these are of a type who will get better with the treatment (B), and .40 or two are of the type who will not get better with the treatment (O).

1   *2*   *3*   *4*   *5*
B   B   B   O   O

Now let us suppose that the investigator selects a *random* sample of two subjects from this population. If the sample is not randomly selected, then we cannot use our deductive probability model to test the hypothesis. The deductive probabilities of interest to us are based upon the premise that *every outcome in a given situation is equally likely.* This means that every possible sample of two subjects must have an equal chance of being chosen. By random sampling, every sample of two is equally likely and we satisfy the basic requirement of our deductive probability model. Without random sampling, we cannot estimate the probability of an experimental result, and have no grounds for making an inference about the population from which the sample came.

If two subjects are selected from the population, three experimental results are possible: Both selections will be type B schizophrenics; one selection will be type B and one type O; both selections

Table 7.1
Possible Outcomes in the Random Selection of Two Subjects from a Population of Five

Hypothesis: The population consists of three type B and two type O subjects

EXPERIMENTAL RESULTS:	2 TYPE B	1 TYPE B	NO TYPE B
OUTCOMES:	1,2	1,4	4,5
	2,1	4,1	5,4
	1,3	1,5	
	3,1	5,1	
	2,3	2,4	
	3,2	4,2	
		2,5	
		5,2	
		3,4	
		4,3	
		3,5	
		5,3	
	$n_1 = 6$	$n_2 = 12$	$n_3 = 2$

$$N = n_1 + n_2 + n_3 = 6 + 12 + 2 = 20$$

will be type O schizophrenics. The three experimental results are given in Table 7.1, and below each result is shown the possible outcomes (selections) which could produce that result. For example, in order to obtain a result in which both subjects are of type B, it is necessary to select two of the three subjects in the population which are of this type. These are Subjects 1, 2, and 3. The result could be produced by selecting Subject 1 first and then Subject 2, or vice versa. Each of these counts as a separate outcome. The same holds for Subjects 1 and 3 and for Subjects 2 and 3. Altogether, there are six outcomes which will produce a sample in which both subjects are of type B. By a similar procedure, 12 outcomes are found which will produce a sample in which only one subject is of type B, and two outcomes will produce a sample which includes no type B subjects. The sum of these is $N = 20$, which is the total number of possible outcomes.

Now suppose the investigator has chosen his sample of two subjects. It is one of the samples listed in Table 7.1, but of course he does not know which one it is and all are equally likely. Let us say that the two subjects receive 15 weeks of group psychotherapy and at the end of that time both show improvement. The hypothesis is that 60% will improve, while in this experiment 100% have improved. Was the hypothesis mistaken? Table 7.1 shows that if the hypothesis is true, in the long run six samples out of 20 will produce a result in which both subjects show improvement. Therefore, by formula (7.1) the probability of this result is 6/20 or .30 under the hypothesis. Such a probability does not suggest an unusual event. There is no reason to reject the hypothesis.

What if the result was that neither of the subjects showed any improvement after 15 weeks of group psychotherapy? According to Table 7.1, in the long run two samples out of 20 will give this result. If the hypothesis is true, the probability of this result is 2/20 or .10. The investigator may decide to retain his hypothesis on the assumption that a rather unusual event has occurred, but he cannot feel very comfortable about it. The result in this case can hardly be said to provide support for his hypothesis. He may decide that ".60 will improve" is not a very plausible hypothesis.

Table 7.2

Possible Samples in the Random Selection of Two Subjects from a Population of Five

Hypothesis: The population consists of three type B and two type O subjects

EXPERIMENTAL RESULTS:	2 TYPE B	1 TYPE B	NO TYPE B
SAMPLES:	1,2	1,4	4,5
	1,3	1,5	
	2,3	2,4	
		2,5	
		3,4	
		3,5	
	$n_1 = 3$	$n_2 = 6$	$n_3 = 1$

$$N = n_1 + n_2 + n_3 = 3 + 6 + 1 = 10$$

The same conclusions would be reached if, instead of considering the possible outcomes, we considered the different *samples* possible in this situation. Although selecting the same subjects in a different order provides two different *outcomes*, as we have used this term, the two subjects selected constitute only one sample. Thus, selecting Subject 1 first and then Subject 2 gives the same sample as selecting Subject 2 first and then Subject 1.

The possible results of the experiment are shown again in Table 7.2 and under each result are listed the different samples which could produce that result. The total number of different samples is found to be 10. Formula (7.1) is equally applicable in this situation to determine the probability of each experimental result. Thus, if the hypothesis is true, the probability of randomly selecting two subjects who will improve is 3/10 or .30. The probability of selecting one who improves and one who does not is 6/10 or .60. And the probability of selecting two subjects who do not improve is 1/10 or .10. These are the same probabilities as were previously obtained by substituting the number of different outcomes in formula (7.1). Since the *order* of the subjects in the sample is of no consequence under the hypothesis, the two methods give the same results.

In behavioral research, we are not often concerned about the order in which subjects are selected, or the order in which a sequence of observations occurs. Usually, we are interested in the probability of obtaining a particular sample rather than a particular ordered outcome. We will focus, therefore, upon methods for determining the number of different samples which are possible in a given situation, and how many of these samples could produce a given experimental result. The remainder of this chapter will be devoted to three methods for determining the probability of different random samples drawn from specified binomial populations: (1) when a small sample is selected from a small population; (2) when a small sample is selected from a large or infinite population; (3) when a large sample is selected from a large or infinite population. For our purposes, a sample will be considered small if it contains ten or fewer observations.

Small Sample, Small Population

When a small sample is drawn from a small binomial population, the formula below for *combinations* is convenient for finding the total number of different samples (combinations of outcomes) which are possible.

$$\binom{n}{r} = \frac{n!}{r!(n-r)!} \tag{7.2}$$

where n is the number of subjects in the population and r is the number in the sample. The exclamation point is read *factorial* and means that the preceding number is to be successively multiplied by each lower integer. Thus, in selecting a sample of two subjects from the five schizophrenics of Example 3, the number of possible samples is

$$\frac{5!}{2!(5-2)!} = \frac{5 \times 4 \times 3 \times 2 \times 1}{(2 \times 1)(3 \times 2 \times 1)} = 10$$

This formula gives the denominator N of the formula m/N.

To find the number of samples which will give a particular result, we use the formula

$$\frac{n_1!}{r_1!(n_1-r_1)!} \times \frac{n_2!}{r_2!(n_2-r_2)!} \qquad (7.3)$$

where n_1 is the number of subjects of a given type in the population and r_1 is the number of subjects of that type in the sample; n_2 is the number of subjects of a second type in the population and r_2 is the number of subjects of this second type in the sample. Thus, for the five schizophrenics, the number of different samples which will give two subjects who improve (r_1) when there are three such subjects in the population (n_1), and zero subjects who fail to improve (r_2) although there are two subjects of this type in the population (n_2), is given by

$$\frac{3!}{2!(3-2)!} \times \frac{2!}{0!(2-0)!} = \frac{3 \times 2 \times 1}{(2 \times 1)(1)} \times \frac{2 \times 1}{(1)(2 \times 1)} = 3$$

0! is always taken as equal to 1. We find, therefore, that there are three different samples in which both subjects are of the type which will improve.

Formula (7.3) gives the numerator m of the formula m/N. If all the possible samples are equally likely, then the values found by means of formulas (7.2) and (7.3) may be entered directly into the formula m/N in order to determine the probability of any obtained result.

Thus, the probability under the hypothesis of obtaining a result in which both schizophrenics improve is 3/10 or .30, as was found by the longer method of listing and counting all the possible samples.

The use of formulas (7.2) and (7.3) is illustrated in another example below.

Example 4.   Eight married couples agree to take part in an experiment in which each subject first fills out a questionnaire relating to his or her likes and dislikes. Three of the eight couples are found to be in very close agreement as to their likes and dislikes. The experimenter believes that these three couples will be most successful at the experimental task, which requires close cooperation and mutual reinforcement between a husband and wife pair. He predicts that scores obtained by these three couples will be in the upper half of scores obtained by the eight couples. If in reality each of the eight couples is as likely as every other to score in the upper half (*i.e.*, above the median of the group), what is the probability of obtaining by chance a result in which all three of these couples score above the median?

To illustrate the situation, the three couples found to be in close agreement on the questionnaire are identified as "A" couples and the remaining five as "O" couples. Thus, we have a population of eight which may be symbolized

$$\underbrace{A \; A \; A}_{n_1} \; \underbrace{O \; O \; O \; O \; O}_{n_2}$$

Under the hypothesis that each of the eight couples is as likely as every other to be among the first four in performance, every possible sample of four couples is equally likely to be found above the median on a given trial. The first step, then, is to determine how many different samples of four could be assembled from the population of eight. This will give us the denominator N of formula (7.1). The next step is to determine how many of these samples include all three of the A couples. This will give the numerator of formula (7.1). It will then be possible to solve directly for the probability of this experimental result.

• • STEP 1. Substituting $n = 4$ and $r = 8$ in formula (7.2), we have

$$\frac{8!}{4!(8-4)!} = \frac{8 \times 7 \times 6 \times 5 \times 4 \times 3 \times 2 \times 1}{(4 \times 3 \times 2 \times 1)(4 \times 3 \times 2 \times 1)} = 70$$

There are, then, 70 different samples of four couples which, under the hypothesis, are equally likely to be first in performance.

• • STEP 2. The samples of four which include all three A couples must include one O couple. The problem is analogous to drawing three subjects from the group n_1 and one subject from the group n_2. Substituting $n_1 = 3$, $r_1 = 3$, and $n_2 = 5$, $r_2 = 1$ in formula (7.3) gives

$$\frac{3!}{3!(3-3)!} \times \frac{5!}{1!(5-1)!}$$

$$= \frac{3 \times 2 \times 1}{(3 \times 2 \times 1)(1)} \times \frac{5 \times 4 \times 3 \times 2 \times 1}{(1)(4 \times 3 \times 2 \times 1)} = 5$$

Five of the possible samples include all three A couples.

• • STEP 3. Substituting the values found in Steps 1 and 2 in formula (7.1), we find that the experimental result obtained has a probability under the hypothesis of

$$\frac{m}{N} = \frac{5}{70} = .07$$

If the equally likely hypothesis is true, we would expect this experimental result to occur seven times in 100. This particular experiment may be one of those seven occasions, but on the face of it, it seems more reasonable to conclude that close agreement among couples is a factor in their success on this task. However, the experimenter will have to consider what other variables might have produced the result before he can come to this conclusion.

Small Sample, Large Population

As the population from which a sample is drawn approaches infinity in size, the ratio of formula (7.3) to formula (7.2) approaches a limiting value which is equal to a term in the *binomial expansion*. Thus, when the population is infinite, the probability of a given sample result may be determined directly from the appropriate term of the binomial expansion. Even when the population is not infinite but is large compared to the sample (say, 20 times the sample size) the binomial expansion will give a very close approximation of the exact probability of obtaining a given sample result.

The basic formula for the binomial expansion is

$$(P + Q)^n \tag{7.4}$$

where P is the hypothesized proportion of subjects or observations of a given type in the population; Q is $1 - P$, or the proportion of subjects or observations in the population which are not of this type; and n is the size of the sample.

For example, returning to the investigator who hypothesized that .60 of the population of schizophrenics are of a type who will improve with group psychotherapy, let us now suppose that two subjects are randomly selected from a vast population of schizophrenics. P is .60, Q is .40, and n is 2. We have

$$(.60 + .40)^2 = (.60)^2 + 2(.60)(.40) + (.40)^2$$

The first exponent, 2, indicates a sample in which both subjects come from the hypothesized .60 of the population who will improve. The probability of randomly drawing such a sample under the hypothesis is obtained by multiplying out the term $(.60)^2 = .36$. Thus, the probability under the hypothesis of obtaining a result in which both subjects improve is .36. Or, we would expect 36% of random samples to give this result. Similarly, the exponents of the second term, which are simply 1 and 1, indicate a sample of one subject from the hypothesized .60 of the population and one from the remaining .40. Multiplying out the second term, we get $2(.60)(.40) = .48$ as the probability under the hypothesis of randomly selecting one subject who improves and one who does not. Or, we expect 48% of random samples to give this result. And multiplying out the third term, we get $(.40)^2 = .16$ as the probability of randomly choosing two subjects from the hypothesized .40 of the population who will not show improvement. That is, only 16% of random samples are expected to give this result.

Note that the three probabilities found in this way—.36, .48, and .16—are not the same as the probabilities of .30, .60, and .10 found when sampling was from a population of only five. Probabilities will always be different when samples are drawn from infinite populations as opposed to small, finite populations. This is because the two situations are basically different. Every time a subject is drawn from a small population, the population proportions are changed. Therefore, the probabilities are different for each successive draw. When the population is infinite, drawing any number of subjects has no effect on the population proportions. Therefore, the probabilities are the same for successive draws. Our different formulas, and results, take into account these different situations.

But now the investigator in our example may justifiably feel reluctant to abandon his belief about the population even if both schizophrenics fail to improve, since this result is expected to occur 16% of the time if his hypothesis is true. In order to really test his hypothesis, the investigator must draw enough subjects so that it is at least possible to get a sample which would cause him to reject his hypothesis. If he takes five subjects, he increases by three the experimental results which are possible. That is, with two subjects, only three results were possible: both subjects improved, one improved, or none improved. With five subjects, there are six possible results: all five improve, four improve, three improve, two improve, one improves, none improves. The probability of each of the six results is given by the six terms of the expansion of $(P + Q)^5$, which in this case is $(.60 + .40)^5$ or $(3/5 + 2/5)^5$.

The terms of this expansion are given below. Under each term is its fractional value, obtained by carrying out the multiplications indicated by the exponent(s) and coefficient of the term. Below each fraction is the decimal value of the term, rounded to the nearest second decimal to permit easy scanning of the six probabilities.

5 IMPROVE	4 IMPROVE	3 IMPROVE	2 IMPROVE	1 IMPROVES	0 IMPROVES
$\left(\dfrac{3}{5}\right)^5$	$5\left(\dfrac{3}{5}\right)^4\left(\dfrac{2}{5}\right)$	$10\left(\dfrac{3}{5}\right)^3\left(\dfrac{2}{5}\right)^2$	$10\left(\dfrac{3}{5}\right)^2\left(\dfrac{2}{5}\right)^3$	$5\left(\dfrac{3}{5}\right)\left(\dfrac{2}{5}\right)^4$	$\left(\dfrac{2}{5}\right)^5$
$\dfrac{243}{3125}$	$\dfrac{810}{3125}$	$\dfrac{1080}{3125}$	$\dfrac{720}{3125}$	$\dfrac{240}{3125}$	$\dfrac{32}{3125}$
.08	.26	.35	.23	.08	.01

Now, before even beginning his experiment, the investigator may consider the probabilities of the six results and decide in advance which of the results have probabilities so small that their occurrence will cause him to reject his hypothesis. He will surely decide to reject his hypothesis about the population if none of the schizophrenics in his sample show improvement. If his hypothesis is true, only 1% of random samples are expected to give this result; hence this result represents a rare occurrence indeed. Rather than believe that such a rare event has occurred, the investigator will conclude that his hypothesis was mistaken if this is the result of his experiment. He may even decide, in addition, that he will reject his hypothesis if only one schizophrenic improves. Adding together the probabilities of 1 improvement and 0 improvement gives $.08 + .01 = .09$ as the probability under his hypothesis that one or less subjects will improve.

Short-Cut Methods for Expanding the Binomial

There are short-cut methods for determining the values of terms in the binomial expansion. First, note that the exponents of successive terms ascend and descend in a parallel, serial order. The first exponent of P is always equal to n, the second exponent is $n - 1$, the third exponent $n - 2$, and so on in a descending order. Q, which first appears in the second term of the expansion, begins with an exponent of 1, has an exponent of 2 in the next term, 3 in the following term, and so on in an ascending order. This may be seen below, where only the P and Q portions of the terms are given for $(P + Q)^4$:

$$P^4 + P^3Q + P^2Q^2 + PQ^3 + Q^4$$

All expansions of the binomial follow this pattern.

The coefficients of the terms in the binomial expansion may be read directly from Pascal's Triangle, which is shown in Table 7.3.

Table 7.3
Pascal's Triangle of Binomial Coefficients

											Sum of Coefficients
				1	2	1					4
			1	3	3	1					8
		1	4	6	4	1					16
	1	5	10	10	5	1					32
1	6	15	20	15	6	1					64
1	7	21	35	35	21	7	1				128
1	8	28	56	70	56	28	8	1			256
1	9	36	84	126	126	84	36	9	1		512
1	10	45	120	210	252	210	120	45	10	1	1024

The row at the top of the table gives the coefficients of the terms in the expansion of $(P + Q)^2$, which are simply 1, 2, and 1. The next row gives the coefficients for $(P + Q)^3$, which are 1, 3, 3, and 1, and so on. To illustrate:

$$(P + Q)^4 = P^4 + 4P^3Q + 6P^2Q^2 + 4PQ^3 + Q^4$$

Once the expansion has been written out in this form, the hypothesized values of P and Q may be substituted in those terms which are of interest, and the terms solved individually by carrying out the indicated multiplications.

In carrying out the multiplications of individual terms in the binomial expansion, it is usually easier to keep P and Q in the form of fractions (*e.g.*, 3/5 and 2/5, rather than .6 and .4). When P and Q are fractions with the same denominator, then the fractional value of every term in the expansion will have the same denominator. Thus, when $(3/5 + 2/5)^5$ was expanded, the fractional values of the terms all had the same denominator, 3125. It is only necessary, therefore, to compute the denominator of one term.

Computations are greatly simplified when the hypothesis is that $P = 1/2$, and therefore that $Q = 1/2$ as well. When $P = Q = 1/2$, it will always be true that the value of each term in the expansion will be equal to the coefficient of the term divided by the sum of all the coefficients for that particular expansion. The sums of the coefficients for the expansions given in Table 7.3 are listed in a column at the right of the table. The use of the binomial expansion in solving a problem of this type is illustrated below.

Example 5.   If college students, asked to guess the number of beads in a glass jar, are as likely to guess too many as too few, (a) what is the probability that a random sample of six students will include five or more subjects who guess too many? (b) What results would lead you to reject the hypothesis that guesses of too many are as likely as guesses of too few?

Hypothesizing that the two possibilities in a situation are equally likely means that the population of elements—guesses, in this case—are hypothesized to be half of one type, half of another. Thus, $P = 1/2$ and $Q = 1/2$. There are six subjects in the sample, so we need to expand $(P + Q)^6$. Reading the coefficients from Table 7.3, and remembering that the exponents of P *descend* in serial order while the exponents of Q *ascend* in serial order,

$$(P + Q)^6 = P^6 + 6P^5Q + 15P^4Q^2 + 20P^3Q^3 + 15P^2Q^4 + 6PQ^5Q^6 + Q^6$$

(**a**) Letting P represent the proportion of guesses which are too high, the probability that *five or more* of the subjects will guess too high is given by the sum of the first two terms of the expansion. The first term represents samples in which all six subjects guess too many beads, the second term samples in which five subjects guess too many and one too few. Both of these terms are included by the phrase "five or more."

Since $P = Q = 1/2$ in this problem, the value of each term in the expansion is equal to its coefficient divided by the sum of all the coefficients. The sum of the coefficients of this expansion is 64, as indicated in Table 7.3. The coefficient of the first term is 1, therefore its value is 1/64. The coefficient of the second term is 6, therefore the value of this term is 6/64. The sum of the two terms is 7/64 or .11. Thus, if guesses of too few are as likely as guesses of too many in this situation, we would expect about 11% of the random samples of this size to include five or more guesses of too many. The probability of such a result under the hypothesis is .11.

(**b**) To determine which results would lead to a rejection of the hypothesis in this case, the probabilities at both extremes of the expansion should be considered. Either too many low guesses or too many high guesses would constitute evidence against the hypothesis that both types of guessing are equally likely in the population. Below are given the fractional values of the terms in the expansion, and under these their decimal values rounded to the second place.

1/64	6/64	15/64	20/64	15/64	6/64	1/64
.02	.09	.23	.31	.23	.09	.02

It is evident from these values that an investigator would most likely reject the hypothesis if either of the two extreme results—six guesses of too many beads or six guesses of too few—occurred. The combined probability of these two results is .02 + .02 = .04. Only four percent of random samples are this extreme if the hypothesis is true.

Any other of the results would not ordinarily lead to a rejection of the hypothesis. If the next most extreme results—five guesses of too many or five guesses of too few—are added, the combined probabilities become the original .04 plus .09 and .09, which gives .22. No investigator would feel justified in rejecting a hypothesis on the basis of results which are expected to occur 22% of the time under that hypothesis.

Large Sample, Large Population

As the sample size n increases, the distribution of sample results, represented by the successive terms of the binomial expansion, approaches the form of the normal distribution. If a distribution of sample values is normal in form, the areas under the normal curve may be used to determine the percentage of samples above and below given z values. And if we know the percentage of samples which will give a particular experimental result, then of course we know also the probability of that result.

What is needed is a means of transforming experimental results into z values, which may then be looked up in the table of normal curve areas. This is done by taking as the mean of the normal distribution ($z = 0$) the expected experimental result, as predicted by the hypothesis. Thus, if the hypothesis is that $P = 1/2$ and a random sample of 20 subjects is drawn, the expected result is that 1/2, or 10, of the subjects will be of the type represented by P. This number, the *expected frequency*, will be symbolized F. The actual experimental result, the observed frequency of type P subjects in the sample, will be symbolized f. Then $f - F$ represents the deviation of the observed frequency or actual result from the expected frequency or predicted result. This is analogous to the numerator of the familiar z formula, where $X - \bar{X}$ represented the deviation of an observation from the mean of the distribution.

In the familiar z formula, the denominator was the standard deviation of the distribution. In a binomial distribution, the standard deviation of sample frequencies about the expected frequency F is given by $\sqrt{nPQ}$. The z formula, then, which will permit us to approximate the probabilities of the binomial expansion by referring to the normal curve is

$$z = \frac{f - F}{\sqrt{nPQ}} \qquad (7.5)$$

The approximation given by formula (7.5) is fairly accurate even when the sample is not very large. The general rule is that both nP and nQ must equal at least 5 if the formula is to yield a satisfactory approximation. An even closer approximation to the binomial may be obtained if f is "corrected for discontinuity"* by bringing it half a unit closer to F (either adding or subtracting .5 from f, whichever brings its value closer to that of F). The use of formula (7.5) is illustrated below.

Example 6. If the population of a city's voters is evenly divided between those who favor preservation of a city park and those who favor use of the space for city housing, (a) what is the probability that a random sample of 48 voters will include at least 28 voters who favor retaining the park? (b) What sample results would lead to a rejection of the hypothesis that voters are evenly divided on this issue?

(a) Let P represent the proportion of voters who favor retaining the park, and Q the proportion who favor replacing it with city housing. Since $P = 1/2$, or .5, and $n = 48$, $F = nP = (.5)(48) = 24$. The observed frequency, f, is 28. Substituting these values in formula (7.5) we have

---

* Our model, the normal curve, is a continuous function. Frequencies, being integers, are discontinuous. The frequency f may be thought of as occupying the interval $f - .5$ to $f + .5$ on the baseline of the normal curve. The distance between F and the nearest bound of this interval is then taken in place of the distance $f - F$.

$$z = \frac{28 - 24}{\sqrt{48(.5)(.5)}} = \frac{4}{\sqrt{12}} = 1.15$$

Looking up $z = 1.15$ in the table of normal curve areas, we find that approximately 87% of random samples have observed frequencies less than this f of 28; hence 13% are expected to have observed frequencies greater than 28. If 13% of random samples are expected, under the hypothesis, to give a result in which 28 or more subjects favor retention of the park, then a finding of 28 cannot be regarded as an unusual event. It is not sufficient cause for rejection of the hypothesis.

Usually, the above procedure will be sufficient for making a decision about a hypothesis on the basis of a sample result. When the decision is a close one, the exact probability of the sample result is better approximated by correcting f for discontinuity by bringing its value .5 closer to the value of F. Thus,

$$z = \frac{27.5 - 24}{\sqrt{12}} = \frac{3.5}{3.46} = 1.01$$

This z value is found to surpass approximately 84% of random sample values; hence about 16% of random samples will yield values at least this great. The probability of such a result is .16, greater than our first approximation of .13. The effect of correcting f for discontinuity will always be to raise the probability of the result. Exact probabilities, computed from the binomial expansion, are somewhat larger than the probabilities read from the normal curve for the same problem. Hence, use of the correction will yield a z and a corresponding probability closer to the exact probability.

(b) To determine what sample results—what observed frequencies— would have an occurrence sufficiently rare under the hypothesis to warrant rejecting the hypothesis, one must first decide the probability value which will be regarded as indicating "rareness." It is possible to decide, for example, that samples so extreme as to have a combined probability of .10 shall be regarded as evidence against the hypothesis that the population is evenly divided. The investigator is then said to have adopted a *significance level* of .10. That is, any sample result which deviates so far from the predicted result as to fall into a class of samples whose combined probability is .10 shall be regarded as deviating *significantly* from the predicted result. Such a significant deviation from the predicted result is taken as cause for the rejection of the hypothesis.

In psychological research, the .05 significance level is in very wide use and it will be adopted for this problem for purposes of illustration. Having adopted a combined probability of .05 as identifying the group of samples which will lead to a rejection of the hypothesis, we now work backwards to determine the observed frequencies which produce such samples.

• • STEP 1. Since samples at either extreme of the distribution constitute evidence aginst the hypothesis that the population is evenly divided, the combined probability .05 is divided in half. Sample frequencies that fall *either* among the lowest .025 *or* among the highest .025 of the possible outcomes shall be regarded as significant departures from the expected frequency F, and hence as evidence against the hypothesis. From the normal curve table, the z value which cuts off the most extreme .025 of the area under the normal curve is 1.96.

• • STEP 2. The z value found identifies the "cut-off" points at both extremes of the distribution. That is, $+z$ marks off samples which are significantly higher than F, and $-z$ marks off those which are significantly lower than F. To determine the f values, the observed frequencies of these samples, $+z$ and $-z$, are substituted in turn in formula (7.5), which is then solved for f. Thus,

$$1.96 = \frac{f - 24}{\sqrt{48(.5)(.5)}}, f = 24 + 1.96\sqrt{48(.5)(.5)} = 30.78$$

$$-1.96 = \frac{f - 24}{\sqrt{48(.5)(.5)}}, f = 24 - 1.96\sqrt{48(.5)(.5)} = 17.22$$

We find, then, that if the .05 significance level is adopted, observed frequencies above 30.78 and below 17.22 will lead to a rejection of the hypothesis that voters are evenly divided. Less extreme sample results will not lead to a rejection of the hypothesis.

SAMPLING DISTRIBUTIONS AND PROBABILITY

We have considered in this chapter a number of distributions that describe how random samples from a binomial population are distributed. One of these sampling distributions was derived from "scratch" (Tables 7.1 and 7.2), and in deriving it we used the principles of random selection and equally likely outcomes that are at the foundation of every other sampling distribution. The distribution given in Tables 7.1 and 7.2 is illustrated graphically in Figure 7.1a. Fig. 7.1b is based on the expan-

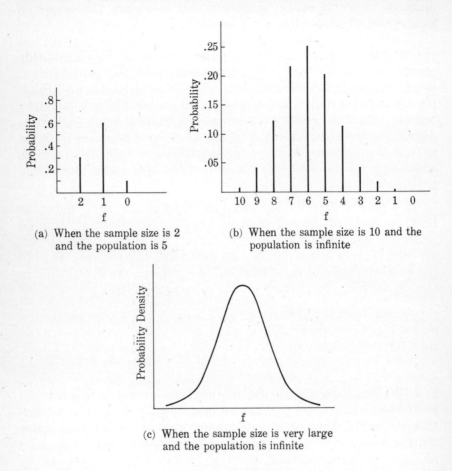

(a) When the sample size is 2 and the population is 5

(b) When the sample size is 10 and the population is infinite

(c) When the sample size is very large and the population is infinite

Figure 7.1

Sampling Distribution of f, the Number of Type B Subjects, When the Population Consists of .6 Type B Subjects and .4 That Are Not Type B

sion of $(P + Q)^{10}$ and shows what the sampling distribution would look like if ten subjects (instead of two) were randomly drawn from a vast population (rather than a population of five) where $P = .6$, $Q = .4$. Note that Fig. 7.1b is already more "normal" in appearance than Fig. 7.1a. If a sample much larger than ten were to be drawn from the population, the number of bars in Fig. 7.1b would be greatly multiplied and much closer together, the skewness would practically disappear, and the resulting graph would be closely approximated by the normal curve of Figure 7.1c.

Observe that the ordinates of the sampling distributions are labeled "Probability," and in the case of the normal curve, "Probability Density." All sampling distributions are probability distributions. The ordinates of Figs. 7.1a and 7.1b might also have been labeled "Proportions" because one can read directly from these ordinates the proportion of samples that will give a particular experimental result. The proportion of samples that will give a result is, of course, the probability of that result. So in giving the proportions of samples having different values, the sampling distribution gives the probabilities of those values.

In the case of the normal curve, because it is continuous, the proportion of samples that will yield a particular result is given by an area rather than by the ordinate. Any "result" in which we might be interested occupies a *distance* along the baseline of the graph, and the proportion of samples having values within that distance would be represented by the area under the curve enclosed by verticals erected at the boundaries of that distance. For example, suppose an experiment gave a result of $z = 1.83$. Usually, we want to know the probability of obtaining a z *as large as this*, so we are interested in the combined probability of all z values that lie beyond 1.83. Even if, for some bizarre reason, we wished to know the probability of obtaining the particular value $z = +1.83$, we would still find ourselves dealing with an area, for the simple reason that the normal curve is continuous and $z = +1.83$ is represented by the distance $z = +1.825$ to $z = +1.835$; the probability would be given by the area under the curve enclosed by verticals erected at these points. However precise a z value is specified (say, $z = +1.8300000$), it is represented by some small distance rather than by a point, and its probability is given by an area rather than by the ordinate. The term *probability density* refers to the height of the curve, but the height of a continuous curve indicates only the density or "thickness" of a probability area in this region, not the probability itself.

All theoretical sampling distributions, whether they are discrete, like Figs. 7.1a and 7.1b, or continuous, like the normal curve of Fig. 7.1c, are derived by mathematical deduction from the premise that every elementary outcome in a given situation is equally likely. When this premise is fulfilled (as by random sampling) the appropriate sampling distribution can be used to determine the probability of a given experimental result. The sampling distributions that will be considered in later chapters are all continuous (or are approximated by continuous curves). This means that to determine the probability of a given result, we will always be referring to an area under the curve of the appropriate sampling distribution. The distributions will often be different in shape from the normal curve, but the principles are the same.

Practice Problems

Answer the following, and tell for each whether the probability you have computed is an empirical estimate *or a* deductive estimate.

1. Of 200 first offenders released from a certain prison, 76 received another sentence and were returned to prison within three years of their release. What is the probability that a first offender released from this prison will not return within three years?

2. At a prep school for boys, all new students are required to begin classes in either Latin, French, German, or Russian. Out of the 138 new students of the past few years, 51 elected to take French, 42 chose German, 25 Latin, and 20 Russian. (a) On the basis of this information, what proportion of the students in this year's entering class are expected to elect French? German? Latin? Russian? (b) If there are 40 students in the entering class, how many are expected to elect French? German? Latin? Russian?

3. In 50 trials with the Müller-Lyer Illusion, a subject makes two correct settings. If he could be given 1000 trials under the same conditions, how many correct settings would he be expected to make?

4. Seventy-three percent of textile workers in a particular region are union members. If the 184 workers at Mill X do not differ in this respect from the region's textile workers, how many of them are expected to be union members?

5. A test constructor plans to include in a test he is assembling a reasoning problem which in a different test was solved correctly by two-thirds of his ten-year-old subjects. He expects that, transferred to the new test he is assembling, the problem can still be solved correctly by two-thirds of the new group of ten-year-olds. To test his hypothesis, he gives the new test, which includes the reasoning problem, to a random sample of ten-year-old subjects.

Imagine that the population of ten-year-olds consists of six subjects and that the investigator gives the test to a random sample of three subjects drawn from this population. What are the possible experimental results, in terms of the number of subjects who solve the reasoning problem correctly? List under each result the different samples (combinations of outcomes) which would produce that result if the population is as hypothesized. If the hypothesis is true, what is the probability of occurrence of each of the experimental results? Would any of these results lead you to reject the hypothesis? Why? Construct a graph of the sampling distribution showing the probability of each experimental result.

6. A colleague of the test constructor in (5) above believes that the context in which the reasoning problem appears in the new test will make the item more difficult than usual. He hypothesizes that only 50% of ten-year-olds can solve the problem correctly in this context. Using the same experiment as in (5), what is the probability of occurrence of each of the experimental results if the colleague's hypothesis is true? Construct a graph of the sampling distribution. Is it possible in this experiment to make a reasonable decision between the test constructor's hypothesis and his colleague's hypothesis (accepting one and rejecting the other)? Under what circumstances (with what result)?

7. Three men are to be sent to an overseas post, and are chosen from among ten draftees available for assignment. How many different samples (combinations) of three men is it possible to select? (a) If the sample is selected by a random procedure, what is the probability that the three friends—Don, Phil, and Ed—will all be chosen? (b) What is the probability that at least two of them will be chosen? (c) What is the probability that the sample will include at least one of them? (d) None of them? (e) Explain why these probabilities do not add up to 1.00.

Use the binomial expansion to answer the following:

8. If blindfolded subjects asked to draw a five-inch line are as likely to draw one which is too long as to draw one which is too short (*i.e.*, if $P = Q = \frac{1}{2}$), what is the probability of obtaining an experimental result in which all four subjects draw lines which are too short? Three of the four subjects draw lines which are too short? All draw lines which are too long?

9. If rats are as likely to turn left as to turn right on their first trial in a T-maze, what is the probability of obtaining a result in which four of the six rats tested turn to the left? Two turn to the left? Three turn right and three turn left?

10. Seven discussion groups, composed of equal numbers of men

and women, each elect a discussion leader for their group. Six of the seven leaders elected are men. If men and women are equally likely to be elected as leaders, what is the probability of obtaining this result? What is the probability that *at least* six will be men?

11. A clinical psychologist is given eight figure drawings, some of which were drawn by normals and some by psychotic patients. He is asked to study the drawings and decide in each case whether the drawing was made by a normal or by a psychotic subject. He is correct in six of his eight judgments. What is the probability of doing this well *or better* by chance?

12. If half of a city's voters intend to vote for Candidate X for mayor and the other half intend to vote for Candidate Y, what is the probability of obtaining a random sample of ten voters at least seven of whom intend to vote for Candidate X? At least eight of whom intend to vote for Candidate X?

13. If there are five true-false items on an exam, what is the probability of getting them all right by chance? All wrong by chance? Three right by chance?

14. If there are five multiple-choice items on an exam and three possible answers are provided for each item, what is the probability of getting all five items right by chance? All wrong by chance? Three items right by chance? (Note that P and Q in this case are *not* $\frac{1}{2}$.)

15. In a study of color preferences among pre-school children, each child is given three trials in which he is asked to choose among four objects which are identical except for color. One of the objects is red, one blue, one yellow, and one green, and the order of the objects from right to left is changed on successive trials. (a) If a child really has no preference among the four colors, what is the probability that he will choose the red object by chance on all three trials? (b) On two of the three trials? (c) What is the probability that he will choose the same color on all three trials? (d) On two of the three trials?

Refer to the areas under the normal curve to answer the following:

16. Determine the probability of (11) above by referring to areas under the normal curve. Compare the probabilities obtained by the two methods and explain why they are different.

17. Determine the probability of (12) above by reference to the normal curve. Compare the probabilities obtained by the two methods. Which probability value is more exact?

18. If the children of a city slum area are as likely to be above

as below average in intelligence, what is the probability of obtaining a random sample of 20 such children in which 14 *or more* are below average in intelligence?

19. A subject claims to have extra-sensory perception. An investigator tests the subject with a deck of 52 cards, 26 of which are red and 26 black. The subject guesses whether successive cards, turned over out of his sight, are red or black. Out of the 52 cards, he guesses correctly 30 times. What is the probability of doing this well *or better* by chance?

20. A random sample of 36 parents in a large school district are interviewed to determine their attitudes towards the quality of the schooling their children are receiving. Of the 36 parents interviewed, 22 express dissatisfaction. Given the hypothesis that the population of parents is evenly divided in its readiness to express dissatisfaction, what is the probability of obtaining a random sample that deviates this much from expectation? On the basis of this probability, should the hypothesis be rejected? Can it be concluded that the majority of parents in this district are dissatisfied with the quality of their children's schooling?

21. On a test of autonomic activity under stress, the median score of a large group of normal subjects is 20.5. An investigator gives the test to a random sample of 40 neurotics and finds that 70% of the neurotics obtain scores above 20.5. Test the hypothesis that the neurotics are a random sample from a population with a median score of 20.5.

22. On a Current Affairs test, 16% of college students obtain scores above 80. A random sample of 300 students at College X are given the test and 28% obtain scores above 80. Test the hypothesis that the 300 students are a random sample from a population in which 16% surpass a score of 80.

Answers

1. .62. Empirical estimate.

2. (a) .37, .30, .18, .14. All are empirical estimates. (b) 15, 12, 7, 6.

3. 40. (The empirical probability estimate is .04.)

4. 134. (.73 is an empirical probability estimate.)

5. The possible experimental results, with the deductive prob-

ability of each under the test constructor's hypothesis, are: all three subjects solve the problem, $P = .20$; two solve the problem, $P = .60$; one solves the problem, $P = .20$; none solve the problem, $P = .00$. Only in the case of this last result can the hypothesis be rejected with confidence because it is not possible to obtain this result if the population is as hypothesized. If the result is obtained, the hypothesis was wrong. The other results (3, 2, or 1 solution) are not unusual samples under the hypothesis and provide no evidence for its rejection.

6. The possible experimental results are the same as above, but under the colleague's hypothesis their deductive probabilities are .05, .45, .45, .05. If all three subjects solve the problem, reject the colleague's hypothesis and accept the test constructor's hypothesis. (If no subjects solved the problem, both hypotheses should be rejected.)

7. 120 different samples. The deductive probabilities are: (a) .008; (b) .18; (c) .71; (d) .29. (e) The events are not all mutually exclusive.

8. .06, .25, .06.

9. .23, .23, .31.

10. .05, .06.

11. .14.

12. .17, .05.

13. .03, .03, .31.

14. .004, .13, .16.

15. (a) .016; (b) .14; (c) .064; (d) .56.

16. $z = 1.41$, $P = .08$.

17. $z = 1.27$, $P = .10$; $z = 1.90$, $p = .03$.

18. $z = 1.79$, $P = .04$.

19. $z = 1.11$, $P = .13$.

20. $z = 1.33$, $P = 2(.0918) = .18$. The probability is doubled so as to include both tails of the normal curve (the area below $z = -1.33$ and the area above $z = +1.33$). The probability of a deviation *as large as* the one observed includes values which deviate this much in either direction from the expected value. Ordinarily, the hypothesis would not be rejected on the basis of such a large probability; the hypothesis is not an implausible one. Therefore, it

cannot be concluded that a majority of the parents in the district are dissatisfied, even though a majority of this sample are dissatisfied.

21. $z = 2.53$, $P = 2(.0057) = .01$. The hypothesis is that 50% of the population sampled would obtain scores above 20.5 (the median). The expected frequency is therefore 20, and the observed sample frequency is $.70(40) = 28$. Since, by our z test, a deviation this large would occur only about one in a hundred times if the hypothesis is true, either a very rare event has occurred or the hypothesis is false. Ordinarily, the hypothesis would be rejected. The median of this population is not 20.5, but almost certainly a higher value.

22. $z = 5.63$, $P < .0001$. The hypothesis $(P = .16, Q = .84)$ would be rejected. At College X, the evidence indicates that more than 16% of the student population would obtain scores above 80.

chapter 8

Formulating
Statistical
Hypotheses

In the preceding chapter, a number of statistical hypotheses were considered. These hypotheses were statements about populations of interest—*e.g.*, that 60% of schizophrenics would show improvement with a given treatment, that college students would be as likely to guess too high as too low in estimating the number of beads in a jar, that voters were evenly divided in the choice between a city park or city housing. The reasonableness of the statement made about the population was evaluated by examining the characteristics of a random sample drawn from that population. Specifically, it was assumed that the statement made about the population was true and the question was asked, "What is the probability of obtaining a random sample with these observed characteristics if the population really is as stated?" If the probability of drawing such a random sample was very small, this cast doubt upon the statement about the population. The tendency was to regard the statement as unreasonable or untenable and to reject it as a false picture of the population. If the probability of drawing such a random sample was not small, the statement made about the population was regarded as reasonable, or at least tenable, and it was not rejected.

This procedure, called hypothesis testing, thus involves two general steps: (1) formulating a statistical hypothesis about a population of interest; (2) evaluating the reasonableness of this hypothesis by examining a random sample drawn from the population.

Most of the remainder of this book is devoted to methods for evaluating the reasonableness of a statistical hypothesis. In this chapter, we turn our attention to the problem of formulating statistical hypotheses.

DEFINITION OF A STATISTICAL HYPOTHESIS

A statistical hypothesis is an explicit statement about some characteristic of a population. The statement must be so explicit that we can deduce from it a similarly explicit *expectation* about the characteristics of a random sample drawn from the population. For instance, the hypothesis that the subjects of a given population are as likely to overestimate as to underestimate the number of beads in a jar leads to the expectation that half of a random sample of such subjects will overestimate and half will underestimate the number of beads.

But suppose the experimenter believes that most subjects will underestimate the number of beads? Can he test the hypothesis that most subjects will underestimate? The answer is no, he cannot. The statement is too vague; it does not lead to a precise expectation about how a random sample will be constituted. How many is "most"? 75%? 90%? We do not know what is expected under such a hypothesis. If the experimenter's statement had been, "75% of subjects will underestimate the number of beads," we should have a testable statistical hypothesis. This hypothesis leads to a specific expectation about the proportion of underestimators in a random sample—namely, .75. *Only statements about populations which give rise to specific, numerical sample expectancies can be tested statistically.*

As we have seen, under the hypothesis that a population is divided half-and-half on some question, a sample division of half-and-half is the "expected" finding. At the same time, we know that most random samples from such a population will not yield perfect half-and-half divisions. The observed proportions will fluctuate from sample to sample even though the values cluster around .50. Similarly, if the mean IQ of a particular population is hypothesized to be 120, the "expected" mean of a random sample is 120. But even if the hypothesis is true, most sample means will depart somewhat from this value. Departures of sample values from expectation are thus the rule rather than the exception. The question is whether the deviation of a sample value from expectation may be attributed to random sampling fluctuation, or whether the deviation is so great that it should be regarded as a contradiction of the hypothesis about the population. All tests of statistical hypotheses make the former assumption—namely, that departures from expectation are entirely due to random sampling fluctuation. A statistical hypothesis is often called a *null hypothesis* to emphasize this assumption that any differences between observed sample values and expected sample values are "null" apart from random sampling fluctuation.

In summary, then, a statistical hypothesis or null hypothesis (1) is an explicit statement about some characteristic of a population, (2) leads to a specific, numerical sample expectancy, and (3) assumes that any obtained sample departure from this expectancy is entirely due to random sampling fluctuation. It is this last assumption which must be invalidated by the data if the hypothesis is to be rejected.

FORMULATING STATISTICAL HYPOTHESES

The particular form in which a statistical hypothesis is stated determines whether it shall be tested by means of a *two-tailed test* or by means of a *one-tailed test*.

The hypothesis that 50% of voters favor a proposal, which may be written "$H: P = .5$" (or $P = Q$), calls for a *two-tailed test*. The hypothesis will be rejected if the obtained sample proportion departs from .5 either in the direction of being too high or in the direction of being too low. Both "tails" or extremes of the sampling distribution are taken into consideration in determining the probability of the sample result, as shown in Figure 8.1(a).

The directional hypothesis that 50% *or more* voters favor a proposal, written "$H: P \geq .5$," calls for a *one-tailed test*. The expected sample proportion is .5 but this hypothesis will be rejected only if the sample proportion departs from .5 in the direction of being too low. Only the lower "tail" of the sampling distribution is considered in determining the probability of the sample result, as shown in Figure 8.1(b).

Some examples of the two kinds of hypotheses are shown in Table 8.1. Across from each hypothesis is its *alternative*, which is simply the logical counter-statement about the population that will be accepted if the hypothesis is rejected.

Choosing the appropriate statistical hypothesis for an experiment is often a roundabout procedure. Since most psychological research originates in beliefs and hunches which are not specific enough to constitute statistical hypotheses, it is usually the case that the investigator must test an opposing hypothesis, the *rejection* of which will provide evidence for his belief. For example, if an investigator suspects that boys will do better than girls on an experimental task,

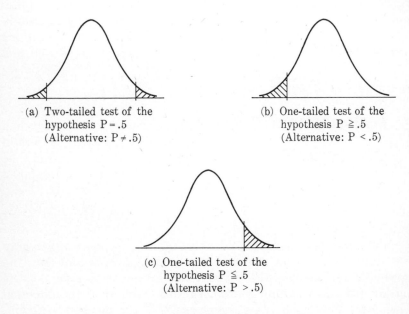

(a) Two-tailed test of the hypothesis P = .5 (Alternative: P ≠ .5)

(b) One-tailed test of the hypothesis P ≧ .5 (Alternative: P < .5)

(c) One-tailed test of the hypothesis P ≦ .5 (Alternative: P > .5)

Figure 8.1

Critical Region for Two-Tailed and One-Tailed Tests. Sample Results Falling in the Shaded Area Will Lead, in Each Case, to Rejection of the Hypothesis

he will probably test (and hope to reject) the opposing statistical hypothesis that girls do as well as or better than boys.

There is an even more important advantage in testing a statistical hypothesis the rejection of which will provide evidence for the investigator's belief. If a statistical hypothesis is rejected, the alternative to that hypothesis may be accepted as true. If the hypothesis that boys and girls do equally well on a task is rejected, the implication is that one sex does better than the other. But if a statistical hypothesis is *not* rejected, this does *not* imply that the hypothesis is true. For example, suppose an investigator hypothesizes that at least 75% of subjects ($P \geq .75$) will underestimate the number of beads

Table 8.1
Some Examples of Statistical Hypotheses

HYPOTHESES THAT CALL FOR A TWO-TAILED TEST:

HYPOTHESIS	ALTERNATIVE	LOCATION OF CRITICAL REGION
$P = Q$	$P \neq Q$	Half in each tail
$P = .75$	$P \neq .75$	Half in each tail
$\mu = 120$	$\mu \neq 120$	Half in each tail
$\mu_1 = \mu_2$	$\mu_1 \neq \mu_2$	Half in each tail
$P_1 = P_2$	$P_1 \neq P_2$	Half in each tail

HYPOTHESES THAT CALL FOR A ONE-TAILED TEST:

HYPOTHESIS	ALTERNATIVE	LOCATION OF CRITICAL REGION
$P \geq Q$	$P < Q$	Lower tail
$P \geq .75$	$P < .75$	Lower tail
$\mu \geq 120$	$\mu < 120$	Lower tail
$\mu_1 \geq \mu_2$	$\mu_1 < \mu_2$	Lower tail
$P_1 \geq P_2$	$P_1 < P_2$	Lower tail
$P \leq Q$	$P > Q$	Upper tail
$P \leq .75$	$P > .75$	Upper tail
$\mu \leq 120$	$\mu > 120$	Upper tail
$\mu_1 \leq \mu_2$	$\mu_1 > \mu_2$	Upper tail
$P_1 \leq P_2$	$P_1 > P_2$	Upper tail

in a jar, and then obtains a sample result in which 70% underestimate. The difference between 70% and 75% may not be meaningful for a small sample (consider $n = 20$, for instance). A z test such as those of the preceding chapter may well show that such a difference has a high probability of occurrence under the hypothesis and therefore the hypothesis cannot be rejected. But obviously a sample finding of 70% who underestimate does not and cannot prove that "at least 75%" are underestimators. The outcome of the statistical test only says, in effect, that the hypothesis of "at least 75%" is not an untenable one. Much ambiguity remains. The investigator cannot say that his belief has been confirmed; it has not been flatly contradicted, but this is hardly the same thing.

It is primarily to avoid the possibility of such an ambiguous result that most investigators follow the roundabout procedure of testing a hypothesis which is opposite to their belief and which they hope to reject. Thus, testing the hypothesis that the proportion of underestimators in the population is equal to or *less than* .75 ($P \leq$ .75) gives the possibility of obtaining unambiguous evidence in favor of the investigator's belief. If the hypothesis is rejected, the only alternative is that *more than* .75 of the population are underestimators. If the hypothesis is not rejected, then of course the investigator has failed to find support for his belief. The important consideration is that the wording of the hypothesis makes it at least possible to obtain unambiguous evidence favoring his belief. The only way this can be done is by identifying his belief with rejection of the hypothesis.

Locating the Critical Region

The student is already familiar with the idea that decisions to reject or to retain hypotheses are made on the basis of probabilities rather than certainties. The investigator chooses a probability value —typically, .10 or .05 or .01—which becomes the *level of significance* in the test of his hypothesis. As pointed out in Chapter 7 (see Example 6), the significance level adopted in testing a hypothesis is the combined probability of those sample results which will lead to rejection of the hypothesis. Thus, when an investigator adopts a significance level for the test of his hypothesis, he specifies thereby a group of possible sample results which deviate so much from expectancy that he will regard the occurrence of any one of them as sufficient cause for the rejection of his hypothesis.

If the hypothesis calls for a two-tailed test, the probability value chosen as the significance level is divided in half to give two equal probability values. These two values define what is called the *critical region*, half of which lies in one tail, half in the opposite tail, of the particular sampling distribution to which the sample result will be referred. The critical region thus embraces all those sample results which will lead to rejection of the hypothesis. If the obtained sample result falls into the critical region in either tail of the distribution, the hypothesis is rejected. If the sample result does not fall into the critical region, the hypothesis is retained.

In a one-tailed test, the probability value chosen as the significance level defines a critical region which lies entirely in one tail of the sampling distribution. As may be seen in Fig. 8.1 and in the examples given in Table 8.1, if the hypothesis states that one parameter is equal to or *greater than* another, the critical region is in the lower tail of the sampling distribution. If the hypothesis states that one parameter is equal to or *less than* another, the critical region is in the upper tail of the distribution. The hypothesis will be rejected only if the sample result falls within the critical region *in that given tail of the distribution.* No other sample result will cause rejection of the hypothesis, however far out it may lie in the opposite tail of the distribution and however small its probability in the distribution.

That the critical region should be located entirely in one tail of the sampling distribution follows logically enough from the nature of a directional hypothesis, but it warns against adopting such a hypothesis without careful consideration of the possibility of obtaining an extreme sample result which falls in the opposite tail of the distribution. Hunches about the outcome of an experiment should not automatically be translated into directional hypotheses. For example, suppose an investigator thinks that the mean score of salesmen (μ_1) on a test will be higher than the mean score of secretaries (μ_2) and he hypothesizes that $\mu_1 \leqq \mu_2$, hoping to reject this hypothesis and accept its alternative that $\mu_1 > \mu_2$. If it now turns out that the mean score of the salesmen is not only lower than that of the secretaries but very remarkably so, his hypothesis permits no explicit recognition of this fact. He is in the embarrassing position of having to retain a hypothesis which includes the possibility that salesmen and secretaries do equally well on the test, even though he can now see that this is unreasonable because the secretaries do better. He cannot change his hypothesis in midstream; the practice of changing hypotheses to fit the data obviously invalidates the whole procedure. But if in the beginning he had hypothesized only that $\mu_1 = \mu_2$, he might now be in a position to reject this hypothesis and assert that the data warrant the conclusion that secretaries do better than salesmen on this test.

The use of directional hypotheses and one-tailed tests is a debated issue. Some writers argue that they should not be used at all and that all tests should be two-tailed; other writers disagree. The fact remains that one-tailed tests are in wide use and the student should understand at least some of their implications.

A disadvantage of the directional hypothesis, as we have just seen, is that it permits no finding of a significant difference opposite to the experimenter's "hunch" or belief. This disadvantage suggests that a directional hypothesis should be adopted only when one of the following circumstances is true: (1) a difference opposite to the investigator's belief is theoretically unsound. Usually, this is because prior investigation of a similar nature has consistently shown differences in one direction—*e.g.*, that hungry rats will perform better than satiated rats, that stress lowers the efficiency of high anxiety subjects, that college graduates have a higher mean income than high school graduates; (2) a difference opposite to the investigator's belief is irrelevant to the purpose of the investigation and therefore would be of no interest even if it occurred.

As an example of (2) above, suppose that an Air Force officer is concerned that some of the pilots under his command are flying too many missions. He is afraid that nervous symptoms are more common among the experienced men who have flown many missions than they are among the more recently graduated and less experienced men. He may hypothesize that the proportion of experienced men who have nervous symptoms (P_1) is equal to or less than the proportion of inexperienced men who have nervous symptoms (P_2), or $P_1 \leqq P_2$. The alternative to this hypothesis is that $P_1 > P_2$, which is the officer's belief. An extreme difference opposite to his belief—namely, that nervous symptoms are *less* common among experienced men—is irrelevant to the purpose of the investigation and needs no explicit recognition. The officer is only interested in detecting the effects of strain (if any) among pilots who have flown many missions. That there may be more nervous symptoms among the inexperienced men does not worry him.

If a directional hypothesis is appropriate for a situation, then there is a distinct advantage in using one. The advantage is that if the investigator's belief is correct, the location of the critical region entirely in one tail of the sampling distribution gives him a better chance of rejecting the hypothesis and so confirming his belief. For instance, in conducting a z test of the nondirectional hypothesis $P = .6$, the critical region for a .05 significance level begins at ± 1.96 of the normal distribution. Thus, the obtained sample z must exceed 1.96 in absolute value in order to fall into the critical region. A z test of the directional hypothesis $P \leq .6$, with the same .05 significance level, is referred to a critical region in one tail of the distribution which begins at $+1.64$. In this case, the obtained z must exceed only 1.64 in order to fall into the critical region. Thus, if the investigator's belief is correct, he gains an advantage in using a one-tailed test.

Choosing a Significance Level

The significance level of a test is generally symbolized α (alpha) and its numerical value is chosen to minimize (or balance) so far as is possible the dangers of rejecting a true hypothesis or retaining a false hypothesis.

If an investigator wants to be very sure that he is right in rejecting a hypothesis, he chooses a very small alpha as the significance level for his test. For example, the admissions officer of a graduate school may want to be very sure that more women than men students fail to complete the course of study before he is willing to set up a quota system which discriminates against women applicants. He may adopt a .01 significance level in his test of the hypothesis that the proportion of women drop-outs is equal to or less than the proportion of men drop-outs, since he does not want to reject this hypothesis if it is true. *Rejecting a hypothesis when it is true is called a* **Type I** **error.** Thus, we may say the admissions officer does not want to make a Type I error.

When the consequences of mistakenly rejecting a true hypothesis are of little importance, an investigator may choose a relatively large significance level for the test of his hypothesis. For instance, suppose that an advertising executive wants to know which of two "free prize" offers (of equal cost to the firm) is most appealing to children. He will hypothesize that the two offers are equally appealing, and he may well adopt $\alpha = .10$ as the significance level for the test of this hypothesis. The .10 significance level gives him a good chance of rejecting the hypothesis and detecting a preference if one actually exists. If the hypothesis of equal appeal or no preference is true, he loses little by mistakenly rejecting it and mistakenly supposing that a preference exists. If there is actually no preference, nothing will be lost whichever prize offer the firm makes. But the firm stands to lose if a preference does exist and the test fails to detect it. So what the executive especially wants to avoid is retaining the hypothesis of no preference if this hypothesis is false. *Retaining a hypothesis when it is false is called a* **Type II error.** Therefore, we may say the advertising executive wants to avoid making a Type II error.

The admissions officer and the advertising executive each chose an alpha value which would help him guard against the particular kind of error he was most anxious to avoid. In most research, the investigator is concerned with avoiding both kinds of error. He does not want to reject a true hypothesis, neither does he want to retain a false hypothesis. Yet, if he makes alpha small in order to reduce the probability of rejecting a true hypothesis, the probability of retaining a false hypothesis is increased. If alpha is made large in order to reduce the probability of retaining a false hypothesis, the probability of rejecting a true hypothesis is increased.

In the effort to keep both of these risks at an acceptable level, the middling value .05 has come to be widely adopted as the significance level in tests of hypotheses. It does not follow, however, that .05 is an appropriate level for all statistical tests. The value of the significance level should not be adopted blindly and automatically. Rather, the investigator should first answer these questions about his hypothesis: What are the consequences of mistakenly rejecting this hypothesis if it is true? If the consequences are serious, make alpha small. The probability of rejecting a true null hypothesis (making a Type I error) is given by alpha. To make this probability small, it is only necessary to reduce the size of alpha. What are the consequences of mistakenly retaining my hypothesis if it is false? If the consequences here are serious, make alpha large. The probability of retaining a false null hypothesis (making a Type II error) depends upon many factors and is not easily determined. The size of alpha is one of these factors. Some other ways of reducing the risk of a Type II error are considered in the next section.

POWER OF A TEST

The *power* of a statistical test refers to the probability that the given test will detect a population difference that actually exists. Power, in this context, is the probability of rejecting a null hypothesis that is false and therefore should be rejected.*

For example, suppose the hypothesis is $P = .5$ while actually, in the population, the true proportion is .6. Thus the hypothesis is false (although of course this will not ordinarily be known.) One experimenter tests the hypothesis $P = .5$ with a random sample of 20 subjects. A second experimenter tests the same hypothesis with a random sample of 100 subjects. Other things equal, the second experimenter with his larger sample clearly has a better chance of detecting that the hypothesis is false and that $P \neq .5$. Regardless of the outcome of the two experiments, the test conducted by the second experimenter is said to have more *power* than the test of the first experimenter because the second experimenter's test has a better chance of rejecting the false hypothesis.

The power of a test depends upon many factors. First, of course, power depends upon the difference between the true characteristics of the population as opposed to the hypothesized characteristics.

* Procedures for estimating the power of a statistical test are beyond the scope of this text. Many of the more useful procedures may be found in Dixon, W. J., and Massey, F. J., *Introduction to Statistical Analysis*, Rev. Ed., McGraw-Hill, 1957.

The larger this difference, the more likely it is to be detected; the smaller the difference, the more likely it is to escape detection. Thus, any given statistical test is automatically more powerful against a large population difference than against a small one.

Other factors that influence the power of a test are (1) the size of the sample, (2) the size of alpha, and (3) the location of the critical region. It should be intuitively clear that a large sample has a better chance of reflecting the true characteristics of the population than does a small sample. If a population difference exists, a large sample is more likely to detect it. Increasing the size of the sample is thus a dependable and very effective means of increasing the power of one's statistical test.

It has already been pointed out that the size of alpha, the level of significance adopted for a test, plays a crucial role in the likelihood of making Type I and Type II errors. A Type II error was defined as accepting a false null hypothesis. The power of a test is the probability of rejecting a false null hypothesis, hence it is the probability of avoiding a Type II error. A large alpha, it was noted, reduced the risk of a Type II error. Increasing the size of alpha, therefore, raises the power of a statistical test. This means of increasing the power of a test must be used judiciously, since increasing the size of alpha also increases the risk of a Type I error. However, in studies where samples are necessarily small and large population differences are not expected, the power of a test may be so low as to constitute a bias against rejection of the null hypothesis. The facts, as it were, are not given a fair chance to become manifest. Clearly, in such cases, a larger significance level than is commonly used should be given serious consideration.

For a given level of significance, a one-tailed test is more powerful than a two-tailed test. We have already seen that in the case of testing a hypothesis about a population proportion, a larger z value is required to reject a nondirectional hypothesis than would be required to reject a directional hypothesis at the same level of significance. In a one-tailed test, the power of the test is concentrated against a difference in the predicted direction, and there is no attendant increase in the risk of a Type I error. Where a one-tailed test is appropriate, then, its use will increase the power of one's statistical test without incurring any added risks.

Practice Problems

For each of the following: (a) formulate the appropriate statistical hypothesis; (b) state the alternative which will be accepted if the hypothesis is rejected; (c) if the hypothesis is directional, give the location of the critical region.

1. A pollster would like to make a forecast about which of two candidates for congress will win a coming election. He interviews a random sample of voters from the district in question to determine whether they intend to vote for Candidate A or Candidate B. He compares the proportions who intend to vote for each candidate.

2. An experimenter wonders whether blindfolded subjects, asked to draw a line of given length, are as likely to draw a line which is too short as to draw a line which is too long. He tests a random sample of students from his classes and determines the proportion who draw too-short lines and the proportion who draw too-long lines.

3. An experimenter believes that on their first trial in a T-maze, rats are as likely to turn left as to turn right. He tests a random sample of rats from the laboratory colony and determines the proportion who turn left and the proportion who turn right on their first trial in the maze.

4. On the basis of previous observation, an experimenter believes that Rat A has a "position habit," and in the long run will turn right in a T-maze more often than he will turn left. To check on his belief, the experimenter tests Rat A at a number of randomly chosen times over several experimental days. He compares the proportion of right turns and the proportion of left turns made by the animal.

5. The experimenter of (2) above found that a majority of his subjects, when deprived of vision, drew lines which were too short. To confirm this finding, he repeats the experiment with a new sample of subjects.

6. On the basis of theory and his own clinical experience, a psychotherapist believes that patients who have dependency problems are less likely to drop out of psychotherapy before its completion than are patients whose main problems are not of this type. To test this belief, he selects a random sample of cases from the clinic's file of "drop-outs." He determines the proportion of drop-outs who re-

ceived a diagnosis of dependency problems and the proportion who did not receive this diagnosis.

7. An investigator suspects that among gifted children the proportion of girls interested in science as a career is the same as the proportion of boys with this interest. He questions a random sample of gifted children from the city's schools and determines the proportion of boys and the proportion of girls who are planning a science career.

8. An investigator has listed four leisure-time activities of college students. He wants to know whether there is any preference among college students for one or more of these activities. He asks a random sample of college students which of the four activities they each prefer, and determines the proportion of students naming each of the activities.

9. An investigator suspects there is a difference in intelligence between two minority groups living in a large city. He obtains two random samples, one from each minority group, and determines the mean IQ of each sample.

10. An experimenter wishes to test the effect, if any, of a new drug on reaction time. Subjects are randomly assigned to an Experimental group (who receive the drug) and a Control group (who receive a placebo). The reaction time of the subjects is then measured and the mean reaction time of each group is computed and compared.

11. A psychologist working in a settlement house believes that the teen-agers of the neighborhood are below average in IQ (their mean score is below 100) and that this is a major factor in the difficulties they have at school. He tests a random sample of teen-agers from the neighborhood and determines their mean IQ.

12. An experimenter has constructed a "masculinity-femininity" test which he hopes to validate by showing that men obtain higher scores on the test than do women. Similar tests have consistently shown differences in this direction. He gives the test to large samples of men and women randomly chosen from several adult populations which are available to him. He then computes separately the mean score for the men and the mean score for the women and compares the two means.

13. The psychotherapist of (6) above finds that among the patients who drop out of psychotherapy the proportion with diagnoses of dependency is not significantly smaller than the proportion with other diagnoses. He is unable to reject the hypothesis that $P \geq Q$. He observes, however, that among the patients of his sample those with dependency problems did not drop out of therapy as

soon as other patients. The mean number of weeks the "dependency" patients remained in therapy was considerably greater than the mean number of weeks other patients remained in therapy. To validate this finding, he selects another random sample of patients from the clinic's file and separates them into two groups according to whether or not they received a diagnosis of dependency problems. For each group he computes the mean number of weeks the patients continued in psychotherapy.

14. An experimenter is interested in the effectiveness of propaganda in altering attitudes. A group of subjects who are fairly homogeneous in their attitudes toward a supposed government policy are randomly assigned to three different groups. One group is subjected to propaganda in the form of a lecture and a second group receives propaganda in the form of a movie. The third group serves as a control and receives no propaganda. All subjects then fill out an attitude questionnaire, and the mean attitude score for each group is determined. The three means are compared.

Answers

1. $H: P = Q$. The proportion of voters who intend to vote for Candidate A is equal to the proportion who intend to vote for Candidate B. Alternative: $P \neq Q$. The proportions are not equal; either more voters intend to vote for A or more intend to vote for B.

2. $H: P = Q$. In the population from which the subjects were drawn, the proportion who would draw lines which are too short is equal to the proportion who would draw lines which are too long. Alternative: $P \neq Q$. The proportions are not equal; either more of the population would draw short lines or more would draw long lines under these conditions.

3. $H: P = Q$. The proportion of animals in the colony who would turn left in this situation is equal to the proportion who would turn right. Alternative: $P \neq Q$. The proportions are not equal; either more would turn left or more would turn right. Note that in this case the experimenter's belief coincides with the statistical hypothesis, not with its alternative. He cannot, therefore, expect actually to confirm his belief. He can only hope to show that his belief is not an untenable one.

4. Let P stand for the proportion of right turns and Q for the proportion of left turns. $H: P \leq Q$. The proportion of right turns this animal will make in the long run is equal to or less than the

proportion of left turns he will make. Alternative: $P > Q$. The proportion of right turns is greater than the proportion of left turns. The critical region is in the upper tail of the sampling distribution.

5. Let P stand for the proportion of subjects who draw a line which is too short, and Q for the proportion who draw one that is too long. $H: P \leq Q$. The proportion of the population who draw short lines under these conditions is equal to or less than the proportion who draw long lines. Alternative: $P > Q$. The proportion who draw short lines is greater than the proportion who draw long lines. The critical region is in the upper tail of the sampling distribution.

6. If theory predicts a difference in a given direction, then a directional hypothesis is appropriate. The hypothesis becomes essentially a test of the theoretical notions which predict this particular difference. In this example, therefore, it is appropriate to test $H: P \geq Q$. The proportion of drop-outs who received diagnoses of dependency is equal to or greater than the proportion of drop-outs who did not receive this diagnosis. Alternative: $P < Q$. The proportion receiving diagnoses of dependency is less than the proportion not receiving this diagnosis. The critical region is in the lower tail of the sampling distribution.

But there is a serious fault in the design of this study. The investigator is considering only the file of drop-outs. What proportion of all patients coming to the clinic receive diagnoses of dependency? What proportion do not? If these proportions are .30 and .70, for example, we would expect to find fewer "dependency" cases in the drop-out file simply because there are fewer such patients in general. Not all questions about the difference between two proportions can be handled by dichotomizing a sample into the two dependent proportions P and Q. In this example, a better procedure would be to compare the proportion of all "dependency" patients who drop out of psychotherapy with the proportion of all "non-dependency" patients who drop out of psychotherapy. Such proportions, because they are independent, are usually symbolized P_1 and P_2 rather than P and Q. A hypothesis of this kind is illustrated in (7) below.

7. $H: P_1 = P_2$. Among the gifted children of this city, the proportion of girls planning a science career is equal to the proportion of boys planning such a career. Alternative: $P_1 \neq P_2$. The two proportions are not equal; either more boys or more girls are planning a science career. Note that for this hypothesis we do not use the notation $P = Q$. Such notation implies that P and Q are dependent proportions, as they must be if $P + Q = 1$. The proportions P_1 and P_2 of this study are independent—that is, knowing one of the proportions does not give us any information about the other one because their sum need have no fixed value. Hypotheses of this kind

cannot be tested by means of the z formula given in Chapter 7. A method for testing such hypotheses is given in Chapter 9.

8. H: $P_1 = P_2 = P_3 = P_4$. In the population of college students from which the sample was drawn, the proportions of students who prefer each of the four activities are equal. (Three of these proportions are independent; the fourth is not. Why?) Alternative: The four proportions are not equal; one or some of the activities are preferred over the others. A method for testing a hypothesis of this kind is given in Chapter 9.

9. H: $\mu_1 = \mu_2$. The mean IQ of the two minority groups is equal. Alternative: $\mu_1 \neq \mu_2$. The means are not equal; one of the minority groups has a higher mean IQ than the other. Methods for testing hypotheses about means are given in Chapter 10.

10. H: $\mu_1 = \mu_2$. This hypothesis refers to the two populations of random samples which would result if the random assignment of these subjects to an Experimental group and a Control group were to be repeated an infinite number of times. The hypothesis states that the mean of all possible random samples taking the drug is equal to the mean of all possible random samples taking the placebo. Hence, the drug has no effect on the reaction time of these subjects. The procedure does *not* insure any generalizations beyond this particular group of subjects because the subjects themselves were not randomly selected from an identified population. Alternative: $\mu_1 \neq \mu_2$. The mean reaction time of all possible samples taking the drug is not the same as the mean reaction time of all possible samples taking the placebo; one mean is greater than the other. Hence, the drug has an effect on reaction time, either speeding it up or slowing it down.

11. H: $\mu \geq 100$. The mean IQ of the teen-agers in this neighborhood is equal to or greater than 100 (average or above average). Alternative: $\mu < 100$. Their mean IQ is below 100 (below average). A directional hypothesis is permissible here because the psychologist is concerned with the reason the teen-agers have trouble in school, and a finding that their mean IQ is above average has no bearing on his purpose. He is only interested in the possibility that their mean IQ is below average. If it is not below average, he will look for other reasons to explain their difficulties with school work.

12. Let μ_1 represent the mean score of men and μ_2 the mean score of women. H: $\mu_1 \leq \mu_2$. The mean score of men is equal to or less than the mean score of women. Alternative: $\mu_1 > \mu_2$. The mean score of men is higher than the mean score of women.

13. H: $\mu_1 \leq \mu_2$. Among patients who drop out of psychotherapy, the mean number of weeks that "dependency" patients remain in therapy is equal to or less than the mean number of weeks that

"non-dependency" patients remain in therapy. Alternative: $\mu_1 > \mu_2$. The mean number of weeks "dependency" patients remain in therapy is greater than the mean number of weeks "non-dependency" patients remain in therapy. Because the two means in question are not dependent upon the relative proportions of "dependency" and "non-dependency" patients in the population, such knowledge is not necessary to this investigation.

14. H: $\mu_1 = \mu_2 = \mu_3$. This hypothesis refers to the three populations of random samples which would result if the random assignment of these subjects to three groups were to be repeated an infinite number of times. The hypothesis states that the means of these three populations are equal, hence that propaganda in lecture or in movie form has no effect on attitudes toward this policy. As in (10) above, the procedure insures no generalizations beyond this particular group of subjects. Alternative: The three means are not equal; one or two of the means is greater than the other(s). Hypotheses of this kind are tested in Chapter 11.

chapter 9

The
Chi-Square
Test

In Chapter 7, the population of interest could always be defined in terms of two proportions: right or wrong, Democrat or Republican, "for" or "against." When two proportions are dependent in the sense that their sum must always equal a fixed number, they are said to have one *degree of freedom*. That is, only one of the two proportions is independent or "free to vary." If votes can only be Democratic or Republican and the proportion of Democratic votes in a sample has been determined, the proportion of Republican votes is automatically known. The two proportions are not independent of each other. If 80% of a student's test answers are correct, then 20% must be incorrect. If we know one proportion, the other is completely predictable; it is not "free to vary." Hence, although there are two proportions, we say that there is only one degree of freedom.

When more than two categories are being compared, there is usually more than one degree of freedom. If votes can be either Democratic, Republican, or Liberal, then determining the proportion of Democratic votes in a sample does not tell us what either of the other two proportions is. They may vary quite independently of the proportion of Democratic votes. But if, in addition to the proportion of Democratic votes, the proportion of, say, Republican votes is determined, then the proportion of Liberal votes will automatically be known. Thus, two (any two) of the three proportions may be thought of as free to vary; but whatever values they take, these values completely determine the value of the third proportion. So when there are three categories and three proportions to be compared, there are two degrees of freedom.

In general, when the data of a single variable have been classified into k categories and there are k proportions to be compared, there are $k - 1$ degrees of freedom.

The z test of Chapter 7 was used to compare observed frequencies with expected frequencies when data had been classified into two categories. When frequencies have been classified into more than two categories, or have been cross-tabulated into the cells of a bivariate table, the *chi-square test* is used. The general formula for computing chi-square, symbolized χ^2, is

$$\chi^2 = \Sigma \frac{(f - F)^2}{F} \tag{9.1}$$

where f is the observed frequency for a given category or cell and F is the corresponding expected frequency for that category or cell. The degrees of freedom, abbreviated df, must also be determined in order to evaluate χ^2.

Like z, which gives a distance along the baseline of the theoretical normal curve, chi-square gives a distance along the baseline of a theoretical distribution called the *chi-square distribution*. Thus, if an obtained chi-square value is found to be way out in the "tail" of the chi-square distribution, it has a correspondingly small probability of occurrence. Actually, there are many chi-square distributions; they differ according to the degrees of freedom on which chi-square is based. It is necessary, then, to refer an obtained chi-square to the theoretical distribution of chi-square values having the same degrees of freedom. This is easily done by means of Table C in the Appendix. This table gives the probability of selected chi-square values from each of many theoretical chi-square distributions. To determine the probability of an obtained chi-square with given df, it is only necessary to locate in the table the distribution having this number of df and compare the obtained chi-square with the values of that distribution.

The probabilities given in Table C of the Appendix are for a two-tailed test. Chi-square tests are of necessity two-tailed. Because differences between observed and expected frequencies are always squared (see formula 9.1), χ^2 is always positive regardless of the direction of the differences. Hence, only the magnitude of differences, not their direction, can be examined by means of the chi-square test.

There is one important instance when χ^2 can conveniently be used in the test of a directional hypothesis. This is when χ^2 has 1 df. Whenever χ^2 has 1 df, it can be converted to a z value by taking advantage of the relationship

$$z = \sqrt{\chi^2}, \text{ when } \chi^2 \text{ has 1 } df \tag{9.2}$$

The resulting z value may be referred to a critical region in either the upper tail or the lower tail of the normal distribution, as the direction of the hypothesis dictates. This use of χ^2 is illustrated in Example 3 of this chapter.

Requirements for the Use
of the Chi-Square Test

The chi-square test, like the z test of Chapter 7, provides only an approximation of exact probabilities and is therefore only appropriate for relatively large samples. The general rule is that every expected frequency F must be equal to or greater than five for the satisfactory use of the chi-square test. This rule may be abrogated to some extent when there are many categories (say, at least five) representing a single variable, or in the case of a bivariate table having more than 1 df. In these cases, the chi-square test is satisfactory if no more than 20% of the cells or categories have expected frequencies smaller than five and none smaller than two.

A second important requirement for the use of the chi-square test is that the data consist of independent observations. That is, when an inference is to be made about a population of subjects, each subject sampled contributes only *one* frequency to the data. Five observations made on one subject cannot be summed with five observations made on another subject to give ten frequencies. If only one subject is used in an experiment, then observations made on this one subject *may* be regarded as independent when the purpose is to make inferences about the population of *this subject's responses*. Whenever more than one subject is used, each subject may contribute only one frequency to the data.

The use of the chi-square test for data of a single variable is illustrated in Examples 1 and 2 below. Applications of the chi-square test to bivariate data are given in Examples 3 and 4.

DATA OF A

SINGLE VARIABLE

Example 1. An advertising firm wishes to determine which of four advertising displays is preferred by housewives. A random sample of 40 housewives are asked to choose among the four displays and the first choice of each is recorded. The results are:

	NUMBER OF TIMES
DISPLAY	CHOSEN FIRST
A	8
B	10
C	13
D	9

Do the results warrant concluding that among the population of housewives from which this sample was drawn, there are preferences regarding the displays?

• • STEP 1. Begin by stating the hypothesis which is to be tested, and choose a level of significance for its evaluation. In this case, the hypothesis may be stated as follows: $H: P_1 = P_2 = P_3 = P_4 = 1/4$ or .25. The proportions of housewives in the population preferring each of the four displays are equal, each proportion therefore having the value 1/4 or .25. Since rejection of this hypothesis, if it is false, is very important to the advertising firm, and little will be lost by rejecting the hypothesis even if it is true, a large alpha is chosen in order to maximize the chances for rejection. Let us say the advertising firm is willing to invest money in the most frequently chosen display (or displays, in case of a tie) if the results of the study are such that they could occur by chance only once in ten times. If the result of the study has some probability larger than .10, the firm will regard the study as inconclusive and consider other courses of action.

• • STEP 2. The hypothesis that on the variable in question the population is divided into equal quarters ($P = 1/4$) leads to the expectation that a random sample will also be divided into equal quarters. Since $n = 40$, the expected frequency in each category is given by $F = nP = 40(1/4) = 10$. The expected frequencies are listed in a column opposite the observed frequencies, as shown in Table 9.1.

• • STEP 3. Carry out the operations called for by the formula for χ^2, as shown in the successive columns of Table 9.1. Note that differences between observed and expected frequencies are squared before being divided by F. The sum of the column $(f - F)^2/F$ gives the value of χ^2, in this case 1.4.

• • STEP 4. Determine the degrees of freedom available. In this case, there are four categories, so $df = k - 1 = 4 - 1 = 3$. In Table C of the Appendix, find the row which gives values of χ^2 for 3 df. Search across the row until you find a value (or values) close to your obtained χ^2. For the present problem, we find the value 1.42, which is very close to the obtained 1.4. According to the column heading

Table 9.1
Chi-Square Test of the Hypothesis That
$$P_1 = P_2 = P_3 = P_4 = 1/4$$

DISPLAY	OBSERVED FREQUENCIES (f)	OBSERVED FREQUENCIES (F)	$(f - F)$	$(f - F)^2$	$(f - F)^2/F$
A	8	10	-2	4	.4
B	10	10	0	0	0
C	13	10	3	9	.9
D	9	10	-1	1	.1
	40	40			$\Sigma = 1.4$

$$\chi^2 = \Sigma \frac{(f - F)^2}{F} = 1.4 \text{ with } 3 \ df$$

$$P \cong .70$$

which appears at the top of the table, χ^2 values as large as and larger than 1.42 have a combined probability of .70 when χ^2 has 3 df. Since our obtained χ^2 is 1.4, we say that our χ^2 has a probability of approximately .70, or $P \cong .70$.

• • STEP 5. If the obtained χ^2 has a probability of occurrence larger than alpha, the hypothesis is retained. If the obtained χ^2 has a probability smaller than alpha, the hypothesis is rejected. Since alpha is .10 in this case and the obtained χ^2 has a probability of approximately .70, it is clear that the hypothesis cannot be rejected.

• RESULTS AND DISCUSSION

By the rule adopted for the test, the hypothesis that $P_1 = P_2 = P_3 = P_4$ is retained. The data do not warrant concluding that one of the displays would be preferred over the others among the population of housewives. What shall the advertising firm do? If there is some basis other than consumer appeal for making a decision among the displays—such as relative costs, etc.—then the firm should choose among the displays on this basis. If consumer appeal is the only relevant factor in arriving at a decision, the results of the study suggest, in effect, that the firm may as well make the decision by flipping coins or drawing straws. There is no reason to believe that housewives prefer one of the displays more than the others.

The student may feel reluctant to accept this last statement. Observing that Display C was chosen by 13 housewives and Display A by only eight housewives, he may feel that there is at least some "evidence" favoring Display C. The situation is analogous to this: if you were to toss six coins once and four of the coins were to turn up heads and two tails, would this result lead you to believe that the coins were not fair? If you think about it, you will surely answer "no." Such an outcome could occur too easily by chance. If the coins are fair, the probability of obtaining a result as deviant as four heads and two tails is almost .70. That is, results as deviant as this are expected to occur 70% of the time when the coins are fair. In exactly the same manner, the χ^2 we found with its attendant probability of .70 tells us that differences at least as deviant as those we observed between the various display categories are expected to occur 70% of the time when the displays have equal appeal in the population. Such differences could occur by chance so easily in random sampling that they cannot possibly be regarded as "evidence" against the hypothesis of equal appeal.

It is true that if the displays have equal appeal, nothing is lost by choosing Display C. The point is that there is no reason to believe anything has been gained.

Test for Goodness of Fit

Example 2. It has been observed that infants generally do not develop a hand preference before the age of six months but will reach for an object as readily with one hand as with the other. A researcher believes the shift to a preferred hand begins before this age, but is so gradual as to be difficult to establish by merely observing the individual child. To investigate his belief, the researcher tests a total of 267 infants who are between the ages of 22 and 24 weeks. A small, brightly colored cube is placed within the child's reach and the investigator observes which hand the child uses in reaching for the object. Each infant is tested in this way until five observations have been made. The child is then classified in a category according to the number of times he used each hand. The results are:

NUMBER OF TIMES EACH HAND WAS USED

	5 RIGHT 0 LEFT	4 RIGHT 1 LEFT	3 RIGHT 2 LEFT	2 RIGHT 3 LEFT	1 RIGHT 4 LEFT	0 RIGHT 5 LEFT
No. OF CHILDREN	10	53	101	59	40	4

Does the distribution reveal a tendency among the children to use one hand more often than the other?

•• STEP 1. The problem here is to arrive at the correct hypothesis. It obviously does not make sense to hypothesize that the proportions of infants classified in the six categories will all be equal. If, in fact, the children will reach with one hand as often as with the other, the middle categories (3 Right, 2 Left and 2 Right, 3 Left) should have the highest frequencies, and the frequencies should become progressively smaller as the categories become more extreme. This familiar picture should remind you of the normal curve, except that since we are dealing with discrete categories the binomial distribution is the appropriate model.

What we really have is a distribution of samples, each based on five observations. When observations can take only one of two forms (left hand or right hand), the samples are from a binomial population. Given the values of P and Q, we can readily determine from the binomial distribution how such samples should be distributed. Under the hypothesis that an individual child is as likely to reach with one hand as with the other $(P = Q = 1/2)$, the proportions in the six categories of our table should approximate the terms of the expansion of $(P + Q)^5$ where P and Q are each $1/2$. When $P = Q = 1/2$, these proportions are given by the coefficient of each term in the expansion divided by the sum of the coefficients. The coefficients and their sum may be read from Table 7.3, p. 166. For $n = 5$, the proportions are $1/32, 5/32, 10/32, 10/32, 5/32, 1/32$. The chi-square test is to determine the probability that the 267 samples of this study are from a population of samples distributed in these proportions. The hypothesis may be written:

$$H: P_1 = 1/32, P_2 = 5/32, P_3 = 10/32, P_4 = 10/32,$$
$$P_5 = 5/32, P_6 = 1/32$$

• • STEP 2. Choose alpha, the level of significance for the test of the hypothesis. The researcher does not anticipate great deviation from equal-handedness among these children, only some small shift in the direction of favoring one hand. This consideration suggests a large alpha, perhaps .10. If small differences are really present, they are more likely to be detected when alpha is large. But if alpha is large, the researcher may be accused (with considerable justification) of making it too easy to reject a hypothesis which, after all, is supported by evidence from other studies. This consideration suggests a small alpha, such as .01. The argument for a small alpha and the argument for a large alpha are both valid and important. The most sensible course is to compromise between the two. We will suppose that the researcher chooses .05 as the level of significance for his test.

• • STEP 3. List the observed frequencies in a column and write the expected frequencies opposite them. The expected frequencies

Table 9.2
Chi-Square Test of the Hypothesis That $P_1 = 1/32$, $P_2 = 5/32$, $P_3 = 10/32$, $P_4 = 10/32$, $P_5 = 5/32$, $P_6 = 1/32$

Category	Observed Frequencies (f)	Expected Frequencies (F)		$(f - F)$	$(f - F)^2$	$(f - F)^2/F$
5 Right	10	$267(1/32) =$	8.34	1.66	2.76	.33
4 Right	53	$267(5/32) =$	41.72	11.28	127.24	3.05
3 Right	101	$267(10/32) =$	83.44	17.56	308.35	3.70
2 Right	59	$267(10/32) =$	83.44	-24.44	597.31	7.16
1 Right	40	$267(5/32) =$	41.72	-1.72	2.96	.07
0 Right	4	$267(1/32) =$	8.34	-4.34	18.84	2.26
	267		267.00	0.00		$\Sigma = 16.57$

$$\chi^2 = \Sigma \frac{(f - F)^2}{F} = 16.57 \text{ with } 5 \; df$$

$$P < .01$$

will be given by $F_1 = nP_1 = 267(1/32) = 8.34$, etc., as shown in Table 9.2. As a check, the sum of the expected frequencies should equal n, or 267 in this case.

•• STEP 4. Carry out the operations called for by the χ^2 formula, as shown in Table 9.2. As a further check, the sum of the column $(f - F)$ should equal zero. The sum of the last column gives the value of χ^2, 16.57. Since there are six categories, $df = 6 - 1 = 5$. From Table C in the Appendix, we find that with 5 df, χ^2 values as large as and larger than 15.09 have a combined probability of .01. Our obtained χ^2 is larger than 15.09 and falls, therefore, into a class of values whose combined probability is less than .01. Hence, we may write $P < .01$.

•• STEP 5. The probability of the obtained χ^2 is clearly smaller than the chosen alpha of .05, so the hypothesis is rejected. The observed distribution is said to be *significantly different* from the hypothesized binomial distribution, which is another way of saying that the difference cannot reasonably be attributed to random sampling fluctuation. The data do not "fit" a binomial distribution in which $P = Q$.

• RESULTS AND DISCUSSION

The researcher's question is still not answered. The chi-square test is able to detect significant differences, but it does not tell where those differences lie. For example, below are given several distributions all of which depart significantly from the binomial distribution of $(P + Q)^5$. The occurrence of any one of these distributions would have led to rejection of the hypothesis.

	5 RIGHT 0 LEFT	4 RIGHT 1 LEFT	3 RIGHT 2 LEFT	2 RIGHT 3 LEFT	1 RIGHT 4 LEFT	0 RIGHT 5 LEFT
DISTRIBUTION A:	0	33	100	100	34	0
DISTRIBUTION B:	80	15	68	69	15	20
DISTRIBUTION C:	10	53	101	59	40	4
EXPECTED BINOMIAL DISTRIBUTION (ROUNDED TO NEAREST INTEGER):	8	42	83	83	42	8

Consider Distribution A. This distribution, with frequencies so heavily concentrated in the middle categories, suggests that not only is there no hand preference among the children, but alternation in the use of the two hands must be the characteristic pattern of behavior. Otherwise, sheer randomness would produce some frequencies in the extreme categories. If this distribution occurred, the statistical hypothesis tested by chi-square would be rejected, but so would the researcher's belief that there is a shift toward a preferred hand.

Consider Distribution B. This distribution, with relatively large frequencies in the extreme categories, suggests a fully developed hand preference for some children. But there is no evidence of a "shift" among the other children. From this distribution, it would seem that children of this age either have a fully developed hand preference, or else they alternate in the use of the two hands. There is no evidence of a gradual shift, and again the researcher's belief, while not entirely contradicted, is not wholly substantiated either. Many children of this age consistently seem to use one hand, but the change from alternation to consistency is apparently sudden, not gradual.

Distribution C gives the frequencies which yielded our χ^2 of 16.57 and led to the rejection of the hypothesis in this study. It is important to understand why they do so. The researcher's belief of a gradual shift towards a preferred hand is supported by the very large difference in the frequencies of the two middle categories. The expected frequencies for these two categories are equal, 83 and 83, as given by the binomial distribution. If one hand is as likely to be used as the other, then it is expected that equal numbers of children will fall into the categories of 3 Right–2 Left and 2 Right–3 Left. But in this study, 101 children were classified in the category of 3 Right–2 Left and only 59 in the category of 2 Right–3 Left. Since most children do become right-handed, the fact that so many more children were classified in the 3 Right–2 Left category strongly suggests a beginning tendency to favor the right hand. And it is this kind of tendency that our researcher predicted.

Before concluding that the researcher's belief has been confirmed, one more step is necessary. Discrepancies between observed and expected frequencies may look "large" yet contribute little to the value of an obtained χ^2 when the expected frequencies themselves are large. One should always look at the values which were summed to obtain χ^2. For this study, these are the values given in the last column of Table 9.2. There it is apparent that by far the largest single contribution to the value of χ^2 comes from the category of 2 Right–3 Left, which has fewer than the expected number of frequencies. The next largest contributions to χ^2 come from the 3 Right and 4 Right categories, which have more than the expected number of frequencies. These findings are consistent with the researcher's prediction—none are inconsistent—and this information, together with the significant obtained χ^2, provide a confirmation of the researcher's belief.

When interpreting a significant χ^2, it is always necessary to examine the original data. χ^2 itself gives no information about the *direction* of differences between observed and expected frequencies, and no information about *where* these differences occurred.

BIVARIATE DATA

The chi-square test may also be used when a researcher wishes to compare two or more independent proportions, or is interested in the relationship between two variables both of which are represented by categories rather than measures. The first step in tests of this kind is to set up a bivariate table and cross-tabulate the observations into the cells of the table, as in Example 2 of Chapter 1.

After the observations have been cross-tabulated and the marginal totals entered, expected frequencies can be computed for each cell of the table. The observed frequencies may then be compared with the expected frequencies by means of the χ^2 formula. The only difference is that χ^2 will not now have $k - 1$ degrees of freedom.

Because the marginal totals of the table are used in computing the expected frequencies (as will be seen), the cells in the table are not all "free to vary." In such cases, an easy way of computing the df is to multiply the number of rows in the table less 1, by the number of columns in the table less 1. Thus, for these problems we may write $df = (r - 1)(c - 1)$, where r stands for rows and c for columns.

Example 3. A number of personality theories imply that the tendency to repress or forget incidents of early childhood is greater among neurotics than among normals. On this basis, an investigator predicts that fewer neurotics than normals will have memories dating back to early childhood. He interviews a random sample of 20 neurotic patients who have been accepted for treatment at a city clinic, and a random sample of 30 normals from the area served by the clinic. Each subject is asked what is his earliest memory and how old he was at the time.

In order to determine what age range shall constitute "early childhood" for the study, the distribution of ages given by the subjects as the time of their first memory is divided at the median. Ages below the median of the distribution are regarded as belonging to "early childhood"; ages above the median are regarded as "late childhood." A bivariate table is set up and each subject is classified according to his group (normal or neurotic) and the time of his first memory (early or late childhood). The results are:

| | TIME OF FIRST MEMORY | | |
	EARLY CHILDHOOD	LATE CHILDHOOD	TOTAL
NORMAL	18	12	30
NEUROTIC	7	13	20
TOTAL	25	25	50

Should it be concluded that fewer neurotics than normals have "early childhood" memories?

A directional hypothesis and one-tailed test would be reasonable in this situation. Theory predicts a difference between the two populations, normals and neurotics, in a specified direction—namely, that *fewer* neurotics than normals have "early childhood" memories. However, if an investigator doubts the truth of a theoretical formulation, or, in general, if there is little evidence in support of a theoretical formulation, he may be unwilling to commit himself to a directional hypothesis. In this case, he will conduct a two-tailed test. For illustrative purposes, we shall carry out both a two-tailed test and a one-tailed test. But it should be emphasized that in practice only one of these tests is carried out, and the decision as to which test will be carried out is made *before* inspecting the data, ideally before the data are even collected.

Two-Tailed Test

• • STEP 1. The hypothesis may be stated in any one of several ways: Either, $H: P_1 = P_2$, the proportion of neurotics having "early childhood" memories is the same as the proportion of normals having such memories. Or, H: The variables "Normal-Neurotic" and "Time of First Memory" are independent (uncorrelated). Also, because a median split was used to obtain the categories representing the variable "Time of First Memory," the hypothesis may take the form that normals and neurotics have the same median on this variable, or $H: \text{Median}_1 = \text{Median}_2$. All three statements of the hypothesis have the same implications and are automatically tested by the chi-square test whether or not they receive explicit recognition.

Let us suppose that .05 is chosen as the level of significance for the test.

• • STEP 2. Compute the expected frequency F for each cell of the bivariate table. This has been done in Table 9.3 by using the column totals to determine what proportion of each group should

Table 9.3
Chi-Square Test of the Hypothesis That $P_1 = P_2$

TIME OF FIRST MEMORY

	EARLY CHILDHOOD	LATE CHILDHOOD	TOTAL
NORMALS	18 ⑮	12 ⑮	30
NEUROTICS	7 ⑩	13 ⑩	20
TOTAL	25	25	50

COMPUTATION OF EXPECTED FREQUENCIES:
  "Early Childhood" Cells
    NORMALS: $F = (25/50)(30) = 15$
    NEUROTICS: $F = (25/50)(20) = 10$

  "Late Childhood" Cells
    NORMALS: $F = (25/50)(30) = 15$
    NEUROTICS: $F = (25/50)(20) = 10$

$$\chi^2 = \Sigma \frac{(f - F)^2}{F} = \frac{(18 - 15)^2}{15} + \frac{(12 - 15)^2}{15} + \frac{(7 - 10)^2}{10} + \frac{(13 - 10)^2}{10} = 3.0$$

$$df = (r - 1)(c - 1) = (2 - 1)(2 - 1) = 1$$
$$.05 < P < .10$$

appear in a particular cell under the hypothesis that there is no difference between the groups. Thus, if 25/50 of all the first memories are classified in the "Early Childhood" category, then it is expected that 25/50 of normals' first memories will fall in that category and 25/50 of neurotics' first memories will fall in that category. The same is true for the "Late Childhood" category since 25/50 of all the first memories are classified in that category. The expected frequencies are shown in the cells of Table 9.3, where they are circled to distinguish them from the observed frequencies. As a check, their row and column sums should be the same as the marginal totals of the table.

• • STEP 3. Compute χ^2 in the usual manner, squaring the difference between the observed and expected frequencies of each cell and dividing by the expected frequency for that cell. In this case, χ^2 is found to equal 3.0.

• • STEP 4. The degrees of freedom are given by $df = (r - 1)(c - 1)$, which in this case equals 1. Note that in the table, if the marginal totals are regarded as fixed (and they were so regarded in determining the expected frequencies), then only one of the cells is free to vary. That is, an entry in any one of the cells completely determines the frequencies of the remaining cells, since the row and column sums of the cells must equal the given marginal totals. There is indeed only one degree of freedom in the table.

• • STEP 5. Turning to Table C of the Appendix, we find that $\chi^2 = 3.0$ with 1 df has a probability between .05 and .10, which may be written $.05 < P < .10$. Since the probability is greater than .05, the significance level chosen for the test, the hypothesis cannot be rejected. It cannot be concluded that fewer neurotics than normals have "early childhood" memories.

• DISCUSSION

The hypothesis that equal proportions of normals and of neurotics have "early childhood" memories is retained. We also retain the hypothesis that the variables "Nornal-Neurotic" and "Time of First Memory" are independent, and the hypothesis that normals and neurotics have the same median on the variable "Time of First Memory."

The probability of the obtained χ^2 is small, less than .10. The result is "close" to being significant. No investigator will feel altogether comfortable retaining a hypothesis of no difference between two parameters when the observed sample difference would occur less than 10% of the time under this hypothesis. At the same time, it is not correct to say that although the result is not significant, there is " a trend" in the predicted direction. *Significant results themselves only indicate trends, not amounts or magnitudes.* Non-significant results, by the rule adopted by the investigator when he chooses alpha, must be attributed to random sampling fluctuation.

There is, however, a legitimate way to make the decision a more certain one. The investigator can increase the size of his sample. A fixed and previously determined number of new subjects may be randomly selected from the population(s) previously sampled, and additional observations made in the same way as before. (We stress that the number of new subjects must be previously determined and adhered to; it is *not* legitimate simply to add subjects until some desired outcome is achieved.) These new observations may be combined with the previous sample and the statistical test conducted again on this larger sample. If the original result was in fact due to an unusual random sample, the addition of more random observations is almost certain to yield a result with some probability larger than was found for the original sample. On the other hand, if the original result reflects a real difference between the two populations, the addition of random observations is very likely to result in a smaller probability value.

When an investigator follows this procedure, increasing the size of his sample and conducting a second test, he gives himself, in effect, a second chance to reject the null hypothesis. If the hypothesis is true, his adopted significance level, whatever it may have been, no longer represents exactly the probability of making a Type I error (rejecting a true null hypothesis.) The probability of making this error is now somewhat larger. For two tests only, the increase in probability is so small that it is usually overlooked. But if the procedure is repeated and the investigator gives himself additional opportunities to reject the null hypothesis, the probability of a Type I error grows apace. The adopted significance level becomes an increasingly uncertain guide to decision-making. An extreme instance of this problem is discussed in Example 4 of this chapter.

One-Tailed Test

• • STEP 1. Formulate the hypothesis. Let P_1 represent the proportion of neurotics who have "early childhood" memories and P_2

represent the proportion of normals who have such memories. Theory predicts that $P_1 < P_2$, the proportion of neurotics will be smaller than the proportion of normals. If the hypothesis $P_1 \geqq P_2$ can be rejected, then the alternative $P_1 < P_2$ may be accepted. The .05 significance level is adopted for this test also.

• • STEP 2. χ^2 is computed in the usual manner. This has already been done in Table 9.3, where χ^2 was found to be 3.0.

• • STEP 3. Because χ^2 has only 1 df, it may be converted to a z value by formula (9.2). Thus,

$$z = \sqrt{\chi^2} = \sqrt{3.0} = \pm 1.73$$

If the *observed* proportions are such that $P_1 < P_2$, -1.73 is taken as the value of z. If the observed proportions are such that $P_1 > P_2$, $+1.73$ is taken as the value of z. From the data given in Table 9.3, we find that $P_1 = 7/20 = .35$ and $P_2 = 18/30 = .60$. It is evident that $P_1 < P_2$, so -1.73 is the value of z.

• • STEP 4. The z value found in Step 3 is referred to the normal curve table, Table B of the Appendix. Because the hypothesis is that $P_1 \geqq P_2$, the critical region is in the lower tail of the normal curve. Our z value of -1.73 falls in the lower tail of the distribution; it only remains to discover whether or not it falls in the critical region. From Table B, we find that z values equal to and below -1.73 have a combined probability of .04. Since this probability is smaller than .05, the significance level adopted for the test, it is clear that our z value falls in the critical region. The hypothesis is rejected and we accept the alternative that $P_1 < P_2$: the proportion of neurotics having "early childhood" memories is smaller than the proportion of normals having such memories.

• DISCUSSION

By this one-tailed test, the hypothesis is rejected and the answer to the original question is yes: it may be concluded that fewer neurotics than normals have "early childhood" memories. By the two-tailed test previously carried out on the same data, the hypothesis is retained and the answer to the original question is no: it cannot be concluded that fewer neurotics than normals have "early childhood" memories. Our two tests lead to opposite conclusions. How can we tell which is the correct conclusion? We cannot tell. The investigator formulates his hypothesis, chooses a significance level, and abides by the results of the statistical test. If he did not do this, he would be like a man who places a bet on one team, then wants to change his bet when that team appears to be losing. If someone will take his bet, the odds by now will be very different. In the same way, if hypotheses or significance levels are changed when they appear to be "losing," the odds are changed—probabilities computed in the usual way cannot be taken at face value—and we cannot arrive at any dependable conclusion.

Example 4. A psychologist working in a rehabilitation center is concerned about the job adjustment of disabled workers who have been retrained and placed in new jobs. Many of these men seem unable to adjust to their new jobs; others, equally handicapped, make a good adjustment. An examination of the men's records reveals no correlation between type of disability and job adjustment, and no correlation between job adjustment and type of job previously held. The psychologist decides to investigate emotional factors. Before leaving the rehabilitation center, all of the men take a psychological test on which they are asked to compare themselves with a variety of descriptive statements which are largely of an emotional nature. For each item of the test, the examinee is asked to compare himself with the description given by checking a five-point rating scale that extends from "Not at all like me" (1) to "Very much like me" (5). The psychologist sets up a bivariate table for each item of the test and cross-tabulates the answers to that item with the men's present job adjustment. For the test item "I feel frustrated most of the time," the answers given by 120 men randomly selected from the files are distributed as shown below:

ANSWERS TO TEST ITEM

JOB ADJUSTMENT	"NOT AT ALL LIKE ME" 1	2	3	4	"VERY MUCH LIKE ME" 5	TOTAL
Good	2	5	18	8	8	41
Fair	3	3	19	10	7	42
Poor	0	2	5	12	18	37
TOTAL	5	10	42	30	33	120

Is there some correlation between job adjustment and answers to this test item, or are the two variables independent?

• • STEP 1. The hypothesis, of course, is that the two variables are independent. If this hypothesis could be rejected, we could be reasonably sure that some degree of correlation exists between the answers to this test item and the men's job adjustment. The hypothesis could be stated in terms of proportions—*e.g.*, that the proportions of men giving each of the test answers is the same for the three job adjustment categories. It is this circumstance which is assumed by the phrase "no correlation."

• • STEP 2. We shall not adopt a significance level for the test of this particular hypothesis. A whole series of statistical tests is being conducted, one for each item of the questionnaire, under the overall hypothesis that job adjustment is not related to the emotional factors reflected in these items. It would be inappropriate to evaluate any single hypothesis outside of this context. Instead, we shall obtain for this item a χ^2 value, determine its probability as usual, then consider the meaning of this probability value within the context of various outcomes for all of the items taken together.

• • STEP 3. To obtain χ^2, we begin as usual by computing the expected frequencies for the cells of the table. The first column total is 5. Dividing this by $n = 120$, we obtain $5/120 = .04$. Thus, .04 of each job-adjustment group are expected to be in the first column. These groups number 41, 42, and 37, so the expected frequencies for the first column are $.04(41) = 1.64, .04(42) = 1.68$, and $.04(37) = 1.48$. These expected frequencies are extremely small. According to the requirements given on p. 201, such expected frequencies are too small for the satisfactory use of the chi-square test. In such cases, if adjoining categories are logically related, it is appropriate to combine the frequencies of adjoining cells until the expected frequencies are large enough to meet the requirement for chi-square. It would be reasonable, for example, to combine test-answer categories 1 and 2 into one category representing the low end of the answer scale. It would also be reasonable to combine the Good and Fair job-adjustment categories into one category representing "acceptable" job adjustment. It would *not* be reasonable to combine the Fair and Poor job-adjustment categories into one category since such a category would have no clear meaning. Because the column totals are small for both test-answer categories 1 and 2, we will combine these two categories and see whether this results in large enough expected frequencies. As may be seen in Table 9.4, where the categories have been combined, the expected frequencies are now large enough to meet the requirement for the chi-square test and we may proceed to compute χ^2.

• • STEP 4. χ^2 is computed in the usual manner, as shown in Table 9.4. Its value is found to be 19.62. Since there are three rows and four columns in the table, $df = (3 - 1)(4 - 1) = 6$. Turning to Table C in the Appendix, we find that a χ^2 as large as 16.81 with 6 df has a probability of .01. Since our obtained χ^2 is larger than this value, its probability is smaller and we write $P < .01$.

Table 9.4
Chi-Square Test of the Hypothesis That Two Variables Are Independent

JOB ADJUSTMENT	ANSWERS TO TEST ITEM				TOTAL
	1 & 2	3	4	5	
GOOD	7 ⟦5.12⟧	18 ⟦14.35⟧	8 ⟦10.25⟧	8 ⟦11.28⟧	41
FAIR	6 ⟦5.25⟧	19 ⟦14.70⟧	10 ⟦10.50⟧	7 ⟦11.55⟧	42
POOR	2 ⟦4.62⟧	5 ⟦12.95⟧	12 ⟦9.25⟧	18 ⟦10.18⟧	37
TOTAL	15	42	30	33	120

COMPUTATION OF EXPECTED FREQUENCIES

$(15/120)(41) = 5.12$ $(42/120)(41) = 14.35$
$(15/120)(42) = 5.25$ $(42/120)(42) = 14.70$
$(15/120)(37) = 4.62$ $(42/120)(37) = 12.95$, etc.

$$\chi^2 = \Sigma \frac{(f-F)^2}{F} = \frac{(7-5.12)^2}{5.12} + \frac{(18-14.35)^2}{14.35} + \cdots + \frac{(18-10.18)^2}{10.18} = 19.62$$

$$df = (r-1)(c-1) = (3-1)(4-1) = 6$$
$$P < .01$$

• DISCUSSION

If only one test item and one hypothesis were being investigated, we would almost surely conclude from this chi-square test that answers to the test item "I feel frustrated most of the time" are correlated with job adjustment. Looking back at the data, it also appears that the greatest departures from expectancy are among the poor adjustment group, who more frequently claimed that the item was "very much" like them and only rarely said that it was not like them. A relatively large number of these men thus reported chronic feelings of frustration before they even began their new jobs. The investigator's interest, of course, is in whether these conclusions may be generalized to the population of disabled workers who come to the rehabilitation center. Before using this test item to identify men who may need special help, the psychologist will want to be sure (reasonably sure) that these results are not an accident of random sampling. But in this case, unlike the examples previously considered, more information is required before the decision can be made.

It will be recalled that a whole series of statistical tests is being conducted, one for each item of the questionnaire. When an investigator adopts, say, a significance level of .05 for the test of his hypothesis, and that hypothesis happens to be true, the probability is .05 that the data will nevertheless be such as to cause a rejection of the hypothesis. If he could repeat his experiment a vast number of times, in the long run 5% of his experimental results would lead to a rejection of the hypothesis even though it is a true hypothesis. From this reasoning, it follows that in the long run 5% of true hypotheses are going to be mistakenly rejected.

Now the investigator of this study is going to test a large number of hypotheses. Suppose they are all true? If there are 100 items and therefore 100 hypotheses and these hypotheses are all true, then the expectation is that ten of these true hypotheses will be rejected if alpha is .10, five will be rejected if alpha is .05, one will be rejected if alpha is .01, and so on. These expectations only apply, it should be emphasized, when all of the hypotheses to be tested are true. Most investigators run little risk of testing large numbers of true hypotheses, unless they test the same hypothesis over and over again and that hypothesis happens to be true. But our investigator is in just such a position. He could be wrong that job adjustment is related to the emotional factors tapped by this particular psychological test, and in that case he will be testing over and over again for each item of the test what is essentially the same true hypothesis. If the test consists of 100 items, he is in danger of testing 100 true hypotheses. Once he recognizes this danger, he can adopt any given significance level *with the expectation that this proportion of his hypotheses will be rejected by the data*, and therefore that the occurrence of such a proportion of rejections does not by itself constitute evidence that the particular test items involved are significantly related to job adjustment.

The point is that whenever an investigator has many hypotheses, or many opportunities to reject a hypothesis, chance factors alone are expected to produce some proportion of rejections. A single rejection cannot be evaluated outside of this context.

Studies of this kind require *cross-validation*—a repetition of the study with another sample of subjects and with a definite set of predictions. Those test items which, on the basis of the preliminary study, appear to be related to job adjustment provide the basis for a set of hypotheses that are now formally tested in the second study.

In general, the cross-validation of statistical results on a new sample is necessary whenever a specific set of outcomes is not predicted prior to the investigation. Random sampling is expected to produce some chance differences, and we cannot find differences first and then proceed as though we had predicted them. The probabilities that guide our decisions are based upon *the coincidence of prediction and outcome,* not upon outcome alone.

Practice Problems

For each of the following, state the appropriate statistical hypothesis; adopt a .05 level of significance, and test the hypothesis by using the chi-square test. On the basis of the results, answer the investigator's question.

1. An investigator is interested in the dating patterns of students at a university. He asks a random sample of 60 students whether most of the dates they go on are "solo" dates which do not include other friends, double-dates with one other couple, or whether they typically join a party or group of friends when they go out on a date. Of the 60 students questioned, 28 say that most of the time they go out on "solo" dates, 22 go on double-dates most often, and ten usually join a group or party. Is there reason to believe from these data that one mode of dating prevails over others at this university?

2. Among a random sample of 40 pre-school children who show a definite color preference, 16 prefer red, 11 prefer blue, nine yellow, and four green. Do these results indicate that one color or some colors are more popular than others among such children?

3. A maze has five straight alleys extending out from the starting point. An experimenter wishes to determine whether the rat he plans to use in an experiment has a tendency to turn in some particular direction so that he will enter some alleys more frequently than others. On 100 trials in the empty maze, the rat entered each alley the following number of times:

Alley A—17; Alley B—15; Alley C—12; Alley D—25; Alley E—31

Does the rat show a tendency to enter some alleys more frequently than others?

4. The experimenter of (3) above now places a different food incentive at the end of each alley of the maze. He wishes to determine whether the incentives will have a differential effect on the number of times each alley is entered, thus bringing about a change in the animal's previous pattern of behavior. On 100 trials in this situation, the rat enters each alley the following number of times:

Alley A—20; Alley B—22; Alley C—24; Alley D—16; Alley E—18

Do these results indicate a significant change in the animal's pattern of behavior?

5. Ninety-six students in Experimental Psychology classes each determine the auditory threshold of one subject for a given tone, using what is called the method of limits. The method gives a threshold value that is presumed to be the tone just loud enough so that the subject will hear it half of the time. After the threshold is determined by this method, the subject is given another short series of trials which include four presentations of the previously determined threshold tone. The students record for their subjects the number of times this threshold tone was heard during the last series. Each subject is then classified according to whether he heard the threshold tone 4, 3, 2, 1, or 0 times during the last series. The distribution of the 96 subjects is as follows:

	NUMBER OF TIMES THRESHOLD TONE WAS HEARD				
	4	3	2	1	0
NUMBER OF SUBJECTS	10	26	29	28	3

Is this distribution consistent with the assumption that each subject has a 50-50 chance of hearing the threshold tone?

6. A pollster believes that a "tough" attitude towards the Communist nations is more common among Korean War veterans than it is among World War II veterans. He questions a random sample of 100 Korean War veterans and 200 World War II veterans and finds the following:

Korean War veterans: 64 favor a tough policy, 36 do not.
World War II veterans: 146 favor a tough policy, 54 do not.

Should it be concluded that Korean War and World War II veterans differ in this respect?

7. An investigator is interested in the effect of set on problem-solving. He divides 40 subjects randomly into an Experimental group and a Control group of 20 each. Both groups are given the same problem to solve, but the Experimental group receives misleading instructions while the Control group is given the usual neutral instructions. Among the Experimental group, five subjects solve the problem, 15 do not. Of the Control group, 13 subjects solve the problem, seven do not. Should it be concluded that the differing instructions have an effect on the problem-solving of these subjects?

8. A psychologist is interested in the relationship between achievement motivation and the tendency to conform to group opinion. A random sample of 50 college students are given a "need-achievement" test to determine the strength of their achievement

motivation. The distribution of scores is divided at the median to give "high" and "low" need-achievement groups that are as nearly equal in size as possible. Each subject is also given a series of trials in a group situation where all the other members of the group have previously been instructed by the experimenter to concur in a clearly mistaken opinion. The number of trials on which the subject consents to the mistaken judgment of the group is taken as his "yielding score." This distribution of scores is also divided at the median to give a group of "high yielders" and a group of "low yielders." Cross-classifying the subjects on both variables gives the following results:

ACHIEVEMENT MOTIVATION	HIGH YIELDERS	LOW YIELDERS
High	9	18
Low	13	10

Do the results indicate a relationship between need-achievement score and the tendency to yield to group opinion?

9. A psychologist believes that much of the anti-social behavior of delinquents springs from the delinquent's view of himself as "no good anyway." As a first step towards investigating his theory, the psychologist compares the self-attitudes of a random sample of delinquents and a random sample of non-delinquent children drawn from the same neighborhoods. The results are as follows:

	SELF-ATTITUDE		
	POSITIVE	NEUTRAL	NEGATIVE
DELINQUENTS	8	18	24
NON-DELINQUENTS	18	22	10

Do the data warrant asserting that a negative self-attitude is found more often among delinquents than among non-delinquent children?

10. An experimenter is interested in the relative effects of different kinds of stress upon task performance. A sample of 90 subjects is randomly divided into three groups of 30 each. The three groups perform the same experimental task, but under different conditions. One group is subjected to failure stress, the subjects being told that they are performing very poorly. The second group is subjected to distraction stress in the form of loud noises and other distracting stimuli. The third group serves as a control, performing the task without interruption under quiet conditions. Performance on the task is classified as "Good," "Average," or "Poor," according to previously established criteria. The results for the three groups are:

	PERFORMANCE		
	GOOD	AVERAGE	POOR
FAILURE STRESS	7	13	10
DISTRACTION STRESS	8	20	2
NON-STRESS CONTROL	15	12	3

Can it be concluded that these subjects perform differently under the different stress conditions?

11. In a study of cognitive development, ten school children randomly selected from each of grades 1 through 8 are given a series of tasks and questions designed to reveal their characteristic way of perceiving and understanding the world around them. On the basis of his performance, each child is classified according to whether his characteristic mode of thinking is predominantly "Abstract," "Functional," or "Concrete." The number of children in each grade who were classified in each of these categories is shown below:

| | CHARACTERISTIC COGNITIVE MODE | | |
GRADE	ABSTRACT	FUNCTIONAL	CONCRETE
1	1	3	6
2	0	5	5
3	1	4	5
4	2	5	3
5	4	4	2
6	3	5	2
7	7	3	0
8	6	3	1

Is there evidence in these results of a shift in the characteristic mode of thinking with increasing age (grade level)?

Answers

1. $\chi^2 = 8.40$ with 2 df, $P < .02$. The hypothesis that students of this university engage equally in the three patterns of dating is rejected. From an inspection of the differences and their direction, joining a party or group of friends appears to be much less common than double-dating and especially "solo" dating.

2. $\chi^2 = 7.40$ with 3 df, $P > .05$. The hypothesis that the colors are equally popular among such children cannot be rejected. Therefore, it is not possible to conclude from this study that one or some of the colors are more popular.

3. $\chi^2 = 12.20$ with 4 df, $P < .02$. The hypothesis is rejected that, with repeated sampling of this animal's behavior under the same conditions, the proportion of times each alley is entered will be the same for all of the alleys. From an inspection of the differences and their direction, the rat shows a tendency to favor Alley E and perhaps Alley D, while Alley C appears to be neglected.

4. $\chi^2 = 24.49$ with 4 df, $P < .001$. The hypothesis of no significant change from the previously observed pattern of behavior is

rejected. (Note that the observed frequencies for the empty-maze condition are the expected frequencies for this condition.) The incentives provided by the experimenter do have a differential effect on the rat's behavior.

5. $\chi^2 = 6.36$ with 4 df, $P > .10$. The hypothesis is that each subject has a 50-50 chance of hearing the tone ($P = Q = \frac{1}{2}$), from which it follows that the 96 outcomes will be distributed in accordance with the expansion of $(P + Q)^4$, since each subject received four trials. Because the probability of a chi-square value as large as 6.36 is greater than .10, the hypothesis cannot be rejected. The observed distribution is consistent with the assumption that the subjects have a 50-50 chance of hearing the tone. At least, it has not been found to be inconsistent with this assumption.

6. $\chi^2 = 2.57$ with 1 df, $P > .10$. The hypothesis of no difference between Korean War and World War II veterans in this attitude ($P_1 = P_2$, or the same proportion of each group favor a tough policy) cannot be rejected. It cannot be concluded that the two groups of veterans differ in this respect.

7. $\chi^2 = 6.46$ with 1 df, $P < .01$. The nondirectional hypothesis, $P_1 = P_2$, is rejected. It may be concluded that the differing instructions have an effect on the problem-solving of these subjects, and an inspection of the direction of the differences indicates that the performance of the Experimental group was poorer than that of the Control group. A directional hypothesis would also be appropriate here because the "set" of a subject has been shown in many studies to influence performance. If P_1 represents the proportion of Experimental group subjects who solve the problem, it might be hypothesized that $P_1 \geq P_2$. This hypothesis would also be rejected ($z = -2.54$, $P = .0055$) and its alternative, $P_1 < P_2$, would be accepted.

8. $\chi^2 = 2.71$ with 1 df, $P = .10$ approximately. The hypothesis that yielding to group opinion is independent of the level of achievement motivation cannot be rejected. The results do not indicate that there is a relationship between these two variables.

9. $\chi^2 = 10.01$ with 2 df, $P < .01$. The hypothesis that there is no difference in the self-attitudes of normals and delinquents is rejected. An inspection of the size and direction of the differences indicates that a negative self-attitude occurs more often among the delinquent children.

10. $\chi^2 = 13.93$ with 4 df, $P < .01$. The hypothesis that performance of this task is independent of stress condition is rejected. It may be concluded that performance is related to the condition under

which the subject is tested. An inspection of the size and direction of the differences indicates that "Failure stress" had the greatest negative effect on performance, and that neither of the stressed groups had as many "Good" performers as the non-stressed control group.

11. The expected frequencies for this three-by-eight table are too small to permit the satisfactory use of a chi-square test. The situation can be rectified, however, by combining adjacent grades (1 and 2, 3 and 4, etc.) to give a three-by-four table. For this combination of the frequencies, $\chi^2 = 24.42$ with 6 df, and $P < .001$. The hypothesis that cognitive mode is independent of grade level (and presumably of age) is rejected. Inspection of the data reveals that the largest contributions to the value of χ^2 come from the four corners of the table, and the differences indicate that relatively more of the younger children were classified as "Concrete" and relatively more of the older children as "Abstract." And the shift appears to occur gradually with increasing age.

chapter 10

The *t* Test

So far, our discussion of probability and hypothesis testing has been concerned almost entirely with data classified into categories. The hypotheses tested were about proportions: that a certain proportion of the population is in a given category; that two population proportions are equal; etc. When data are in the form of measures, analogous hypotheses are made about the mean—that the population mean has a certain value, that two population means are equal, and so on. In this and the next chapter, we take up procedures that are used to test hypotheses about the mean.

THE t DISTRIBUTION

In Chapter 5, it was stated that the sampling distribution of means is approximately normal when the sample size n is 30 or more. This is true even when the parent population (the population from which the samples are drawn) is not itself normal. If the samples are large enough, the distribution of means will be normal regardless of the shape of the parent population. Therefore, determining a confidence interval for μ by the method of Chapter 5 requires no assumptions about the distribution of the parent population. The method of Chapter 5 does assume, though, that the population standard deviation σ is known. Because s is a reliable estimate of σ when n is as large as 30, approximate confidence intervals were obtained by substituting s for σ in the formulas of that chapter.

In this chapter, we consider problems in which it is assumed that the parent population is normally distributed, but there is no restriction on the sample size because we take into account the fact that s is used in place of σ. The statistic obtained under this set of assumptions is called t, and it is not normally distributed. For large samples, the sampling distribution of t approaches the shape of the normal curve and t may be referred to normal curve tables. But for small samples, t must be referred to the special tables of the t distribution.

The t distribution, like the χ^2 distribution, is a family of theoretical curves that vary with the degrees of freedom available. Since the t distribution assumes that s is used in place of σ, the degrees of freedom for t are the same as those for s—namely, $n - 1$. Table D in the Appendix gives the probability of obtaining selected t values for given degrees of freedom. The t distribution is symmetrical, like the normal distribution, with mean $t = 0$. Table D gives only $+t$ values, from the upper half of the distribution. The probabilities given at the top of the table are for a two-tailed test, and thus represent the proportion of cases that lie beyond both $+t$ and $-t$. For a one-tailed test, these probabilities should be halved.

CONFIDENCE INTERVAL FOR THE MEAN

Confidence limits for μ may be obtained by substituting the sample values $\overline{X}$, s, and n in the formula

$$\overline{X} \pm t_o \frac{s}{\sqrt{n}} \qquad (10.1)$$

where the value of t_o is determined by the confidence level chosen and the degrees of freedom that are available. We illustrate below.

Example 1. A Current Affairs test is given to a random sample of 12 college students. They obtain a mean score of 45 with $s = 6$. (a) Determine a 95% confidence interval for μ, the mean of the parent population from which the students were drawn. (b) A score of 50 has previously been established as the minimum score for well-informed persons. Could the mean for this population of students be as high as 50?

• • step 1. Determine the value of t_o. There are $12 - 1 = 11$ degrees of freedom. The 95% confidence limits are desired, which means that we want the t values that include the middle 95% of the distribution, or that cut off .025 of the cases in each tail of the distribution. From Table D, for 11 df, the value of t_o is 2.20.

• • STEP 2. Substitute the obtained sample values and the value of t_o in formula (10.1). Thus,

$$45 \pm 2.20 \frac{6}{\sqrt{12}} = 45 \pm 3.81$$

Adding and subtracting 3.81 as indicated, we obtain the interval:

$$41.19 < \mu < 48.81, \text{ with } 95\% \text{ confidence.}$$

• DISCUSSION

According to our confidence interval, the population mean μ is a value between 41.19 and 48.81. The answer to part (b) is yes, μ could be 50—μ *could* be 150—because confidence is not certainty. But we doubt that μ is as large as 50.

Notice that the confidence limits found by this procedure have not been referred to as "approximate" confidence limits. Confidence limits for μ determined by the normal curve procedure of Chapter 5 were called "approximate confidence limits" because that procedure assumed that σ was known when in fact σ was estimated by s. Confidence limits determined by reference to the t distribution take into account that s is used in place of σ, with the result that these are *exact* confidence limits. *Exact* confidence intervals are confidence intervals about which we can make exact probability statements. Thus, when we claim "μ is some value between 41.19 and 48.81," the probability is .95 that our statement is true. In the long run, with repeated sampling, the procedure we used will lead to true statements (intervals that contain μ) 95% of the time and false statements (intervals that do not contain μ) 5% of the time.

A particular statement about μ is, of course, either true or false, but we do not know into which of these two categories the statement falls. Since our procedure leads to 95 true statements for every 5 that are false, the probability is .95 that a particular statement is among the true ones. It is a little like flipping a coin that rolls out of sight. The coin has landed and one of the events, heads or tails, has occurred. But as long as we cannot see the coin, our probability statement remains the same—.5 that it landed heads. In the same way, we determine a 95% confidence interval and the interval either contains μ or does not contain μ. Since we do not know which of these events has occurred, our probability statement remains the same—.95 that the interval contains μ.

To understand just what is "approximate" about the confidence intervals of Chapter 5, consider the 95% confidence interval for μ obtained from the same sample data, but using formula (5.4):

$$41.61 < \mu < 48.39, \text{ with } 95\% \text{ confidence.}$$

This confidence interval is inexact because the probability is *not* .95 that μ is within the limits given. The exact probability that these limits include the value of μ cannot be read from the normal curve table (as the formula assumes) because σ was not used in the computation of the confidence limits, s was used. By interpolation in the t table, for 11 df, the probability that μ is within the given limits is only about .92.

Because of discrepancies like these the normal-curve procedure of Chapter 5 was recommended only for samples as large as 30. When n is 30 or more, the t distribution is so close to normal that confidence limits obtained by formulas (5.4) and (10.1) will be almost identical. Therefore, for large samples either formula may be used. But for small samples formula (10.1) must be used.

One Sample: Hypothesis
That μ Is a Certain Value

In Example 1, we "doubted" that the population mean was as high as 50 because 50 fell outside the 95% confidence limits established for μ. How "doubtful" should we be? Our sample mean was 45. What is the probability of obtaining such a sample from a population where μ is 50?

The hypothesis that μ is a particular value like 50 may be stated with its alternative as follows:

$$H: \mu = 50 \qquad \text{Alternative: } \mu \neq 50$$

The directional hypothesis that μ is *at least* 50 (equal to or greater than 50) is stated:

$$H: \mu \geq 50 \qquad \text{Alternative: } \mu < 50$$

The critical region for this hypothesis, it will be remembered, is in the *lower* tail of the probability distribution.

The directional hypothesis that μ is equal to or less than 50 is stated:

$$H: \mu \leq 50 \qquad \text{Alternative: } \mu > 50$$

The critical region for this hypothesis is in the *upper* tail of the probability distribution.

Hypotheses such as these may be tested by substituting the hypothesized value for μ in the formula

$$t = \frac{\overline{X} - \mu}{s/\sqrt{n}} \qquad\qquad (10.2)$$

and referring the t value obtained to Table D, to the t distribution with $n - 1$ degrees of freedom.

Example 2. A random sample of 12 students were found to have a mean score of 45 with $s = 6$ on a Current Affairs test. What is the probability that this sample came from a population where μ is 50?

• • STEP 1. The value 50 is substituted for μ in formula (10.2) along with the given sample values. Thus,

$$t = \frac{45 - 50}{6/\sqrt{12}} = \frac{-5}{1.73} = -2.89$$

• • STEP 2. The value 2.89 is referred to the t distribution for $12 - 1 = 11$ degrees of freedom. In the row for 11 df, we find the values 2.72 and 3.11. Since 2.89 falls between these values, it has some probability between the probabilities given for 2.72 and 3.11. The probability of our obtained t, then, is less than .02 but greater than .01.

• DISCUSSION

The results of our test indicate that a sample mean as deviant as 45 will occur less than two times in a hundred if μ is 50. Ordinarily, this would lead to rejection of the hypothesis that μ is 50. If "well-informed" is defined as achieving a score of 50 or above, we would be led to conclude that as a group, this population of students falls somewhat short of being well-informed. Many individuals have scores above 50, but it is very unlikely that the group mean is as high as 50.

The general outcome of this test—though not the exact probability value—was already clear from the confidence interval computed earlier. Since .95 was the confidence level used, any values outside the obtained interval are automatically among the least probable 5% of the possible values of μ. In general, a confidence interval implies a rejection of all hypotheses about μ that lie outside of the confidence limits. Values within the interval constitute "acceptable" hypotheses about μ.

Two Independent Samples:
Hypothesis That $\mu_1 = \mu_2$

Often, in research, we want to compare the means of two groups of subjects who were independently and randomly selected from different populations (*e.g.*, six-year-olds and ten-year-olds, males and females, churchgoers and non-churchgoers). It also happens often that we want to compare the means obtained by subjects who were selected from the same population but then assigned randomly to two different experimental conditions. In both of these cases, we would test the null hypothesis that there is no difference between the parameter means, or that $\mu_1 = \mu_2$. Or, if it is predicted that $\mu_1 > \mu_2$, the directional hypothesis $\mu_1 \leqq \mu_2$ may be tested by locating the critical region in the upper tail of the probability distribution, and so on.

Such hypotheses about the means of two independent samples may be tested by applying the formula

$$t = \frac{(\overline{X}_1 - \overline{X}_2) - (\mu_1 - \mu_2)}{\sqrt{\dfrac{s^2}{n_1} + \dfrac{s^2}{n_2}}} \tag{10.3}$$

and referring the obtained t to Table D, with $df = n_1 + n_2 - 2$. The term $(\mu_1 - \mu_2)$ is equal to 0 when the hypothesis is that the parameter means are equal; this term may therefore be dropped from the formula in testing such hypotheses. s^2 is an estimate of σ^2, the variance of the identical populations assumed by the hypothesis. (The variance, it will be recalled, is the square of the standard deviation.) s^2 is the weighted average of the two sample variances, and may be obtained by substituting the sample values s_1^2 and s_2^2 in the formula

$$s^2 = \frac{(n_1 - 1)s_1^2 + (n_2 - 1)s_2^2}{n_1 + n_2 - 2} \tag{10.4}$$

When n_1 and n_2 are equal, the sample values s_1^2 and s_2^2 may be substituted directly into formula (10.3), and it is not necessary to compute the s^2 of formula (10.4).

The use of formula (10.3) to compare two sample means is based on the assumption that the two samples come from normally distributed populations that have equal variances. For a given investigation, there is usually no way of knowing whether these assumptions are met or not. There is no way of determining from sample data that a population is normal or that two population variances are equal.* Fortunately, moderate—and even certain extreme—violations of these assumptions have been found to have little effect on the probabilities of calculated t values. But, certain other violations may have a large effect. Without going into the matter further, some suggestions are offered for avoiding the more serious consequences of failing to meet the assumptions of the t test: (1) obtain samples that are as large as possible; (2) if samples must be small, try to have them equal in size; (3) use a two-tailed test in preference to a one-tailed test.

Example 3. An investigator is interested in how differing motives may influence the answers given on personality tests. A class of 28 students is randomly divided into two groups of 14 each. Both groups are given a personality test designed to measure Social Responsiveness. Group 1 is told the test will become part of their file, while Group 2 is told they need not put their names on the test, since the investigator is only interested in how college students as a group score on this test. Afterwards, the tests are scored and means and standard deviations are obtained for the two groups. The results are:

Group 1: $\bar{X}_1 = 62.1$, $s_1 = 10.0$, $n_1 = 14$
Group 2: $\bar{X}_2 = 51.1$, $s_2 = 13.0$, $n_2 = 14$

Can it be concluded that the different motivating conditions have an effect on test scores?

In order to answer the question affirmatively, we must first be able to reject the hypothesis $\mu_1 = \mu_2$, that the parameter means for these two conditions are equal. Because we have two independent samples, formula (10.3) is used to test the hypothesis. A significance level of .05 will be used.

• • STEP 1. The first step is to determine the value of s^2, the estimate of the common population variance. Since s_1 and s_2 are given, these values are squared to obtain $s_1{}^2 = 100.0$ and $s_2{}^2 = 169.0$. Substituting in formula (10.4) we obtain

$$s^2 = \frac{(14 - 1)100.0 + (14 - 1)169.0}{14 + 14 - 2}$$

$$= \frac{1300 + 2197}{26}$$

$$= 134.5$$

* A test for the hypothesis that $\sigma_1{}^2 = \sigma_2{}^2$ is given in Chapter 11, but of course failure to reject this hypothesis does not establish that the variances *are* equal.

It was not necessary in this case to compute s^2 because the two samples are equal in size. We did so to illustrate the more general procedure.

• • STEP 2. The value of s^2 is substituted with the sample means and n's in formula (10.3) to obtain

$$t = \frac{62.1 - 51.1}{\sqrt{\frac{134.5}{14} + \frac{134.5}{14}}} = \frac{11.0}{\sqrt{\frac{269}{14}}} = 2.51$$

If we had wished to take advantage of the fact that the samples are equal in size, the sample variances 100.0 and 169.0 could have been substituted directly into formula (10.3). Thus,

$$t = \frac{62.1 - 51.1}{\sqrt{\frac{100.0}{14} + \frac{169.0}{14}}} = \frac{11.0}{\sqrt{\frac{269}{14}}} = 2.51$$

When the sample n's are equal, the two procedures yield the same results.

• • STEP 3. The obtained t value is referred to Table D with $df = 14 + 14 - 2 = 26$. There we find that a t as large as 2.51 has a probability of less than .02. Since this value is smaller than our alpha of .05, the hypothesis that $\mu_1 = \mu_2$ is rejected.

• DISCUSSION

The hypothesis is rejected and we accept the alternative that $\mu_1 \neq \mu_2$. Therefore, we are led to conclude that the conditions under which the subjects were tested do have an effect upon their scores on this test. Group 1, who were told the test would be part of their file, obtained the higher scores, suggesting that Social Responsiveness (or whatever the test seemed to the students to measure) is regarded as a desirable "attribute" to be included in one's file.

We have rejected that $\mu_1 = \mu_2$, but what populations are μ_1 and μ_2 the means of? To what populations do our conclusions apply? A class of students is not a random sample of students, so there is no statistical basis for drawing conclusions about some larger student population. Randomization (and the basis for making a statistical inference) entered into the *assignment of subjects* to the two experimental conditions. The particular division of the subjects that resulted from this procedure is one division out of a vast number of other possible divisions which could as easily have occurred. It is this vast number of possible divisions of the subjects that constitutes the population from which a sample was drawn. The population consists of all the different samples (divisions of the subjects) that can be obtained by randomly selecting 14 subjects from a total of 28. Over 40 million different sample divisions can be obtained by this procedure (if you doubt it work out 28!/14!14!), and it is to this population of 40 million sample divisions that our conclusions apply.

Imagine for a moment these 40 million sample divisions. Each division of the subjects yields two groups and two $\bar{X}$'s. One of these groups is always designated Group 1 and its mean is $\bar{X}_1$. The mean of all the $\bar{X}_1$'s (40 million of them) is μ_1. Similarly, for each division of the subjects there is always a Group 2 and $\bar{X}_2$. The mean of all the $\bar{X}_2$'s is μ_2. In rejecting the hypothesis that $\mu_1 = \mu_2$, we reject that the subjects' scores will be the same under the two conditions of testing. Specifically, we reject that the means will be the same.

To generalize beyond this particular class of 28 students (on other than an impressionistic basis) the study must be repeated with other subjects. Similar findings on diverse groups would provide a kind of common-sense support for the notion that the different motivating conditions regularly affect scores in the manner observed. Or better, the study may be repeated on a random sample from a population of interest so that the findings may at least be generalized to this population. The present study has demonstrated that the different motivating conditions *can* make a difference in performance on this test.

Two Correlated Samples:
Hypothesis That a Mean
Difference = 0

A widely used experimental design in psychological research is that in which the subjects act as their own controls. Typically, each subject is tested twice under different conditions (*e.g.*, before and after taking a tranquilizer, or with two different types of reward), and the difference in his performance under the two conditions provides a measure of their different effects. The obvious advantage of this design is that it controls for individual differences by using the same subjects for both conditions. Sometimes, instead of using the same subjects, pairs of subjects are matched on some relevant variable (*e.g.*, intelligence) and the members of each pair are randomly assigned to the two experimental conditions.

In both of these cases, the two samples of measures are usually correlated because either the same subjects or matched groups of subjects provided both samples. The t test for independent samples is therefore not appropriate for this situation. However, the design yields a set of difference scores—one for each subject or for each pair of matched subjects—and formula (10.2) can be used to test a hypothesis about the parameter mean μ_D of the difference scores. Thus,

$$t = \frac{\bar{X}_D - \mu_D}{s_D/\sqrt{n}} \tag{10.5}$$

where $\bar{X}_D$ is the mean of the difference scores and s_D is their standard deviation. Under the hypothesis that scores will be the same for the two conditions, the mean difference $\mu_D = 0$. In this case, t may be computed directly from the difference scores by the more convenient formula,

$$t = \frac{\Sigma D}{\sqrt{\dfrac{n\Sigma D^2 - (\Sigma D)^2}{n-1}}} \tag{10.6}$$

where n is the number of difference scores, and ΣD is their algebraic sum. The obtained t is referred to Table D, with $df = n - 1$.

Example 4. A new drug for depressed mental patients is to be tested. A random sample of ten depressed patients is selected from a large number of recently admitted hospital patients who received this diagnosis. The ten patients are given a test of psychomotor efficiency that measures their mental alertness in terms of a combined time and error score, transformed so that high scores indicate high efficiency. After the patients are receiving the drug on a regular basis, they are tested again. Their scores before and after receiving the drug are shown in the first two columns of Table 10.1. Is there evidence of a significant change in psychomotor efficiency after receiving the drug? Test the hypothesis that $\mu_D = 0$ using an alpha of .10.

• • STEP 1. For each pair of scores, determine the difference D, being careful to indicate by a plus or minus sign the direction of the difference. In Table 10.1, minus signs indicate that the second score was the larger, plus signs that the first score was the larger. The column of difference scores are summed algebraically, as shown, to obtain ΣD. This sum should be equal to the difference between the sums of the original columns of scores. Thus, $86 - 92 = -6$ also.

• • STEP 2. Square each of the difference scores, as shown in the last column of Table 10.1. The sum of this column gives ΣD^2.

Table 10.1
t Test of the Hypothesis That a Mean Difference Is 0

EFFICIENCY SCORE			
BEFORE DRUG	AFTER DRUG	D	D^2
5	10	−5	25
9	14	−5	25
7	5	+2	4
3	6	−3	9
10	9	+1	1
15	15	0	0
4	1	+3	9
16	20	−4	16
12	10	+2	4
5	2	+3	9
⎯	⎯	⎯	⎯
86	92	−17	$\Sigma D^2 = 102$
		+11	

$$\Sigma D = -6$$

$$t = \cfrac{\Sigma D}{\sqrt{\cfrac{n\Sigma D^2 - (\Sigma D)^2}{n-1}}} = \cfrac{-6}{\sqrt{\cfrac{10(102) - (-6)^2}{9}}} = -.57$$

• • STEP 3. Enter ΣD and ΣD^2 in formula (10.6). (Remember that n is the number of difference scores, *not* the number of original scores.) For these data, formula (10.6) gives $t = -.57$.

• • STEP 4. Refer the obtained t value to Table D in the Appendix, with $df = n - 1$. In this case, $df = 10 - 1 = 9$. For a two-tailed test, with 9 df, a t as large as .57 has a probability greater than .50. Such a probability is very much larger than the alpha of .10 chosen as the significance level for the test; therefore the hypothesis that $\mu_D = 0$ cannot be rejected. If the hypothesis is true, differences as large as those we found will occur in more than 50% of random samples. Such differences cannot be regarded as evidence against the hypothesis.

• DISCUSSION

Failing to reject the hypothesis $\mu_D = 0$ means, of course, that no evidence has been found that the drug has any effect on the psycho-motor efficiency of depressed patients. Observe, however, that while we are able to say "no evidence has been found," we are not able to say "it has been shown that the drug has no effect." As was pointed out earlier and bears repeating: Failure to reject a null hypothesis does not establish that the hypothesis is true. It is especially important to remember this when samples are small. When samples are small, and when the population difference or "effect" being investigated is not a very large one, the probability of a Type II error is usually high. Even with the increased power afforded by an alpha of .10, the probability is high that we shall fail to reject the null hypothesis even though it is false.

Consider the following example. Suppose we have a biased coin, a coin that will in the long run land heads up .80 of the time. We do not know this and wish to test that the coin is fair—*viz.*, that P(Heads) $= .5$. We flip the coin five times and observe that heads come up on four of the five trials. Under the hypothesis that $P = .5$, a result as deviant as this has a probability of 12/32 or about .38. We shall certainly not reject the hypothesis that the coin is fair, and of course we shall be making a Type II error in not doing so. We continue to flip the coin for a total of ten trials and observe a total of eight heads. The probability of a result as deviant as this is about .11, so again the hypothesis will not be rejected and again we will have made a Type II error. The coin all this time is behaving perfectly appropriately—landing heads up on .80 of the trials—but we are making Type II errors because our samples are not large enough to permit the finding that a sample value of .80 is significantly different from the hypothesized value .50. Only if the coin deviates somewhat from its "true" nature in the direction of giving nine or ten heads shall we be lucky enough to reject the false hypothesis that $P = .5$.

In the same way, the failure of our drug experiment to find a significant difference may be due to the low power of the statistical test rather than to the absence of a difference in the population that was sampled. Thus, in failing to reject the null hypothesis we may have made a Type II error. This is always a possibility, of course, in any statistical test, but it becomes an especially likely possibility when samples are small. When the null hypothesis cannot be rejected and samples are small, it is usually best to suspend all judgment. That there is no difference in the population is likely, and that there is a substantial difference which the test failed to detect is also likely. The results are inconclusive. Wherever possible, take a large sample!

Testing the Hypothesis of Zero Correlation

The hypothesis that the population correlation ρ is zero may be tested by substituting an observed sample r in the formula

$$t = \frac{r\sqrt{n-2}}{\sqrt{1-r^2}} \qquad (10.7)$$

and referring the obtained t to Table D, with $df = n - 2$.

For example, suppose that a correlation of .46 is found between two variables in a random sample of 20 subjects. Can we reject the hypothesis that the correlation is zero in the population from which the sample came? We compute

$$t = \frac{.46\sqrt{20-2}}{\sqrt{1-(.46)^2}} = \frac{.46(4.2426)}{\sqrt{.7884}} = 2.20$$

The degrees of freedom are $20 - 2 = 18$. For a two-tailed test, the probability of obtaining a t as large as this is less than .05. If alpha is .05, the hypothesis that $\rho = 0$ would be rejected. This does not allow us to conclude, of course, that ρ is "around .46," only that ρ is very unlikely to be as low as zero.

If formula (10.7) is solved for r, it is possible to substitute values of n and t into the formula and determine what value of r is necessary for a given size sample in order to reject the hypothesis that $\rho = 0$. This has been done for various sample sizes and significance levels to give the table of significant r's that appears in the Appendix as Table E. Thus, turning to this table, we find that with 18 df an r of .444 is significant at the .05 level (two-tailed test). Since our sample r of .46 is larger than this value, it clearly falls in the critical region (when alpha is .05) and the hypothesis that $\rho = 0$ is rejected without further ado.

Practice Problems

1. A random sample of nine subjects memorize a list of 20 nonsense syllables. The following day they are tested to determine how

many of the syllables they can recall. The mean number is 8.7 with $s = 3.0$. Compute 95% and 99% confidence intervals for μ.

2. A random sample of 16 young rats are each trained to run a multiple-T maze. The number of errors (blind alley entrances) made by each of the animals in learning the maze is recorded. The mean number of errors made by the group is 75.2 with $s = 16.0$. Compute 95% and 99% confidence intervals for μ.

3. A random sample of 25 college students are asked to keep a record of time spent in study over a two-week period. The mean number of hours reported by the students is 17.4 with $s = 6.0$. (a) Compute 95% and 99% confidence intervals for μ. (b) Supposing these same results had been obtained for a sample of 225 students, what would the 95% and 99% confidence intervals be?

4. On a projective personality test, the mean number of responses given by normals is 20. A random sample of 15 schizophrenic patients give a mean of 14 responses with $s = 7.5$. Using an alpha of .05, test the hypothesis that the schizophrenics are a random sample from a population whose mean is 20.

5. A youth worker whose task it is to help place young people in suitable jobs is concerned because of the large number of young job applicants who failed to finish high school. He administers individual IQ tests to a random sample of 20 of these high school dropouts and finds that their mean IQ is 92.0 with $s = 10.2$. What is the probability that this sample comes from a population where the mean IQ is at least 100? Test the directional hypothesis that $\mu \geq 100$ using an alpha of .05.

6. At a reception center for Army inductees, the mean physical fitness rating of a random sample of 12 men is 75.6 with $s = 17.3$. During the war years, the mean physical fitness rating of inductees was 61. Is the present population of inductees a more "fit" group? Using an alpha of .01, test the directional hypothesis that the 12 men are a random sample from a population whose mean fitness rating is no higher than 61 (equal to or less than 61).

7. A random sample of 20 sixth-graders are randomly divided into two groups of ten each. Both groups are given the same science lesson to learn, but Group 1 reads the lesson from a standard text book, while Group 2 learns the lesson from a teaching machine. At the end of the hour, all the students are given a test to determine how well they learned the lesson. Group 1 obtains a mean grade of 71.3 with $s = 9.2$. Group 2 obtains a mean grade of 79.7 with $s = 8.7$. Do the results warrant concluding that one of these learning methods

is superior to the other? Use an alpha of .05 to test the hypothesis that $\mu_1 = \mu_2$.

8. A personnel psychologist concerned with staffing a factory department that will be engaged in the assembly of small parts feels that women workers will do better at this task than men. From among the first applicants for the job, he chooses a random sample of ten men and ten women and gives them a test of manual dexterity. The women obtain a mean score of 25.2 with $s = 4.0$. The mean for the men is 22.5 with $s = 4.9$. On the basis of these results, should the psychologist recommend that women be hired for this job in preference to men? Use an alpha of .10 to test the hypothesis that $\mu_1 = \mu_2$.

9. The mean IQ of eight pupils randomly selected from the public school of a certain area is found to be 103.4 with $s = 10.0$. The mean IQ of six pupils chosen randomly from a parochial school serving the same area is 106.5 with $s = 8.0$. Do the results indicate that the parochial school children of this area have a higher mean IQ than the public school children? Use an alpha of .10 to test the hypothesis that $\mu_1 = \mu_2$.

10. Previous studies have found that reaction time is faster when the stimulus is presented soon after the "ready" signal than when a longer waiting period is required. In line with these findings, an investigator sets up the null hypothesis that $\mu_S \geq \mu_L$ (mean reaction time for a short waiting period is equal to or greater than mean reaction time for a long waiting period), and adopts an alpha of .01 for the test of his hypothesis. A single practiced subject is tested under two conditions: a two-second waiting period (short), and a six-second waiting period (long). The short and long waiting periods are randomly alternated over a series of 100 trials. For 50 short-period trials, the subject's mean reaction time is 151 milliseconds with $s^2 = 325$. For 50 long-period trials, his mean reaction time is 159 milliseconds with $s^2 = 225$. Do these results permit the investigator to reject the null hypothesis?

11. Ten subjects chosen randomly from a large class of freshmen at College X are given a questionnaire relating to their attitudes towards college life. Two years later, when they are juniors, the same subjects are asked to fill out the questionnaire again. Their scores on both occasions are shown below, with higher scores indicating a generally more favorable attitude. Is there evidence of a significant change in favorableness of attitude over the two-year interval? Use an alpha of .05 to test the hypothesis that $\mu_D = 0$.

As Freshmen	Two Years Later
22	29
32	27
18	22
29	46
36	45
25	35
25	38
23	31
30	41
27	25

12. In a study of perception, 12 subjects with normal vision are given a test in which they are to locate geometrical figures that are embedded in more complex designs. In Part A of the test, the figures to be located consist of regular and familiar geometrical shapes (triangles, circles, etc.). In Part B of the test, the figures to be located are unfamiliar, irregular shapes. The investigator is interested in whether the regular shapes will be located more easily than the irregular shapes. All subjects take both parts of the test. To balance out order effects, six subjects are randomly assigned to take Part A first while the remaining six take Part B first. Afterwards, the scores made by each subject on the two parts of the test are compared. The results are:

NUMBER OF FIGURES LOCATED

Regular Shapes	Irregular Shapes
16	13
12	10
20	20
18	19
20	15
14	11
14	16
15	11
13	14
15	12
15	12
10	10

Do the results support the investigator's hunch that regular shapes are more readily perceived than irregular shapes? Use an alpha of .05 to test the hypothesis that $\mu_D = 0$.

13. To investigate the effects of distraction on attention and concentration, a random sample of ten subjects are given a letter cancellation test (*e.g.*, to cross out all the f's in a printed passage) under two different conditions: normal conditions in a quiet room, and distraction conditions in a busy and noisy room. Two different printed passages are used, equated for the number of letters to be canceled. To balance out possible difference in the difficulty of the

two passages, five subjects are randomly chosen to receive one of the passages, five the other, under the quiet condition. For the distraction condition that follows, each subject then receives the passage he has not yet seen. Afterwards, the scores made by each subject under the two conditions are compared. The results are:

NUMBER OF CORRECT CANCELLATIONS

QUIET CONDITION	DISTRACTION CONDITION
30	28
34	29
25	27
26	23
29	30
35	35
21	24
40	36
30	32
22	25

Is there a significant difference in scores made under the two conditions? Use an alpha of .05 to test the hypothesis that $\mu_D = 0$.

14. A control group of ten subjects randomly selected from the same population as the subjects of (13) above are treated in the same manner as those subjects except that the control group takes both letter cancellation tests under quiet conditions. To determine whether there is a practice effect, difference scores are computed between the first and second testing. The mean difference score is found to be 3.4 with $s^2 = 11.1$. Compute the mean and s^2 of the difference scores obtained by the subjects of (13) above. Compare this mean with the control group mean, using formula (10.3) and an alpha of .05 to test the hypothesis that $\mu_{D_e} = \mu_{D_c}$, the mean change (difference) in the scores of experimental group subjects is equal to the mean change in control group scores.

15. For a random sample of 27 college students, the correlation between reported hours of study and grade point average is .50. (a) Should it be concluded that there is a relationship in the student population between these two variables? Use formula (10.7) and an alpha of .01 to test the hypothesis that $\rho = 0$ in the population from which these students came. (b) From Table E, what value of r is significant at the .01 level for this test?

16. A random sample of 18 nursery school children are rated by their parents and by their teachers for creativeness in play. The correlation between the two sets of ratings is .40. (a) Does this correlation indicate a tendency for teachers and parents to rate a child similarly? Use formula (10.7) and an alpha of .05 to test the hypothesis that $\rho = 0$ between such ratings for the population of

nursery school children. (b) From Table E, what value of r is significant at the .05 level for this test?

17. For a random sample of 200 suburban commuters, a correlation of $-.18$ is found between reported income and time spent at home. Use Table E to determine the probability of obtaining such a sample from a population where $\rho = 0$. Do the results indicate a relationship in this commuter population between income and time spent at home?

18. If the .05 significance level is chosen, determine from Table E the value of r that is necessary to reject the hypothesis that $\rho = 0$ when the sample size is (a) 5, (b) 10, (c) 15, (d) 30, (e) 52, (f) 102. (g) What do these successively smaller values indicate about the sampling distribution of r when $\rho = 0$ and the sample size is made larger and larger?

Answers

1. 95% interval: 6.39 to 11.01. 99% interval: 5.34 to 12.06.

2. 95% interval: 66.68 to 83.72. 99% interval: 63.41 to 86.99.

3. (a) 95% interval: 14.92 to 19.88. 99% interval: 14.04 to 20.76. (b) 95% interval: 16.62 to 18.18. 99% interval: 16.37 to 18.43. Observe the much narrower intervals obtained with a sample of 225. When samples are large, the variability of the sampling distribution is reduced and 95% or 99% of the samples fall within a relatively small range. (For these intervals, with 224 df t_o is virtually identical with z_o and the normal curve z values are used in place of t. For all practical purposes, when $df > 30$, t may be referred to the normal curve table. The values at the bottom of the t table, for $df = \infty$, are the same as the z values that would be read from the normal curve table.)

4. $t = -3.10$ with 14 df. This t falls within the critical region, which begins at ±2.14. For a two-tailed test, $P < .01$. The hypothesis is rejected. The evidence is that, as a group, the patient population that was sampled gives fewer responses than normals on this test.

5. $t = -3.51$ with 19 df. The critical region for this one-tailed test is in the *lower* tail of the t distribution, beginning at $t = -1.73$. Our obtained t is well within the critical region; the probability under the hypothesis of obtaining a t as large as this is less than .005 (half the probability given by the column heading). The hypothesis is

rejected. We conclude that the mean IQ of the dropouts is less than 100.

6. $t = +2.92$ with 11 df. The critical region for this test $(H:\mu \leq 61)$ is in the *upper* tail of the t distribution, beginning at $+2.72$. Our obtained t is within the critical region, $P < .01$, so the hypothesis is rejected. It is highly unlikely that this group of men are a random sample from a population whose mean physical fitness rating is as low as 61.

7. $t = 2.10$ with 18 df, $P = .05$. Since a .05 significance level was adopted, the hypothesis is rejected. We conclude that for this science lesson, the teaching machine is superior to the text book for this pupil population.

8. $t = 1.35$ with 18 df, $P > .10$. The hypothesis cannot be rejected. There is no basis for concluding that women applicants obtain higher dexterity scores than men. The samples are small and the psychologist may want to repeat his study before making a negative decision, but as the matter now stands, there is no evidence for the superiority of women applicants.

9. $t = .62$ with 12 df, $P > .50$. The hypothesis cannot be rejected; more than 50% of random samples will show a difference as great as this if the population means are equal. There is no evidence that the parochial school children have a higher mean IQ than the public school children.

10. $t = -2.41$ with 98 df. For this one-tailed test, the critical region is in the lower tail of the t distribution and begins at -2.36. Our obtained t is below this value so it falls in the critical region. $P < .01$, and the hypothesis is rejected. The investigator may conclude that *for this subject* (only this subject's behavior was sampled) mean reaction time is faster following a two-second waiting period than a six-second waiting period.

11. $t = -3.42$ with 9 df, $P < .01$. The hypothesis is rejected. The minus t value (due to a minus ΣD) indicates that the second scores were generally larger than the first. We conclude that scores are higher, and attitudes generally more favorable, in this population of juniors than in the population as freshmen.

12. $t = +2.41$ with 11 df, $P < .05$. The hypothesis is rejected. The plus t value indicates that the first set of scores are generally larger than the second set, hence that more of the regular shapes were correctly located, supporting the investigator's hunch. This experimental design is similar to that of Example 3 in that the subjects are not themselves a random sample and there is no statistical basis for generalizing to some larger group. What was randomized

in the experiment was their assignment to a particular *order*—Part A first or Part B first—which constitutes two experimental conditions. There are $12!/6!6! = 924$ different ways in which the subjects can be assigned to the two conditions. For each such assignment, a set of difference scores could be obtained (in theory if not in practice) and the mean difference $\overline{X}_D$ computed. The hypothesis states that the mean of this distribution of 924 $\overline{X}_D$'s is zero. In rejecting this hypothesis, the investigator is able to conclude that regardless of the order in which the embedded figures are presented, more regular than irregular shapes are perceived by these subjects.

13. $t = +.32$ with 9 df, $P > .50$. The hypothesis cannot be rejected; there is no evidence of a difference in performance under the two conditions. In fact, the plus t value indicates that these subjects performed somewhat better under distraction than they did in a quiet room. In experiments such as this one, and such as Example 4 of this chapter, there is a definite need for a control group. In this case, for example, there may be a practice effect due to the first testing. If so, distraction during the second test may act to reduce the scores from what they ordinarily would be, but this effect of distraction appears only as a blunting of the increase in scores due to practice. The difference scores of a control group, tested twice in a quiet room, would provide a basis for comparison. Similarly, in Example 4, a control group might reveal that depressed patients who do not receive the drug become in the same period of time even more depressed and obtain much lower efficiency scores than they did at the initial testing. The drug may act to inhibit this trend, an effect no investigator would wish to overlook.

14. The mean of the difference scores obtained in (13) is .3 and $s^2 = 8.9$. Using these and the corresponding values for the control group, formula (10.3) gives $t = -2.19$. With 18 df, $P < .05$ for this two-tailed test. We conclude that the difference between means is significant, and thus that distraction does have an effect on performance. The control group shows an increase in score, supporting the notion of a practice effect, and the results for the experimental group suggest that this increase is obliterated by distraction. (These findings were, of course, invented to make the point, but such problems arise very often in experimental work and the student should become sensitive to the need for a control group before he plunges into research.)

15. (a) $t = 2.89$ with 25 df, $P < .01$. The hypothesis is rejected. Yes, there is evidence of a relationship between hours of study and grade point average. (b) .487. Because our r of .50 is larger than this value, we know from Table E that it falls in the critical region and

thus that the hypothesis $\rho = 0$ may be rejected at the .01 level of significance.

16. (a) $t = 1.75$ with 16 df, $P = .10$. The hypothesis cannot be rejected. It cannot be concluded that parents and teachers tend to rate the children similarly. The sample is small and we can hardly conclude the opposite—that there is no relationship between the ratings of parents and teachers. Without additional evidence, judgment must be suspended. (b) .468. Because our r is smaller than this value, we know immediately that it does not fall in the critical region and the hypothesis cannot be rejected.

17. $P = .01$. (The difference in significant r values when $df = 198$ and $df = 200$ is so minute as to be entirely negligible.) Yes; it is very unlikely that $\rho = 0$ in this population. With such a large random sample r is highly reliable and it is also unlikely that ρ is much larger than $-.18$. We conclude that there is a slight negative relationship in this population between income and time spent at home.

18. (a) .878; (b) .632; (c) .514; (d) .361; (e) .273; (f) .195; (g) As the sample size increases, the variability of the sampling distribution becomes progressively reduced, with 95% of sample r's falling within a smaller and smaller range about the mean of 0. Thus, when samples are large, even a small r value will fall outside of this range and cause the rejection of the hypothesis that $\rho = 0$. When samples are small, the range is larger, and only a relatively large r value will fall outside of this range. Thus, a relatively large r is required to reject the hypothesis of zero correlation when the sample is small.

chapter 11

The F Test
and
Analysis
of Variance

We will be concerned in this chapter with procedures for testing two kinds of hypotheses: (1) that $\sigma_1{}^2 = \sigma_2{}^2$, the variances of two populations are equal; and (2) that $\mu_1 = \mu_2 = \mu_3 = \ldots = \mu$, the means of several populations are equal.

In both of these instances, the hypothesis is tested by means of an F test that takes the basic form

$$F = \frac{s_1{}^2}{s_2{}^2} \tag{11.1}$$

where $s_1{}^2$ and $s_2{}^2$ are two independent sample estimates of the population variance σ^2.

The F distribution, like the t and χ^2 distributions, is a family of theoretical curves that vary with the degrees of freedom available. More specifically, the F distribution varies with the combination of df available, since the numerator and the denominator of the F ratio each has associated with it a particular df. For example, the variance estimate in the numerator may be based on a sample of five cases and the variance estimate in the denominator on a sample of ten cases. Then the degrees of freedom for F will be $5 - 1 = 4$ for the numerator and $10 - 1 = 9$ for the denominator. Table F in the Appendix gives the values of F that are significant at the .05 and .01 levels (one-tailed test) for different combinations of numerator and denominator df. Thus, for 4 and 9 df, $F = 3.63$ marks the beginning of the critical region for a one-tailed test when alpha is .05, and $F = 6.42$ marks the beginning of the critical region for a one-tailed test when alpha is .01. F values equal to or larger than these would, in each case, cause rejection of the hypothesis. For two-tailed tests, the probabilities are doubled. Thus, for a two-tailed test, $F =$

3.63 is significant at the .10 level and $F = 6.42$ is significant at the .02 level.

HYPOTHESIS
THAT $\sigma_1^2 = \sigma_2^2$

Example 1.   In a study of the emotional responsiveness of schizophrenics, a random sample of 15 patients and 30 normal controls are tested in a variety of emotion-provoking situations. The amount of affective arousal in each situation is measured and a combined arousal score is obtained for each subject. The schizophrenics obtain a mean score of 62 with $s = 14$. The normal controls obtain a mean score of 54 with $s = 8$. Using an alpha of .05, test the hypothesis that the normals and schizophrenics are random samples from the same population with respect to affective arousal on this test.

If two samples come from the same or identical populations, then $\mu_1 = \mu_2$ and $\sigma_1^2 = \sigma_2^2$. That is, the populations have identical means and variances. Assuming that the population of measures is normally distributed in each case, there are thus two ways in which the scores of normals and schizophrenics may differ. The two populations may have different means, and quite independently of this, the populations may have different variances. The t tests of Chapter 10 assumed that the population variances were equal and proceeded from this assumption to examine the difference between the means. But in this example, there is a rather large difference in the standard deviations of the two samples: variability is greater among the schizophrenic subjects, suggesting a wider range and more "extreme" arousal scores than is found among the normals. To investigate this possibility, we test the hypothesis that $\sigma_1^2 = \sigma_2^2$, the two population variances are equal.

• • STEP 1. Each s is squared to obtain the variance estimate s^2. Thus, for the schizophrenics, $s^2 = 196$; for the normal controls, $s^2 = 64$.

• • STEP 2. We are conducting a two-tailed test of the hypothesis $\sigma_1^2 = \sigma_2^2$, but in order to use the F table in the Appendix, we must obtain a result that can be referred to the upper tail of the F distribution, since only upper values are given in the table. To accomplish this, and obtain an F value equal to or greater than 1 (the mean of the F distribution), we arbitrarily place the larger of our two variance estimates in the numerator of formula (11.1). Thus,

$$F = \frac{\text{larger } s^2}{\text{smaller } s^2} = \frac{196}{64} = 3.06$$

• • STEP 3. The df for the numerator are $15 - 1 = 14$. For the denominator, $df = 30 - 1 = 29$. We have, then, $F = 3.06$ with $(14, 29)$ df.

• • STEP 4. Referring to Table F, we find that for $(14, 29)$ df, F values as large as 2.77 have a probability of .02 (doubling the .01 probability since this is a two-tailed test). Our F of 3.06 is larger than this value, falling even further out in the tail of the F distribution, and therefore has some probability less than .02. We reject the hypothesis that $\sigma_1{}^2 = \sigma_2{}^2$ and conclude that the two population variances are not equal.

• DISCUSSION

The evidence so far is that the two populations from which our schizophrenics and normals were selected have different variabilities so far as affective arousal scores are concerned. Since the larger variance estimate was obtained from the schizophrenics, it would seem that the schizophrenic population is a less homogeneous group with respect to affective arousal than is the normal population. Relatively, the normals react pretty much alike, while there are large differences among the schizophrenics.

We should like to know also, of course, whether the two populations differ in the amount of affective arousal each shows. That is, we would like to know if the means differ. The t test for independent samples given in Chapter 10 is based on the assumption of equal population variances. We have just rejected the hypothesis that the variances are equal, so this t test is not applicable. Approximate tests are available which take into account that the population variances are not equal. Such an approximation is given below.

Hypothesis That $\mu_1 = \mu_2$
When Population Variances
Are Unequal

To test for a significant difference between two independent sample means when the population variances are unequal, the following formula for t is used:

$$t = \frac{\bar{X}_1 - \bar{X}_2}{\sqrt{\dfrac{s_1{}^2}{n_1} + \dfrac{s_2{}^2}{n_2}}} \qquad (11.2)$$

Instead of referring the result to the t table, the computed t is compared to a significant value t_o obtained from the formula

$$t_o = \frac{t_1 \dfrac{s_1{}^2}{n_1} + t_2 \dfrac{s_2{}^2}{n_2}}{\dfrac{s_1{}^2}{n_1} + \dfrac{s_2{}^2}{n_2}} \qquad (11.3)$$

where t_1 is the tabled value of t that is significant for $df = n_1 - 1$, and t_2 is the tabled value that is significant for $df = n_2 - 1$. If the result obtained from formula (11.2) is equal to or larger than t_o, then the hypothesis that $\mu_1 = \mu_2$ is rejected.

Substituting the data of Example 1 in formula (11.2), we obtain

$$t = \frac{62 - 54}{\sqrt{\dfrac{196}{15} + \dfrac{64}{30}}} = \frac{8}{\sqrt{13.07 + 2.13}} = 2.05$$

The hypothesis that $\mu_1 = \mu_2$ is to be tested with a .05 significance level. From Table D in the Appendix, we find that $t_1 = 2.14$. This is the t value that is significant at the .05 level (two-tailed test) for 14 df. Locating a similar value for 29 df, we find $t_2 = 2.04$. Substituting these values, with the values for s^2/n that were just computed, into formula (11.3), we obtain

$$t_o = \frac{2.14(13.07) + 2.04(2.13)}{13.07 + 2.13} = 2.13$$

Our t of 2.05 is smaller than t_o, and therefore it is not significant. We are unable to reject the hypothesis that $\mu_1 = \mu_2$.

Although we found that our schizophrenic and normal populations have different variabilities, we are unable to conclude that they have different means. The important distinguishing feature between the two groups seems to be not the average amount of affective arousal, but a tendency toward more "extreme" reactions among the schizophrenics—some obtaining much lower scores, some much higher scores, than the normals.

ANALYSIS OF VARIANCE: HYPOTHESIS THAT

$$\mu_1 = \mu_2 = \mu_3 = \ldots = \mu$$

We take up now an application of the F test that is called the *analysis of variance*. The procedure involves a comparison of two variance estimates as before, *but in analysis of variance the underlying purpose is to test the hypothesis that the means of several populations are all equal.* How this is accomplished is illustrated in the sections that follow.

In general, it is assumed in analysis of variance that the different samples come from normally distributed populations that have the same variance. Since even quite substantial violations of these assumptions apparently have little effect on the probabilities of obtained F values, we will proceed here as though the assumptions have been met in all cases. Should the student encounter extreme violations of the assumptions—data that are extremely non-normal, or sample variances that differ very widely—he should consult a more advanced statistics text for procedures to be used in handling such situations.

Using Means and Variances When n's Are Equal

The procedure given here is convenient for testing the null hypothesis that $\mu_1 = \mu_2 = \mu_3 = \ldots = \mu$ when the means and variances of the several groups have already been computed and the groups are all equal in size.

Example 2. An investigator is interested in the relative effectiveness of verbal and material rewards in the learning of young children. Fifteen children of similar chronological and mental age are randomly divided into three groups of five each. Each child is tested individually in a "guessing game" where success depends upon learning to discriminate among a series of geometrical figures. On each trial, correct discrimination is signaled by a light which flashes on. Group 1 receives, in addition, a penny for every correct discrimination. Group 2 is praised for making correct discriminations. Group 3 serves as a control group and receives no additional reward.

The number of correct discriminations are recorded for each child, and the means and variances of the three groups are computed. The results are:

Penny Reward	Verbal Reward	Control Group
$\overline{X}_1 = 16.0$	$\overline{X}_2 = 11.0$	$\overline{X}_3 = 9.0$
$s_1^2 = 5.6$	$s_2^2 = 8.4$	$s_3^2 = 7.0$
$n_1 = 5$	$n_2 = 5$	$n_3 = 5$

Is there evidence of a significant difference in the mean performance of the three groups?

We wish to test the null hypothesis that $\mu_1 = \mu_2 = \mu_3$, the three parameter means are equal, and thus that the different reward conditions have no effect upon performance. Therefore, the three sets of scores may be thought of as random samples from the same population, as illustrated in (a) of Fig. 11.1. The alternative is that the reward conditions do have differential effects and the three sets of scores are not from the same population. *At least two, and perhaps three, different populations are involved.* Such an alternative is illustrated in (b) of Fig. 11.1, where three distinct populations are shown. (It is not necessary, of course, for all three population means to differ from one another in order to reject the null hypothesis. A difference between any two of the population means is also a contradiction of the null hypothesis even though this alternative is not illustrated.)

Our procedure will be to examine the plausibility of Fig. 11.1(a). Specifically, we will obtain two independent estimates of the variance

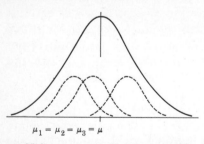

$\mu_1 = \mu_2 = \mu_3 = \mu$

(a) Null hypothesis: The three samples come from the same population

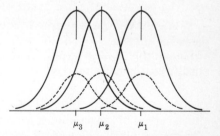

μ_3 μ_2 μ_1

(b) Alternative: The three samples come from different populations

Figure 11.1

Schematic Representation of (a) the Null Hypothesis That Three Samples Come From the Same Population, and (b) an Alternative in Which the Samples Come From Three Different Populations

of this population. If the two estimates are consistent with the idea of a single population—that is, if the estimates are not significantly different—we will accept the null hypothesis. If the two estimates are significantly different, we will reject the idea of a single population of scores and accept the alternative that the samples come from different populations.

• • STEP 1. One way to estimate the variance of our assumed single population is to average the three sample variances that we already have. Thus,

$$s_w^2 = \frac{5.6 + 8.4 + 7.0}{3} = 7.0$$

We have used the symbol s_w^2 to indicate that this is the *within-groups variance estimate*. The within-groups variance estimate is so called because it is based on the variation of subjects *within* each of the groups and does not take into account any differences *between* the groups.

The degrees of freedom for s_w^2 are equal to the sum of the degrees of freedom associated with each of the sample variances. In this case, there are $5 - 1 = 4$ *df* associated with each of the three sample variances, so s_w^2 has 12 *df*.

• • STEP 2. Another, independent way of estimating the variance of our assumed population of scores is to take advantage of the relationship $s_{\bar{x}}^2 = s^2/n$, which is simply the square of the more familiar expression $s_{\bar{x}} = s\sqrt{n}$. In earlier chapters, this relationship was used to estimate the variation of sample means. Now our interest is in s^2, the estimate of the population variance. Solving for s^2, we obtain $s^2 = ns_{\bar{x}}^2$. To obtain $s_{\bar{x}}^2$, we determine the variation of our three sample means about their grand or total mean $\bar{X}_t$. First, the total mean is computed by averaging the three sample means,

$$\bar{X}_t = \frac{16 + 11 + 9}{3} = 12.0$$

The variation of the sample means about $\bar{X}_t$ is determined in the same way that the variance is determined for any set of measures. Thus,

$$s_{\bar{x}}^2 = \frac{(16 - 12)^2 + (11 - 12)^2 + (9 - 12)^2}{3 - 1} = 13.0$$

where one degree of freedom is lost in the denominator because we are using sample values to obtain an *estimate* of the sampling variation of means. $s_{\bar{x}}^2$ is then multiplied by the sample size n to obtain the population variance estimate,

$$s_b^2 = ns_{\bar{x}}^2 = 5(13.0) = 65.0$$

This variance estimate is symbolized s_b^2 and called the **between-means** or **between-groups variance estimate**. As we have just seen, s_b^2 is based entirely on the difference between the means of the groups and does not depend upon any differences among individuals within the groups.

The degrees of freedom for s_b^2 are the same as for $s_{\bar{x}}^2$—namely, the number of sample means minus one. In this case, $df = 3 - 1 = 2$.

• • STEP 3. We now have two independent estimates of the population variance, $s_w^2 = 7.0$ and $s_b^2 = 65.0$. The two estimates are independent because they are derived from different parts of the total information available and these different parts are themselves independent. The difference between group means is not influenced by the magnitude of the differences among individuals within each group, and similarly, the differences among individuals within the groups are unaffected by how far apart the group means are.

Intuitively, our variance estimates of 7.0 and 65.0 seem incompatible. It is hard to imagine that these are estimates of the same population variance. To test this possibility, an F ratio is computed as follows:

$$F = \frac{s_b^2}{s_w^2} = \frac{65.0}{7.0} = 9.29$$

This F test is a one-tailed test. We are only interested in discovering whether s_b^2 is significantly *larger than* s_w^2. It is s_b^2 that is based on the difference between means and provides information as to how large these differences are. Only if s_b^2 is significantly larger than s_w^2 can we reject the hypothesis that $\mu_1 = \mu_2 = \mu_3$. Hence, s_b^2 is always placed in the numerator of the F ratio regardless of its numerical value.

• • STEP 4. The degrees of freedom for F have already been determined. They are 2 for the numerator (s_b^2) and 12 for the denominator (s_w^2). Turning to Table F of the Appendix, we find that for 2 and 12 df, $F = 6.93$ is significant at the .01 level. Since our F of 9.29 is larger than this value, the probability is less than .01 that s_b^2 and s_w^2 are estimates of a common population variance. It is highly improbable that our three samples come from the same population and we reject the null hypothesis that $\mu_1 = \mu_2 = \mu_3$. We conclude that the reward conditions do have a differential effect upon performance.

•• STEP 5. The results of an analysis of variance are usually reported in a summary table as shown below:

SOURCE OF VARIATION	df	VARIANCE ESTIMATE (MEAN SQUARE)	F	P
Reward Conditions	2	65.0	9.29	<.01
Individual Differences (Error)	12	7.0		
Total	14			

The terms in parentheses are frequent synonyms for the terms above them. Thus, the term *mean square* is frequently used in place of variance estimate, and *error* or *error term* is the most frequent and general designation for the denominator of the F ratio in analysis of variance. However, we will retain the term *individual differences* because it is more descriptive of this source of variation in the problems that we will consider.

Formulas that summarize the procedure given above for computing an analysis of variance from means and variances (when n's are equal) are given in Table 11.1.

Table 11.1
Analysis of Variance Formulas Using
Means and Variances

EQUAL n's

$$s_w^2 = \frac{\overset{k}{\Sigma}s^2}{k} \qquad\qquad df = N - k$$

$$s_b^2 = ns_{\bar{x}}^2 = \frac{n\overset{k}{\Sigma}(\overline{X} - \overline{X}_t)^2}{k - 1} \qquad df = k - 1$$

$$F = \frac{s_b^2}{s_w^2}$$

where k is the number of groups, n is the size of one group, and N is the total number of subjects in all groups combined. The symbol $\overset{k}{\Sigma}$ indicates that summation is over *groups*. $\overline{X}_t$ is the grand mean.

• DISCUSSION

Having rejected the hypothesis that our three samples come from the same population, we conclude that the parameter means are not all equal. Pennies, praise, and "no reward" have differential effects on the performance of these children. This is as far as our conclusion takes us. We are not in a position to say that *all three* parameter means are different, nor does our significant F permit statements about particular means—for instance, that the largest mean is significantly greater than the others. We can only assert that the magnitude of differences among the set of means, as measured by s_b^2, is significantly greater than might be expected by chance if such samples were randomly drawn from the same population.

Procedures are available for examining the difference between specific pairs or groups of means after conducting an analysis of variance, but they are beyond the scope of this text.*

Using Raw Data

An analysis of variance may be computed directly from the raw data, without first determining the means and variances of the groups. The procedure given below may be used whether the groups are equal in size or unequal in size.

Example 3. In a survey of women's attitudes towards their role in modern society, an investigator interviews a sample of 23 women chosen randomly from among the recent graduates of a large women's college. As part of the survey, each subject answers a 20-item questionnaire designed to assess how satisfied she is with her own role in society. The number of positive answers given on this questionnaire is taken as the subject's Role Satisfaction score. Of the 23 women interviewed, ten are housewives, seven are unmarried and pursuing a career of some kind, and six are both married and pursuing a career. Their Role Satisfaction scores are:

HOUSEWIVES	UNMARRIED CAREER WOMEN	MARRIED CAREER WOMEN
7	10	8
12	15	13
8	6	14
14	9	9
10	9	10
16	11	16
11	12	
11		
9		
13		

Is there evidence of a relationship between Satisfaction score and the social role of the subject?

* The interested student should see B. J. Winer, *Statistical Principles in Experimental Design*, McGraw-Hill, 1962, pp. 65–92, or A. L. Edwards, *Experimental Design in Psychological Research*, Rev. Ed., Holt, 1960, Chapter 10.

The question asks whether, in this population of women, Satisfaction score varies with social role. If we are able to reject the hypothesis that $\mu_1 = \mu_2 = \mu_3$, the groups have the same mean Satisfaction score, we can then conclude that Satisfaction score does vary with these social roles and there is a relationship between them in this population.

• SUM OF SQUARES

We introduce a term, the *sum of squares*. The term refers to the sum of squared deviations from the mean, as in the expression $\Sigma(X - \overline{X})^2$ or its algebraic equivalent $\Sigma X^2 - \dfrac{(\Sigma X)^2}{n}$. One of these expressions commonly appears in the numerator of variance formulas, and in analysis of variance the term *sum of squares* designates the numerator of a variance estimate. The variance estimate is equal to the appropriate sum of squares (SS) divided by its degrees of freedom. Thus,

$$s_b{}^2 = \frac{SS_b}{k-1} \qquad \textbf{(11.7)}, \qquad \text{and,} \qquad s_w{}^2 = \frac{SS_w}{N-k} \qquad \textbf{(11.8)}$$

From now on, we will distinguish between these two parts of the variance estimate—its numerator, the sum of squares, and its denominator, the degrees of freedom available.

It can be shown that the total sum of squares—that is, the sum of squared deviations of the scores from the grand mean of all groups combined—is equal to the sum of SS_b and SS_w. In other words,

$$\text{Total } SS = SS_b + SS_w$$

We will not attempt to prove this statement here, but we will compute all three sums of squares for our example and show that the relationship holds.

• • STEP 1. For each group, the sum of the scores is obtained, as shown in the first three columns of Table 11.2. This gives ΣX_1, ΣX_2, and ΣX_3. Adding these together gives $\Sigma X = 253$, the sum of all the scores.

• • STEP 2. Each score is squared and the squares are summed for each group, as shown in the last three columns of Table 11.2. This gives $\Sigma X_1{}^2$, $\Sigma X_2{}^2$, and $\Sigma X_3{}^2$. The sum of these is $\Sigma X^2 = 2955$.

• • STEP 3. The total sum of squares is computed. The total sum of squares is given by either $\Sigma(X - \overline{X}_t)^2$ or $\Sigma X^2 - (\Sigma X)^2/N$.

Table 11.2
Analysis of Variance Using Raw Data
(Example 2: Satisfaction scores of women having different social roles.)

X_1	X_2	X_3	X_1^2	X_2^2	X_3^2
7	10	8	49	100	64
12	15	13	144	225	169
8	6	14	64	36	196
14	9	9	196	81	81
10	9	10	100	81	100
16	11	16	256	121	256
11	12		121	144	
11			121		
9			81		
13			169		
SUM: 111	72	70	1301	788	866

$$\Sigma X = 111 + 72 + 70 = 253 \qquad \Sigma X^2 = 1301 + 788 + 866 = 2955$$

$$\text{TOTAL } SS: \quad \Sigma X^2 - \frac{(\Sigma X)^2}{N} = 2955 - \frac{(253)^2}{23} = 172.00$$

$$df = N - 1 = 23 - 1 = 22$$

BETWEEN-GROUPS VARIANCE ESTIMATE

$$SS_b = \frac{(\Sigma X_1)^2}{n_1} + \frac{(\Sigma X_2)^2}{n_2} + \frac{(\Sigma X_3)^2}{n_3} - \frac{(\Sigma X)^2}{N}$$

$$= \frac{(111)^2}{10} + \frac{(72)^2}{7} + \frac{(70)^2}{6} - \frac{(253)^2}{23} = 6.34$$

$$s_b^2 = \frac{6.34}{2} = 3.17 \qquad df = k - 1 = 3 - 1 = 2$$

WITHIN-GROUPS VARIANCE ESTIMATE

$$SS_w = \text{Total } SS - SS_b = 172.00 - 6.34 = 165.66$$

$$s_w^2 = \frac{165.66}{20} = 8.28 \qquad df = N - k = 23 - 3 = 20$$

$$F = \frac{s_b^2}{s_w^2} = \frac{3.17}{8.28} = .38$$

Since the second expression is easier to compute, and we already have the necessary sums from Steps 1 and 2, it is used in Table 11.2 to obtain Total SS. Observe that $N = n_1 + n_2 + n_3$, the number of scores in all groups combined.

• • STEP 4. The between-groups sum of squares, SS_b, is computed by the formula given in Table 11.2. This formula is equivalent to the numerator of formula (11.5) for s_b^2, although here raw scores are used and allowance has been made for unequal group sizes. For each group, the sum of scores is squared, and the square is then divided by the number of scores in that group. The last term, $\frac{(\Sigma X)^2}{N}$, appears in the formula for Total SS and its value can be simply carried down from that computation. The value of SS_b is then divided by its degrees of freedom to obtain s_b^2.

• • STEP 5. The within-groups sum of squares, SS_w, may be obtained in either of two ways. Taking advantage of the relationship Total $SS = SS_b + SS_w$, it is a simple matter to obtain SS_w by subtraction, as has been done in Table 11.2. SS_w can also be computed from the data. It is obtained by adding together the sum of squares for each group:

$$SS_w = \left(\Sigma X_1{}^2 - \frac{(\Sigma X_1)^2}{n_1}\right) + \left(\Sigma X_2{}^2 - \frac{(\Sigma X_2)^2}{n_2}\right) + \left(\Sigma X_3{}^2 - \frac{(\Sigma X_3)^2}{n_3}\right)$$

$$= \left(1301 - \frac{(111)^2}{10}\right) + \left(788 - \frac{(72)^2}{7}\right) + \left(866 - \frac{(70)^2}{6}\right)$$

$$= 68.90 + 47.43 + 49.33$$

$$= 165.66$$

This value agrees with the value obtained by subtraction, as of course it should if all computations have been carried out correctly.

The value of SS_w is then divided by its degrees of freedom to obtain s_w^2.

• • STEP 6. An F ratio is computed, dividing s_b^2 by s_w^2 as before. F is .38 with (2,20) df, a nonsignificant value. (From Table F in the Appendix, F must equal or exceed 3.49 in order to be significant at the .05 level.) We are therefore unable to reject the hypothesis that $\mu_1 = \mu_2 = \mu_3$. There is no basis for concluding that Role Satisfaction score varies with social role in this population of women.

• • STEP 7. The analysis of variance is summarized in a table as shown below:

SOURCE OF VARIATION	SUM OF SQUARES	df	VARIANCE ESTIMATE	F	P
Social role	6.34	2	3.17	.38	>.05
Individual differences	165.66	20	8.28		
Total	172.00	22			

It is not necessary to include a sum-of-squares column when formally reporting the results of an analysis of variance. The column has been included here to emphasize the point that the between-groups and within-groups sums of squares are *components* of the total sum of squares. Their sum is equal to the total sum of squares, and the sum of their degrees of freedom is equal to the total *df*.

• DISCUSSION

Since we were unable to reject the hypothesis that $\mu_1 = \mu_2 = \mu_3$, we have no evidence of a relationship between social role and Role Satisfaction score in this population. Apparently, there are varying degrees of satisfaction within each social group, but little if any difference between the groups. The samples were small and the investigator may want to study more subjects before accepting this conclusion. But as the matter stands now, there is no reason to abandon the null hypothesis.

The computational procedure used here makes clearer than our initial procedure the mathematical basis of analysis of variance—namely, the breaking down of the total variance into separate components, each of which provides an independent estimate of the population variance. We began with the total sum of squares and found its two parts, SS_b and SS_w. That the total sum of squares should so conveniently consist of these two parts probably seems to the student, at this point, more in the nature of a fortunate coincidence than a mathematical necessity. But consider for a moment what the total variance is. If all the groups are combined into one large group with mean $\overline{X}_t$, the variance of this large group will, of course, be based on the deviation of each score from $\overline{X}_t$. This deviation is the basis for the total sum of squares and the total variance. It can readily be shown that the deviation $(X - \overline{X}_t)$ is the sum of two deviations—the distance of the score from its group mean, and the distance of the group mean from $\overline{X}_t$. For example, suppose we take a score X_1 from a group with mean $\overline{X}_1$. Our claim is that the deviation $(X_1 - \overline{X}_t) = (X_1 - \overline{X}_1) + (\overline{X}_1 - \overline{X}_t)$. The statement is easily proved. Removing parentheses, we have

$$X_1 - \overline{X}_t = X_1 - \overline{X}_1 + \overline{X}_1 - \overline{X}_t$$
$$= X_1 - \overline{X}_t$$

It is easy to see that such a statement could be proved regarding any score from any one of the groups. It requires only further algebra, and some additional notation, to develop from this basic relationship the statement that Total $SS = SS_w + SS_b$.

Although we have considered examples involving only three groups, the analysis of variance can be applied to any number of groups. Examples involving four, five, and six groups are given in the practice problems that follow.

Practice Problems

Use an alpha of .05 to test the appropriate hypotheses in the following situations.

1. Company I employs 12 men whose job it is to assemble the electronic device sold by the company. The men are paid on a piecework basis and work in separate cubicles, having little contact with each other on the job. Under these conditions, the average output of the 12 men in a typical week is 59.0 items with $s^2 = 124.4$. To stimulate competition among the men, the company decides to move them into one large room where they will work at open benches in full view of one another. Several months later, it is found that the average output of the 12 men is again 59.0 items per week, but now $s^2 = 28.0$. Has there been a significant change in the group's performance?

2. In studying the effect of heredity on animal intelligence, an investigator has obtained through selective breeding a strain of rats whose maze performance is superior to that of rats with uncontrolled heredity. To determine whether his animals are also superior at other types of tasks, the investigator sets up a discrimination problem in which the rat must learn to press a bar only when a light is turned on, refraining from bar-pressing when the light is off. He tests a random sample of 11 rats from the inbred strain and records the time required by each animal to learn the discrimination to a given criterion. Their mean learning time is 84.7 minutes with $s^2 = 81.4$. For a random sample of 25 animals with uncontrolled heredity, the mean learning time is 95.2 minutes with $s^2 = 375.0$. Using an alpha of .05, test the hypothesis that the two groups of animals come from identical populations with regard to performance on this task.

3. Twenty trainees in Clinical Psychology are randomly divided into two groups of ten each. Both groups are told that they will observe a play therapy session through a one-way vision window, and that they are to watch especially for signs of anxiety in the child's behavior. Group 1 is told further that this is a disturbed child referred for treatment, while Group 2 is told they will observe a normal child, "to see how normal children respond to the play therapy situation." Both groups then observe the same play therapy session. Afterwards, each subject is asked to list the "signs of

anxiety" he observed in the child's behavior. The experimenter counts the number of "signs" listed by each subject. The results for the 20 subjects are:

Group 1 "Disturbed Child"	Group 2 "Normal Child"
5	6
7	2
11	4
3	5
7	5
12	4
7	3
6	4
9	4
3	3

Does the different information given have an effect on how many "signs of anxiety" are reported? Compute $\bar{X}$ and s^2 for each group and test for significant differences in the performance of the two groups.

4. The reaction time of a subject is measured to three different stimuli: light, sound, and touch. There are 60 trials, in which the stimuli are each presented 20 times in a random order. The results (reaction time in hundredths of a second) for the three stimuli are:

Light	Sound	Touch
$\bar{X} = 21$	$\bar{X} = 18$	$\bar{X} = 18$
$s^2 = 18$	$s^2 = 12$	$s^2 = 15$
$n = 20$	$n = 20$	$n = 20$

Should it be concluded that this subject's reaction time differs to these different stimuli? Test the hypothesis that $\mu_1 = \mu_2 = \mu_3$.

5. In a study of leadership, 24 boys at a summer camp are randomly divided into three groups of eight each. Each group is to build a "clubhouse" with materials provided by the camp. Group 1 is told they are to elect one of themselves as the group leader. For Group 2 the camp supervisor appoints one of the boys as the group leader. Group 3 works without a formal leader. After completing the clubhouses, the boys are queried individually about their experience in the group. For each boy, the investigator records the number of favorable answers given to a list of specific questions about his perception of other group members and the way they worked together. The number of favorable answers per boy is then averaged for each of the groups. The results are summarized below:

Group 1 Elected Leader	Group 2 Appointed Leader	Group 3 No Formal Leader
$\bar{X} = 19$	$\bar{X} = 18$	$\bar{X} = 14$
$s^2 = 9$	$s^2 = 16$	$s^2 = 11$
$n = 8$	$n = 8$	$n = 8$

Is there a relationship between type of leadership experience and the number of favorable answers given?

6. An experimenter is interested in the effect of sleep deprivation on mental alertness. Twenty subjects are randomly divided into four groups of five each. All subjects are given a task requiring a high level of mental alertness, but after differing amounts of sleep deprivation. Group 1 is deprived of sleep for 16 hours, Group 2 for 20 hours, Group 3 for 24 hours, and Group 4 for 28 hours. Scores on the task are averaged for each group. The results are:

GROUP 1 (16 HOURS)	GROUP 2 (20 HOURS)	GROUP 3 (24 HOURS)	GROUP 4 (28 HOURS)
$\bar{X} = 30$	$\bar{X} = 22$	$\bar{X} = 25$	$\bar{X} = 15$
$s^2 = 24$	$s^2 = 18$	$s^2 = 30$	$s^2 = 24$
$n = 5$	$n = 5$	$n = 5$	$n = 5$

Can it be concluded that amount of sleep deprivation influences mental alertness as measured by this task?

7. An investigator is interested in tracing the development of the slang vocabulary of teen-agers. To determine whether there is a distinct age level when this vocabulary appears, he selects a random sample of ten school children at each age level from nine through fourteen years. On the basis of a preliminary study of teen-agers, the investigator has compiled a list of slang words known to at least 80% of the teen-agers. These words have been made up into a vocabulary test which the investigator now gives to all the children. The mean score is computed for each age group, with results as shown below:

9 YEARS	10 YEARS	11 YEARS	12 YEARS	13 YEARS	14 YEARS
$\bar{X} = 12$	$\bar{X} = 11$	$\bar{X} = 12$	$\bar{X} = 18$	$\bar{X} = 25$	$\bar{X} = 24$
$s^2 = 10$	$s^2 = 9$	$s^2 = 16$	$s^2 = 20$	$s^2 = 17$	$s^2 = 12$
$n = 10$	$n = 10$	$n = 10$	$n = 10$	$n = 10$	$n = 10$

Is there a significant difference among the mean scores of the different age groups?

8. An investigator suspects that two tranquilizing drugs used in the treatment of mental patients have negative side effects on their intellectual functioning. He conducts an experiment in which 21 mental patients who would ordinarily receive such drugs are randomly divided into three groups of seven patients each. Group 1 receives Drug A, Group 2 receives Drug B, and Group 3 serves as a Control group receiving placebos. At the end of a two-week period during which the patients receive no other treatment, they are all given a series of tests. One of these tests requires the subject to learn a simple stylus maze, where the number of trials needed to learn the maze is taken as an index of intellectual functioning. The results are:

GROUP 1 DRUG A	GROUP 2 DRUG B	GROUP 3 CONTROL
5	5	6
5	8	4
2	4	7
4	8	2
3	10	2
7	7	4
2	7	3

Is there evidence that the two tranquilizer drugs have a negative effect on intellectual functioning? (a) Compute the analysis of variance using the means and variances of each group. (b) Compute the analysis of variance using the sums of squares.

9. In a Word Fluency test, the subject is asked to give as many words as he can that begin with a certain letter. The test is timed and the subject's score is the number of words he is able to give in the time allowed. To determine whether the manner of administering the test has an effect upon test scores, a group of 34 students are randomly divided into two groups of ten subjects each and one group of 14 subjects. The group of 14 subjects takes the test as a group, in a room together, writing their answers. Subjects of the other two groups are given the test individually, subjects of one group writing the words, subjects of the other group speaking them aloud. Their Word Fluency scores are:

INDIVIDUAL- ORAL	INDIVIDUAL- WRITTEN	GROUP- WRITTEN
25	29	34
34	35	48
50	21	22
34	56	52
42	41	36
32	58	37
39	26	38
48	31	46
24	35	29
35	38	48
		30
		39
		26
		40

Is there evidence that the mode of test administration influences scores on this test? (*Note:* Subtracting a constant from each score has no effect on the sums of squares, and will give smaller numbers to work with.)

10. A random sample of 40 voters from a township are given an attitude test that measures political liberalism-conservatism. The subjects are also classified according to their income into one of four income groups: low, low-average, high-average, and high. The scores

of subjects in the four groups are then compared. Their test scores are:

Low	Low-Average	High-Average	High
40	31	47	36
48	32	51	51
37	39	54	35
52	36	44	38
45	40	40	42
45	45	48	37
55	33	46	46
50	35	53	
39	35	39	
43	44	45	
	41	37	
	40		

Is there evidence of a relationship between income group and liberalism-conservatism score? (High scores indicate high liberalism.)

11. In a study of group influence on memory, 40 subjects listen to a 20-minute recorded speech. Afterwards, the subjects are divided randomly into five groups of eight subjects each and sent to five separate rooms. There they are asked to recall the number of times the speaker said "uh" in the course of the speech they heard. Without previous intention to remember, the task is quite impossible, but the subjects of each group are urged to "help one another" and do the best they can. A group member records the number finally decided upon by each member of his group. The number of "uh's" that are "remembered" by the subjects are:

Group 1	Group 2	Group 3	Group 4	Group 5
5	10	7	15	5
8	8	9	20	13
3	15	10	10	8
6	12	12	12	10
7	12	16	18	7
5	10	5	25	6
10	6	10	20	15
7	11	13	17	9

Is there a significant difference among the means of the five groups?

Answers

1. There is no change in mean output, but the variability of the group appears to have shrunk. $F = 4.44$ with $(11,11)$ df, a value that almost reaches the .02 level of significance ($F = 4.46$). Our F

has a probability just slightly larger than .02 and certainly less than .05. We reject the hypothesis that $\sigma_1^2 = \sigma_2^2$. Variability is less in the new situation. Working together in one room does not seem to breed competition; the men become more alike in output than they were before in separate cubicles.

2. $F = 4.61$ with $(24,10)$ df, $P < .02$. The hypothesis $\sigma_1^2 = \sigma_2^2$ is rejected. The inbred strain of rats, as might be expected, is less variable in performance than the rats with uncontrolled heredity. Comparing the means by formula (11.2), we obtain $t = 2.22$. Formula (11.3) gives $t_o = 2.12$ as the value of t that is significant at the .05 level for a two-tailed test. Since our t is larger than this value, $P < .05$ and the hypothesis that $\mu_1 = \mu_2$ is also rejected. We conclude that the two groups of animals come from populations having both different variances and different means with regard to performance on this task. The inbred strain has a lower variability and a higher mean.

3. $F = 9.11/1.33 = 6.85$, $P < .02$. The hypothesis $\sigma_1^2 = \sigma_2^2$ is rejected. $t = 2.93$, which is larger than $t_o = 2.26$, the t value significant at the .05 level for a two-tailed test, so the hypothesis $\mu_1 = \mu_2$ is also rejected. The trainees who believed they were observing a disturbed child tended, as a group, to report more signs of anxiety than did trainees who believed they were observing a normal child. The difference in means is significant, indicating different population means for these two conditions of observation. The significant difference in variability under the two conditions suggests relatively large individual differences in the reports of trainees observing a "disturbed" child, as compared with the relatively small differences among trainees when the child is believed to be normal.

4. $F = 60/15 = 4.0$ with $(2,57)$ df. The F table gives 3.17 as significant at the .05 level for $(2,55)$ df, the nearest df to ours. Since our F is larger than 3.17, $P < .05$. The hypothesis $\mu_1 = \mu_2 = \mu_3$ is rejected. We conclude that the subject's reaction time is different to these different stimuli. Because the mean reaction time to the sound and touch stimuli is the same in this sample of the subject's behavior (.18 seconds), our significant F value must arise from the subject's reaction time to the light stimulus (.21 seconds) since this is the only mean that differs. In this case, then, we are able to draw the further conclusion that (for the given situation) this subject's reaction time to light is significantly different from his reaction time to sound and touch.

5. $F = 56/12 = 4.67$ with $(2,21)$ df. Since our F is larger than the tabled value 3.47, $P < .05$. We reject the hypothesis that $\mu_1 = \mu_2 = \mu_3$ and conclude that there is a relationship between type

of leadership and group members' evaluations of how well the group worked together. Note, however, that the interpretation of this conclusion depends upon nonstatistical factors. To be confident that the different evaluations given by the groups resulted from their different leadership experience, we should want to know that the conditions were the same for all groups except for those factors arising directly from type of leadership. For example, were the groups about equal in skill? Was there competition between the groups? (The group who finished last may perceive their group in a less favorable light for this reason.) On what basis was the appointed leader chosen? (Appointing an unpopular boy could result in an essentially leaderless situation.) Did an informal leader emerge in the group that had no appointed or elected leader? In short, we should want to be satisfied that the observed relationship is not a product of conditions that were not or could not be controlled.

6. $F = 196.67/24.0 = 8.19$ with $(3,16)$ df. This F is larger than the tabled value of 5.29, which is significant at the .01 level, so $P < .01$. The hypothesis that $\mu_1 = \mu_2 = \mu_3 = \mu_4$ is rejected. We conclude that amount of sleep deprivation does affect performance of this task, or that there is a relationship between amount of sleep deprivation and mental alertness as measured by this task.

7. $F = 400.0/14.0 = 28.57$ with $(5,54)$ df. For $(5,55)$ df, the nearest df to ours in the F table, the value 3.37 is significant at the .01 level. Since our F is larger than this value, $P < .01$. The hypothesis $\mu_1 = \mu_2 = \ldots = \mu_6$ is rejected. There is a significant difference among the age groups in their knowledge of this slang vocabulary. An inspection of the means suggests little if any difference between 9 and 11 years, with sizeable increases in score occurring at 12 and 13 years. Further statistical tests are needed ·to confirm these as significant differences. The investigator will also need to show that the differences he obtained in slang vocabulary scores are not a product of general vocabulary level—since it is well known that general vocabulary also increases over these ages. If the investigator has also a measure of general vocabulary for each subject, he can control for this factor by applying a procedure called *analysis of covariance*, which the interested student will find described in more advanced texts.

8. For both (a) and (b), $F = 21.0/3.67 = 5.72$ with $(2,18)$ df, and $P < .05$. The hypothesis $\mu_1 = \mu_2 = \mu_3$ is rejected. From this, we can conclude only that there is a significant difference in the mean performance of the three groups. Since it happens that the mean of subjects receiving Drug A is exactly the same as the mean of the Control group, we are able to conclude at once that there is no significant difference in performance under these two conditions.

Our significant F must arise from a difference in the performance of subjects receiving Drug B, who have a higher mean and therefore required more trials to learn the maze. Thus, there is evidence that Drug B has a negative effect on intellectual functioning, but there is no such evidence for Drug A.

9. $F = 4.20/96.95 = .04$ with $(2,31)$ df, and is a nonsignificant F value. We are unable to reject the hypothesis of equal parameter means. There is no evidence that these modes of test administration have an effect upon Word Fluency scores.

10. $F = 172.24/29.68 = 5.80$ with $(3,36)$ df, and $P < .01$. The hypothesis of equal population means is rejected; liberalism-conservatism score does vary with income group in this township. Inspection of the means reveals that the Low-Average and High income groups have lower mean scores than do the Low and High-Average income groups. Further tests would almost certainly be carried out to determine whether these differences are significant.

11. $F = 125.41/11.75 = 10.67$ with $(4,35)$ df, and $P < .01$. The hypothesis of equal parameter means is rejected; there is a significant difference among the means. Since the conditions of the experiment were outwardly the same for all groups, and randomization argues against inherent group differences, to what can we attribute the significant difference among means? The only variable condition was the social interaction of the separate groups. With no accurate remembrances possible of the number of "uh's" in the recorded speech, this group interaction apparently created in some way a "norm" around which individual estimates then clustered. Since there was no interaction between groups, the "norms" of the groups tended to differ more than did the individuals within any one group. We would conclude that where accurate recall is not possible, there is a strong group influence on what is "remembered."

chapter 12

**Which
Statistic
to Use:
A Summary**

Choosing the appropriate statistical procedure for analyzing a set of data is often a puzzling matter to the student. In this book, as in most statistics texts, examples of research data are presented together with procedures for their analysis. The student's own research efforts are not accompanied by instructions telling him what to do with the data, and it is here that he often stumbles. In this chapter we review and summarize, as general guidelines, the main considerations that enter into choosing a statistical procedure.

The class of statistics appropriate for a particular study depends upon the answers given to the following questions:

(1) *What kind of data are the statistical procedures to be applied to?* In any study, the group of statistics available for use depends in large part upon the answer to this question. When the data are scores or measures, it is possible to use many statistical techniques that are not applicable when observations can only be ranked or classified into categories. A different group of statistics is appropriate for categories, and still another for ranks. Definitions and examples of these three types of data—measures, ranks, and the data of categories— are given in Chapter 1.

(2) *Do the data represent, for the investigator's purpose, a sample or a population?* The answer to this question determines whether or not the procedures of statistical inference will be used. If, for the investigator's purpose, the data constitute a population in the sense that no statistical inferences are to be made to any larger group, only descriptive statistics are needed to present the results of the study. If the data are a random sample and the investigator's purpose is to generalize his findings to the population from which the sample came, then he will need to use inferential statistics as well

as descriptive statistics. Some examples of samples and populations are given on pp. 67–69.

(3) *Supposing the purpose is statistical inference: Has a prediction been made about the outcome of the study?* The answer to this question determines whether the procedures of parameter estimation or of hypothesis testing will be used. If a prediction has been made about the outcome of the study, it is usually possible to formulate and test a null hypothesis. Some examples of null hypotheses are given in Table 8.1, p. 185. If the purpose is not to test a hypothesis but simply to estimate from sample data the value of a population parameter, then the investigator will very likely compute confidence limits for the parameter of interest.

Sometimes, both hypothesis testing and parameter estimation are used in a study. When a null hypothesis has been rejected, the investigator may then be interested in a confidence interval. For example, if the null hypothesis $\mu = 100$ is rejected, the investigator will very likely wish to know a band of values likely to include μ. He may then use his sample data to compute a confidence interval for μ.

In the remainder of this chapter are reviewed the groups of statistics appropriate for different kinds of data. For the most part, the review will be confined to statistics presented in this text. Many additional statistical techniques are available—particularly in the areas of correlation and analysis of variance—and the student should consult a more advanced text if the techniques given here do not seem to "fit" his particular research problem.

CATEGORIES

We have considered many kinds of research problems that involve data classified into categories. The observations are usually words—"agree" or "disagree," "good" or "average" or "poor," "above the median" or "below the median" —and each observation is classified into one of a set of mutually exclusive categories. The only possible summary of such data is to give the frequency, or the proportion, of observations in each category. Descriptive statistics take the form of a table of frequencies or of proportions, and when the results are to be depicted graphically a bar chart is made. These procedures are given in Chapter 1, pp. 4–10.

When the data are a sample, inferences may be made about the population proportion or proportions.

Estimating a Population Proportion

Often the investigator has no hypothesis about the population proportion. His purpose is exploratory; he wants to use his sample to obtain an estimate of the population proportion P. In general, a sample proportion p is an estimate of the corresponding population proportion P. Thus, the inductive probability estimates of Chapter 7 (see p. 154 ff.) are sample estimates of P. When the sample size is large, such that np and nq are both greater than 10, a confidence interval for P may be obtained by the procedure given in Chapter 5, pp. 118–120.

Hypotheses About Population Proportions

Where a prediction has been made about the outcome of the study, it is possible to formulate and test a null hypothesis about the population proportion(s). The particular test that will be appropriate depends upon the number of categories used in classifying the data, and upon the sample size.

• Two Categories

The usual hypothesis here is $P = Q$, although sometimes other values are hypothesized—*e.g.*, $P = .75$. The tests given in Chapter 7 are appropriate for such hypotheses. We summarize: Where the sample size is large enough so that both nP and nQ are greater than 5 (note that P and Q here are the *hypothesized* parameters, not the sample proportions used in obtaining a confidence interval for P), the z test given on p. 169 may be used to test a hypothesis about the value of P. Where the sample size is small and the above condition is not satisfied, the binomial expansion should be used to determine the probability of obtaining a given sample result under the hypothesis (see pp. 163–168.)

• More Than Two Categories

Under this heading are included classification systems where the several categories represent a *single* variable (*e.g.*, type of TV program preferred), and classification systems involving *two* variables (*e.g.*, type of preferred program and sex of the subject). In both cases, the chi-square test may be used to test the appropriate null hypothesis, provided the assumptions of the chi-square test are met (see p. 201).

In the case of a single variable, the usual hypothesis is that the population proportions falling into each of the categories are equal. An example of this kind is given on p. 201ff. For bivariate data, the hypothesis may be stated in any one of several ways, all equivalent to the statement that there is no relationship between the two variables. Examples are given on p. 209ff.

MEASURES

When the data are quantitative in the sense that each observation is a score or measure of some kind, many forms of analysis are possible. Depending largely upon the purpose of the study, the descriptive statistics used may be few and spare or very elaborate indeed. Where the purpose is primarily statistical inference, it is usually unnecessary to present detailed information about the sample, and descriptive statistics tend to be few. When the data constitute a population, a fuller description is usually desirable.

Descriptive Statistics for Measures

The statistics most widely used in describing a distribution of measures are listed below, along with the page where each is defined.

STATISTIC	PAGE WHERE DEFINED
TO DESCRIBE CENTRAL TENDENCY:	
MEAN	82
MEDIAN	45
MODE	19
TO DESCRIBE VARIABILITY:	
STANDARD DEVIATION	82
RANGE	16
INTERQUARTILE RANGE	59
TO DESCRIBE RELATIONSHIP BETWEEN TWO VARIABLES:	
CORRELATION COEFFICIENT	129

Measures of central tendency and variability provide a summary of the obtained distribution. There is seldom a need to present all of the measures given above. Where the distribution is fairly symmetrical and has only one distinct mode, it is often sufficient to report only the mean and standard deviation of the distribution. If the distribution is skewed, the median should also be given, and possibly the range. The student may find it helpful to review pp. 94–97.

The correlation coefficient serves the special purpose of summarizing the linear relationship between two sets of measures obtained from the same subjects. It is usually desirable in such studies to report also the mean and standard deviation of each of the two distributions.

When it is important to convey in detail the shape of an obtained distribution, graphical representation is the most straightforward procedure. The most useful graphs for this purpose are the histogram (pp. 18, 23) and the frequency polygon (pp. 18, 27). Even when one of these graphs will not be included among the results that are formally reported, the investigator should at least construct a frequency distribution of the data for his own information. As we have seen, a knowledge of how the observations are distributed is important in deciding which descriptive statistics should be presented. And when the data are a sample, knowing their distribution is important in judging whether or not it is reasonable to assume that the parent population meets the requirements of contemplated statistical tests.

Estimating a Population Mean

Where the investigator has no hypothesis about the population mean and wishes to estimate its value, he may use his sample to obtain a confidence interval for the mean of the population. When the sample size is 30 or more, the procedure given in Chapter 5 (pp. 114–117) may be safely used to compute such a confidence interval. When the sample size is smaller than 30, a confidence interval for the population mean may be obtained by the procedure given in Chapter 10 (pp. 226–228), provided the distribution of the sample data is not incompatible with the assumption of a normally distributed population. In practice, moderate population deviations from normality are not a matter for great concern. But where sample data suggest a marked deviation from normality in the population—as, for example, that the population is bimodal, or is extremely skewed—confidence intervals based upon small samples may be seriously in error.

A random sample of scores or measures may be used to determine confidence intervals for other population values: for example, for the median, the variance or standard deviation, the population correlation. We have not taken up these procedures, but the interested student will find them in more comprehensive statistics texts.

Hypotheses About
Population Means

When the data are measures, prediction most often takes the form of a null hypothesis about the mean of the population, or about the difference between population means. Depending upon the number of sample means that are to be compared, and whether or not they are correlated, hypotheses and tests take somewhat different forms:

NUMBER OF SAMPLE MEANS	HYPOTHESIS	TEST
ONE	That μ is a certain value	t test, p. 228
TWO, INDEPENDENT	$\mu_1 = \mu_2$	t test, p. 230
TWO, CORRELATED	$\mu_D = 0$	t test, p. 233
MORE THAN TWO, INDEPENDENT	$\mu_1 = \mu_2 = \mu_3 = \cdots = \mu$	Analysis of variance, p. 251 ff.

All of these tests assume that the population is normally distributed, and where more than one population is concerned, the additional assumption is made that the population variances are equal. For a discussion of these assumptions, see pp. 230 and 251.

When the hypothesis of equal population variances has been tested and rejected (see Example 1, Chapter 11), the t test given on p. 249 should be used to compare two independent sample means.

Other Significance Tests
for Measures

Although interest usually centers upon the mean when data are in the form of scores or measures, significance tests have been developed for a number of other statistics as well. Among the more important of these tests, we have considered the following:

Test that a population correlation is zero, p. 237
Test that two population variances are equal, p. 248
Test that two population medians are equal, p. 209

The last-named test, that two population medians are equal, is not restricted to use with measures since the test requires only classification above and below the median of a group. For this purpose, the median of a set of ranks will serve as well as the median of a set of scores.

Ranks

Ranks are the least common of the three types of data we have considered. In Chapter 1, Examples 3 and 4, the procedure of ranking was illustrated, and there and in Chapter 2 some of the properties of ranks were discussed. We have already pointed out that the test that two population medians are equal (p. 209) may be applied when two groups have been ranked on a variable. Also, the correlation formulas of Chapter 6 may be applied to ranks—when, for example, individuals have been ranked on each of two variables and a measure of the relationship between the two sets of ranks is desired. However, there are simpler ways of determining the correlation between sets of ranks. These procedures, and a number of statistical tests developed especially for use with ranks, are available in more advanced statistics texts.* We will confine ourselves here to indicating the circumstances when the student should seek these tests—that is, circumstances that call for the use of ranks and for statistical tests comparing sets of ranks.

Ordinarily, ranks are not used if measurement is possible. Situations do arise where quantitative measurement of a variable is not possible (see Example 3, Chapter 1). Then, of course, ranks must be used because measures are not available. But probably the main use of ranks in psychological research is as *a replacement for measures that fail in some way to meet the investigator's requirements*. Either the measures are unreliable (but the ranks are not), or, more often, the distribution of measures is incompatible with the assumption of a normally distributed population. Virtually all of the statistical

* Many statistics texts include chapters on *nonparametric* or *distribution-free* statistics, where tests for ranks may be found. A more complete compilation of such tests for behavioral science researchers is in S. Siegel, *Nonparametric Statistics for the Behavioral Sciences*, McGraw-Hill, 1956. All of the tests for ranks listed in Table 12.1 can be found there.

Table 12.1
Descriptive and Inferential Statistics Appropriate for Different Kinds of Data

	Category Data	Scores or Measures	Ranks
Descriptive Statistics			
Tables	Table of frequencies, proportions or percentages	Table of frequencies, proportions or percentages Table of centiles or centile ranks	Table of ranks
Graphs	Bar chart	Histogram; frequency polygon	
Summary Statistics	Modal category	Mean, median, mode Standard deviation, range, inter-quartile range Correlation coefficient	Median *Rank correlation coefficient
Inferential Statistics			
Parameter Estimation	Confidence interval for P	Confidence interval for μ	
Significance Tests	Two categories: Binomial test for small samples z test for large samples More than two categories: Chi-square test	Single sample mean: t test that μ is a certain value Two independent sample means: t test for independent samples Two correlated sample means: t test for correlated samples More than two sample means: Analysis of variance	Two independent samples: *Median test *Mann-Whitney U test Two correlated samples: *Wilcoxon Signed-ranks test More than two samples: *Kruskal-Wallis H test

* See footnote on p. 277.

tests developed for measures assume that the parent population of measures is normally distributed. When this assumption is untenable, the investigator may either transform his measures so that the assumption is met (applicable only in special cases), or, what is more usual, he may substitute ranks for the measures of his sample and conduct a statistical test appropriate for ranks.

Statistical tests for ranks make no assumptions about the population distribution. Hence, when an investigator wishes to avoid the assumption of a normally distributed population, he can convert his measures to ranks and use a test for ranks in place of the usual t test or analysis of variance technique. The names of some of these tests for ranks are given in Table 12.1, opposite the t test and analysis of variance techniques for which they are appropriate substitutes. For example, if the usual t test for comparing two independent samples should be inappropriate because the population is known to be extremely skewed, the samples may be compared by replacing the measures with ranks and conducting a Mann-Whitney U test. Or, the measures may be divided at the median into high and low groups, and a median test using chi square may be conducted on the resulting fourfold table.

Generally, tests for ranks should be resorted to only when the more usual tests for measures are clearly inappropriate. When this is the case, a test for ranks serves as an extremely useful alternative. But where tests for measures are appropriate, nothing is gained by substituting a test for ranks and much may be lost. Tests for ranks are generally less sensitive than tests for measures in such situations. The great value of the tests for ranks is that they enable us to proceed with relevant comparisons precisely in those situations where tests for measures cannot be appropriately conducted.

Appendix

Table A

TABLE OF SQUARES AND SQUARE ROOTS
OF NUMBERS FROM 1 TO 1000

Number	Square	Square Root	Number	Square	Square Root
1	1	1.000	51	26 01	7.141
2	4	1.414	52	27 04	7.211
3	9	1.732	53	28 09	7.280
4	16	2.000	54	29 16	7.348
5	25	2.236	55	30 25	7.416
6	36	2.449	56	31 36	7.483
7	49	2.646	57	32 49	7.550
8	64	2.828	58	33 64	7.616
9	81	3.000	59	34 81	7.681
10	1 00	3.162	60	36 00	7.746
11	1 21	3.317	61	37 21	7.810
12	1 44	3.464	62	38 44	7.874
13	1 69	3.606	63	39 69	7.937
14	1 96	3.742	64	40 96	8.000
15	2 25	3.873	65	42 25	8.062
16	2 56	4.000	66	43 56	8.124
17	2 89	4.123	67	44 89	8.185
18	3 24	4.243	68	46 24	8.246
19	3 61	4.359	69	47 61	8.307
20	4 00	4.472	70	49 00	8.367
21	4 41	4.583	71	50 41	8.426
22	4 84	4.690	72	51 84	8.485
23	5 29	4.796	73	53 29	8.544
24	5 76	4.899	74	54 76	8.602
25	6 25	5.000	75	56 25	8.660
26	6 76	5.099	76	57 76	8.718
27	7 29	5.196	77	59 29	8.775
28	7 84	5.292	78	60 84	8.832
29	8 41	5.385	79	62 41	8.888
30	9 00	5.477	80	64 00	8.944
31	9 61	5.568	81	65 61	9.000
32	10 24	5.657	82	67 24	9.055
33	10 89	5.745	83	68 89	9.110
34	11 56	5.831	84	70 56	9.165
35	12 25	5.916	85	72 25	9.220
36	12 96	6.000	86	73 96	9.274
37	13 69	6.083	87	75 69	9.327
38	14 44	6.164	88	77 44	9.381
39	15 21	6.245	89	79 21	9.434
40	16 00	6.325	90	81 00	9.487
41	16 81	6.403	91	82 81	9.539
42	17 64	6.481	92	84 64	9.592
43	18 49	6.557	93	86 49	9.644
44	19 36	6.633	94	88 36	9.695
45	20 25	6.708	95	90 25	9.747
46	21 16	6.782	96	92 16	9.798
47	22 09	6.856	97	94 09	9.849
48	23 04	6.928	98	96 04	9.899
49	24 01	7.000	99	98 01	9.950
50	25 00	7.071	100	1 00 00	10.000

TABLE OF SQUARES AND SQUARE ROOTS (*Cont.*)

Number	Square	Square Root	Number	Square	Square Root
101	1 02 01	10.050	151	2 28 01	12.288
102	1 04 04	10.100	152	2 31 04	12.329
103	1 06 09	10.149	153	2 34 09	12.369
104	1 08 16	10.198	154	2 37 16	12.410
105	1 10 25	10.247	155	2 40 25	12.450
106	1 12 36	10.296	156	2 43 36	12.490
107	1 14 49	10.344	157	2 46 49	12.530
108	1 16 64	10.392	158	2 49 64	12.570
109	1 18 81	10.440	159	2 52 81	12.610
110	1 21 00	10.488	160	2 56 00	12.649
111	1 23 21	10.536	161	2 59 21	12.689
112	1 25 44	10.583	162	2 62 44	12.728
113	1 27 69	10.630	163	2 65 69	12.767
114	1 29 96	10.677	164	2 68 96	12.806
115	1 32 25	10.724	165	2 72 25	12.845
116	1 34 56	10.770	166	2 75 56	12.884
117	1 36 89	10.817	167	2 78 89	12.923
118	1 39 24	10.863	168	2 82 24	12.961
119	1 41 61	10.909	169	2 85 61	13.000
120	1 44 00	10.954	170	2 89 00	13.038
121	1 46 41	11.000	171	2 92 41	13.077
122	1 48 84	11.045	172	2 95 84	13.115
123	1 51 29	11.091	173	2 99 29	13.153
124	1 53 76	11.136	174	3 02 76	13.191
125	1 56 25	11.180	175	3 06 25	13.229
126	1 58 76	11.225	176	3 09 76	13.266
127	1 61 29	11.269	177	3 13 29	13.304
128	1 63 84	11.314	178	3 16 84	13.342
129	1 66 41	11.358	179	3 20 41	13.379
130	1 69 00	11.402	180	3 24 00	13.416
131	1 71 61	11.446	181	3 27 61	13.454
132	1 74 24	11.489	182	3 31 24	13.491
133	1 76 89	11.533	183	3 34 89	13.528
134	1 79 56	11.576	184	3 38 56	13.565
135	1 82 25	11.619	185	3 42 25	13.601
136	1 84 96	11.662	186	3 45 96	13.638
137	1 87 69	11.705	187	3 49 69	13.675
138	1 90 44	11.747	188	3 53 44	13.711
139	1 93 21	11.790	189	3 57 21	13.748
140	1 96 00	11.832	190	3 61 00	13.784
141	1 98 81	11.874	191	3 64 81	13.820
142	2 01 64	11.916	192	3 68 64	13.856
143	2 04 49	11.958	193	3 72 49	13.892
144	2 07 36	12.000	194	3 76 36	13.928
145	2 10 25	12.042	195	3 80 25	13.964
146	2 13 16	12.083	196	3 84 16	14.000
147	2 16 09	12.124	197	3 88 09	14.036
148	2 19 04	12.166	198	3 92 04	14.071
149	2 22 01	12.207	199	3 96 01	14.107
150	2 25 00	12.247	200	4 00 00	14.142

TABLE OF SQUARES AND SQUARE ROOTS (*Cont.*)

Number	Square	Square Root	Number	Square	Square Root
201	4 04 01	14.177	251	6 30 01	15.843
202	4 08 04	14.213	252	6 35 04	15.875
203	4 12 09	14.248	253	6 40 09	15.906
204	4 16 16	14.283	554	6 45 16	15.937
205	4 20 25	14.318	255	6 50 25	15.969
206	4 24 36	14.353	256	6 55 36	16.000
207	4 28 49	14.387	257	6 60 49	16.031
208	4 32 64	14.422	258	6 65 64	16.062
209	4 36 81	14.457	259	6 70 81	16.093
210	4 41 00	14.491	260	6 76 00	16.125
211	4 45 21	14.526	261	6 81 21	16.155
212	4 49 44	14.560	262	6 86 44	16.186
213	4 53 69	14.595	263	6 91 69	16.217
214	4 57 96	14.629	264	6 96 96	16.248
215	4 62 25	14.663	265	7 02 25	16.279
216	4 66 56	14.697	266	7 07 56	16.310
217	4 70 89	14.731	267	7 12 89	16.340
218	4 75 24	14.765	268	7 18 24	16.371
219	4 79 61	14.799	269	7 23 61	16.401
220	4 84 00	14.832	270	7 29 00	16.432
221	4 88 41	14.866	271	7 34 41	16.462
222	4 92 84	14.900	272	7 39 84	16.492
223	4 97 29	14.933	273	7 45 29	16.523
224	5 01 76	14.967	274	7 50 76	16.553
225	5 06 25	15.000	275	7 56 25	16.583
226	5 10 76	15.033	276	7 61 76	16.613
227	5 15 29	15.067	277	7 67 29	16.643
228	5 19 84	15.100	278	7 72 84	16.673
229	5 24 41	15.133	279	7 78 41	16.703
230	5 29 00	15.166	280	7 84 00	16.733
231	5 33 61	15.199	281	7 89 61	16.763
232	5 38 24	15.232	282	7 95 24	16.793
233	5 42 89	15.264	283	8 00 89	16.823
234	5 47 56	15.297	284	8 06 56	16.852
235	5 52 25	15.330	285	8 12 25	16.882
236	5 56 96	15.362	286	8 17 96	16.912
237	5 61 69	15.395	287	8 23 69	16.941
238	5 66 44	15.427	288	8 29 44	16.971
239	5 71 21	15.460	289	8 35 21	17.000
240	5 76 00	15.492	290	8 41 00	17.029
241	5 80 81	15.524	291	8 46 81	17.059
242	5 85 64	15.556	292	8 52 64	17.088
243	5 90 49	15.588	293	8 58 49	17.117
244	5 95 36	15.620	294	8 64 36	17.146
245	6 00 25	15.652	295	8 70 25	17.176
246	6 05 16	15.684	296	8 76 16	17.205
247	6 10 09	15.716	297	8 82 09	17.234
248	6 15 04	15.748	298	8 88 04	17.263
249	6 20 01	15.780	299	8 94 01	17.292
250	6 25 00	15.811	300	9 00 00	17.321

Number	Square	Square Root	Number	Square	Square Root
301	9 06 01	17.349	351	12 32 01	18.735
302	9 12 04	17.378	352	12 39 04	18.762
303	9 18 09	17.407	353	12 46 09	18.788
304	9 24 16	17.436	354	12 53 16	18.815
305	9 30 25	17.464	355	12 60 25	18.841
306	9 36 36	17.493	356	12 67 36	18.868
307	9 42 49	17.521	357	12 74 49	18.894
308	9 48 64	17.550	358	12 81 64	18.921
309	9 54 81	17.578	359	12 88 81	18.947
310	9 61 00	17.607	360	12 96 00	18.974
311	9 67 21	17.635	361	13 03 21	19.000
312	9 73 44	17.664	362	13 10 44	19.026
313	9 79 69	17.692	363	13 17 69	19.053
314	9 85 96	17.720	364	13 24 96	19.079
315	9 92 25	17.748	365	13 32 25	19.105
316	9 98 56	17.776	366	13 39 56	19.131
317	10 04 89	17.804	367	13 46 89	19.157
318	10 11 24	17.833	368	13 54 24	19.183
319	10 17 61	17.861	369	13 61 61	19.209
320	10 24 00	17.889	370	13 69 00	19.235
321	10 30 41	17.916	371	13 76 41	19.261
322	10 36 84	17.944	372	13 83 84	19.287
323	10 43 29	17.972	373	13 91 29	19.313
324	10 49 76	18.000	374	13 98 76	19.339
325	10 56 25	18.028	375	14 06 25	19.365
326	10 62 76	18.055	376	14 13 76	19.391
327	10 69 29	18.083	377	14 21 29	19.416
328	10 75 84	18.111	378	14 28 84	19.442
329	10 82 41	18.138	379	14 36 41	19.468
330	10 89 00	18.166	380	14 44 00	19.494
331	10 95 61	18.193	381	14 51 61	19.519
332	11 02 24	18.221	382	14 59 24	19.545
333	11 08 89	18.248	383	14 66 89	19.570
334	11 15 56	18.276	384	14 74 56	19.596
335	11 22 25	18.303	385	14 82 25	19.621
336	11 28 96	18.330	386	14 89 96	19.647
337	11 35 69	18.358	387	14 97 69	19.672
338	11 42 44	18.385	388	15 05 44	19.698
339	11 49 21	18.412	389	15 13 21	19.723
340	11 56 00	18.439	390	15 21 00	19.748
341	11 62 81	18.466	391	15 28 81	19.774
342	11 69 64	18.493	392	15 36 64	19.799
343	11 76 49	18.520	393	15 44 49	19.824
344	11 83 36	18.547	394	15 52 36	19.849
345	11 90 25	18.574	395	15 60 25	19.875
346	11 97 16	18.601	396	15 68 16	19.900
347	12 04 09	18.628	397	15 76 09	19.925
348	12 11 04	18.655	398	15 84 04	19.950
349	12 18 01	18.682	399	15 92 01	19.975
350	12 25 00	18.708	400	16 00 00	20.000

TABLE OF SQUARES AND SQUARE ROOTS (*Cont.*)

Number	Square	Square Root	Number	Square	Square Root
401	16 08 01	20.025	451	20 34 01	21.237
402	16 16 04	20.050	452	20 43 04	21.260
403	16 24 09	20.075	453	20 52 09	21.284
404	16 32 16	20.100	454	20 61 16	21.307
405	16 40 25	20.125	455	20 70 25	21.331
406	16 48 36	20.149	456	20 79 36	21.354
407	16 56 49	20.174	457	20 88 49	21.378
408	16 64 64	20.199	458	20 97 64	21.401
409	16 72 81	20.224	459	21 06 81	21.424
410	16 81 00	20.248	460	21 16 00	21.448
411	16 89 21	20.273	461	21 25 21	21.471
412	16 97 44	20.298	462	21 34 44	21.494
413	17 05 69	20.322	463	21 43 69	21.517
414	17 13 96	20.347	464	21 52 96	21.541
415	17 22 25	20.372	465	21 62 25	21.564
416	17 30 56	20.396	466	21 71 56	21.587
417	17 38 89	20.421	467	21 80 89	21.610
418	17 47 24	20.445	468	21 90 24	21.633
419	17 55 61	20.469	469	21 99 61	21.656
420	17 64 00	20.494	470	22 09 00	21.679
421	17 72 41	20.518	471	22 18 41	21.703
422	17 80 84	20.543	472	22 27 84	21.726
423	17 89 29	20.567	473	22 37 29	21.749
424	17 97 76	20.591	474	22 46 76	21.772
425	18 06 25	20.616	475	22 56 25	21.794
426	18 14 76	20.640	476	22 65 76	21.817
427	18 23 29	20.664	477	22 75 29	21.840
428	18 31 84	20.688	478	22 84 84	21.863
429	18 40 41	20.712	479	22 94 41	21.886
430	18 49 00	20.736	480	23 04 00	21.909
431	18 57 61	20.761	481	23 13 61	21.932
432	18 66 24	20.785	482	23 23 24	21.954
433	18 74 89	20.809	483	23 32 89	21.977
434	18 83 56	20.833	484	23 42 56	22.000
435	18 92 25	20.857	485	23 52 25	22.023
436	19 00 96	20.881	486	23 61 96	22.045
437	19 09 69	20.905	487	23 71 69	22.068
438	19 18 44	20.928	488	23 81 44	22.091
439	19 27 21	20.952	489	23 91 21	22.113
440	19 36 00	20.976	490	24 01 00	22.136
441	19 44 81	21.000	491	24 10 81	22.159
442	19 53 64	21.024	492	24 20 64	22.181
443	19 62 49	21.048	493	24 30 49	22.204
444	19 71 36	21.071	494	24 40 36	22.226
445	19 80 25	21.095	495	24 50 25	22.249
446	19 89 16	21.119	496	24 60 16	22.271
447	19 98 09	21.142	497	24 70 09	22.293
448	20 07 04	21.166	498	24 80 04	22.316
449	20 16 01	21.190	499	24 90 01	22.338
450	20 25 00	21.213	500	25 00 00	22.361

Number	Square	Square Root	Number	Square	Square Root
501	25 10 01	22.383	551	30 36 01	23.473
502	25 20 04	22.405	552	30 47 04	23.495
503	25 30 09	22.428	553	30 58 09	23.516
504	25 40 16	22.450	554	30 69 16	23.537
505	25 50 25	22.472	555	30 80 25	23.558
506	25 60 36	22.494	556	30 91 36	23.580
507	25 70 49	22.517	557	31 02 49	23.601
508	25 80 64	22.539	558	31 13 64	23.622
509	25 90 81	22.561	559	31 24 81	23.643
510	26 01 00	22.583	560	31 36 00	23.664
511	26 11 21	22.605	561	31 47 21	23.685
512	26 21 44	22.627	562	31 58 44	23.707
513	26 31 69	22.650	563	31 69 69	23.728
514	26 41 96	22.672	564	31 80 96	23.749
515	26 52 25	22.694	565	31 92 25	23.770
516	26 62 56	22.716	566	32 03 56	23.791
517	26 72 89	22.738	567	32 14 89	23.812
518	26 83 24	22.760	568	32 26 24	23.833
519	26 93 61	22.782	569	32 37 61	23.854
520	27 04 00	22.804	570	32 49 00	23.875
521	27 14 41	22.825	571	32 60 41	23.896
522	27 24 84	22.847	572	32 71 84	23.917
523	27 35 29	22.869	573	32 83 29	23.937
524	27 45 76	22.891	574	32 94 76	23.958
525	27 56 25	22.913	575	33 06 25	23.979
526	27 66 76	22.935	576	33 17 76	24.000
527	27 77 29	22.956	577	33 29 29	24.021
528	27 87 84	22.978	578	33 40 84	24.042
529	27 98 41	23.000	579	33 52 41	24.062
530	28 09 00	23.022	580	33 64 00	24.083
531	28 19 61	23.043	581	33 75 61	24.104
532	28 30 24	23.065	582	33 87 24	24.125
533	28 40 89	23.087	583	33 98 89	24.145
534	28 51 56	23.108	584	34 10 56	24.166
535	28 62 25	23.130	585	34 22 25	24.187
536	28 72 96	23.152	586	34 33 96	24.207
537	28 83 69	23.173	587	34 45 69	24.228
538	28 94 44	23.195	588	34 57 44	24.249
539	29 05 21	23.216	589	34 69 21	24.269
540	29 16 00	23.238	590	34 81 00	24.290
541	29 26 81	23.259	591	34 92 81	24.310
542	29 37 64	23.281	592	35 04 64	24.331
543	29 48 49	23.302	593	35 16 49	24.352
544	29 59 36	23.324	594	35 28 36	24.372
545	29 70 25	23.345	595	35 40 25	24.393
546	29 81 16	23.367	596	35 52 16	24.413
547	29 92 09	23.388	597	35 64 09	24.434
548	30 03 04	23.409	598	35 76 04	24.454
549	30 14 01	23.431	599	35 88 01	24.474
550	30 25 00	23.452	600	36 00 00	24.495

TABLE OF SQUARES AND SQUARE ROOTS (*Cont.*)

Number	Square	Square Root	Number	Square	Square Root
601	36 12 01	24.515	651	42 38 01	25.515
602	36 24 04	24.536	652	42 51 04	25.534
603	36 36 09	24.556	653	42 64 09	25.554
604	36 48 16	24.576	654	42 77 16	25.573
605	36 60 25	24.597	655	42 90 25	25.593
606	36 72 36	24.617	656	43 03 36	25.612
607	36 84 49	24.637	657	43 16 49	25.632
608	36 96 64	24.658	658	43 29 64	25.652
609	37 08 81	24.678	659	43 42 81	25.671
610	37 21 00	24.698	660	43 56 00	25.690
611	37 33 21	24.718	661	43 69 21	25.710
612	37 45 44	24.739	662	43 82 44	25.729
613	37 57 69	24.759	663	43 95 69	25.749
614	37 69 96	24.779	664	44 08 96	25.768
615	37 82 25	24.799	665	44 22 25	25.788
616	37 94 56	24.819	666	44 35 56	25.807
617	38 06 89	24.839	667	44 48 89	25.826
618	38 19 24	24.860	668	44 62 24	25.846
619	38 31 61	24.880	669	44 75 61	25.865
620	38 44 00	24.900	670	44 89 00	25.884
621	38 56 41	24.920	671	45 02 41	25.904
622	38 68 84	24.940	672	45 15 84	25.923
623	38 81 29	24.960	673	45 29 29	25.942
624	38 93 76	24.980	674	45 42 76	25.962
625	39 06 25	25.000	675	45 56 25	25.981
626	39 18 76	25.020	676	45 69 76	26.000
627	39 31 29	25.040	677	45 83 29	26.019
628	39 43 84	25.060	678	45 96 84	26.038
629	39 56 41	25.080	679	46 10 41	26.058
630	39 69 00	25.100	680	46 24 00	26.077
631	39 81 61	25.120	681	46 37 61	26.096
632	39 94 24	25.140	682	46 51 24	26.115
633	40 06 89	25.159	683	46 64 89	26.134
634	40 19 56	25.179	684	46 78 56	26.153
635	40 32 25	25.199	685	46 92 25	26.173
636	40 44 96	25.219	686	47 05 96	26.192
637	40 57 69	25.239	687	47 19 69	26.211
638	40 70 44	25.259	688	47 33 44	26.230
639	40 83 21	25.278	689	47 47 21	26.249
640	40 96 00	25.298	690	47 61 00	26.268
641	41 08 81	25.318	691	47 74 81	26.287
642	41 21 64	25.338	692	47 88 64	26.306
643	41 34 49	25.357	693	48 02 49	26.325
644	41 47 36	25.377	694	48 16 36	26.344
645	41 60 25	25.397	695	48 30 25	26.363
646	41 73 16	25.417	696	48 44 16	26.382
647	41 86 09	25.436	697	48 58 09	26.401
648	41 99 04	25.456	698	48 72 04	26.420
649	42 12 01	25.475	699	48 86 01	26.439
650	42 25 00	25.495	700	49 00 00	26.458

TABLE OF SQUARES AND SQUARE ROOTS (*Cont.*)

Number	Square	Square Root	Number	Square	Square Root
701	49 14 01	26.476	751	56 40 01	27.404
702	49 28 04	26.495	752	56 55 04	27.423
703	49 42 09	26.514	753	56 70 09	27.441
704	49 56 16	26.533	754	56 85 16	27.459
705	49 70 25	26.552	755	57 00 25	27.477
706	49 84 36	26.571	756	57 15 36	27.495
707	49 98 49	26.589	757	57 30 49	27.514
708	50 12 64	26.608	758	57 45 64	27.532
709	50 26 81	26.627	759	57 60 81	27.550
710	50 41 00	26.646	760	57 76 00	27.568
711	50 55 21	26.665	761	57 91 21	27.586
712	50 69 44	26.683	762	58 06 44	27.604
713	50 83 69	26.702	763	58 21 69	27.622
714	50 97 96	26.721	764	58 36 96	27.641
715	51 12 25	26.739	765	58 52 25	27.659
716	51 26 56	26.758	766	58 67 56	27.677
717	51 40 89	26.777	767	58 82 89	27.695
718	51 55 24	26.796	768	58 98 24	27.713
719	51 69 61	26.814	769	59 13 61	27.731
720	51 84 00	26.833	770	59 29 00	27.749
721	51 98 41	26.851	771	59 44 41	27.767
722	52 12 84	26.870	772	59 59 84	27.785
723	52 27 29	26.889	773	59 75 29	27.803
724	52 41 76	26.907	774	59 90 76	27.821
725	52 56 25	26.926	775	60 06 25	27.839
726	52 70 76	26.944	776	60 21 76	27.857
727	52 85 29	26.963	777	60 37 29	27.875
728	52 99 84	26.981	778	60 52 84	27.893
729	53 14 41	27.000	779	60 68 41	27.911
730	53 29 00	27.019	780	60 84 00	27.928
731	53 43 61	27.037	781	60 99 61	27.946
732	53 58 24	27.055	782	61 15 24	27.964
733	53 72 89	27.074	783	61 30 89	27.982
734	53 87 56	27.092	784	61 46 56	28.000
735	54 02 25	27.111	785	61 62 25	28.018
736	54 16 96	27.129	786	61 77 96	28.036
737	54 31 69	27.148	787	61 93 69	28.054
738	54 46 44	27.166	788	62 09 44	28.071
739	54 61 21	27.185	789	62 25 21	28.089
740	54 76 00	27.203	790	62 41 00	28.107
741	54 90 81	27.221	791	62 56 81	28.125
742	55 05 64	27.240	792	62 72 64	28.142
743	55 20 49	27.258	793	62 88 49	28.160
744	55 35 36	27.276	794	63 04 36	28.178
745	55 50 25	27.295	795	63 20 25	28.196
746	55 65 16	27.313	796	63 36 16	28.213
747	55 80 09	27.331	797	63 52 09	28.231
748	55 95 04	27.350	798	63 68 04	28.249
749	56 10 01	27.368	799	73 84 01	28.267
750	56 25 00	27.386	800	64 00 00	28.284

SQUARES AND SQUARE ROOTS   288

TABLE OF SQUARES AND SQUARE ROOTS (*Cont.*)

Number	Square	Square Root	Number	Square	Square Root
801	64 16 01	28.302	851	72 42 01	29.172
802	64 32 04	28.320	852	72 59 04	29.189
803	64 48 09	28.337	853	72 76 09	29.206
804	64 64 16	28.355	854	72 93 16	29.223
805	64 80 25	28.373	855	73 10 25	29.240
806	64 96 36	28.390	856	73 27 36	29.257
807	65 12 49	28.408	857	73 44 49	29.275
808	65 28 64	28.425	858	73 61 64	29.292
809	65 44 81	28.443	859	73 78 81	29.309
810	65 61 00	28.460	860	73 96 00	29.326
811	65 77 21	28.478	861	74 13 21	29.343
812	65 93 44	28.496	862	74 30 44	29.360
813	66 09 69	28.513	863	74 47 69	29.377
814	66 25 96	28.531	864	74 64 96	29.394
815	66 42 25	28.548	865	74 82 25	29.411
816	66 58 56	28.566	866	74 99 56	29.428
817	66 74 89	28.583	867	75 16 89	29.445
818	66 91 24	28.601	868	75 34 24	29.462
819	67 07 61	28.618	869	75 51 61	29.479
820	67 24 00	28.636	870	75 69 00	29.496
821	67 40 41	28.653	871	75 86 41	29.513
822	67 56 84	28.671	872	76 03 84	29.530
823	67 73 29	28.688	873	76 21 29	29.547
824	67 89 76	28.705	874	76 38 76	29.563
825	68 06 25	28.723	875	76 56 25	29.580
826	68 22 76	28.740	876	76 73 76	29.597
827	68 39 29	28.758	877	76 91 29	29.614
828	68 55 84	28.775	878	77 08 84	29.631
829	68 72 41	28.792	879	77 26 41	29.648
830	68 89 00	28.810	880	77 44 00	29.665
831	69 05 61	28.827	881	77 61 61	29.682
832	69 22 24	28.844	882	77 79 24	29.698
833	69 38 89	28.862	883	77 96 89	29.715
834	69 55 56	28.879	884	78 14 56	29.732
835	69 72 25	28.896	885	78 32 25	29.749
836	69 88 96	28.914	886	78 49 96	29.766
837	70 05 69	28.931	887	78 67 69	29.783
838	70 22 44	28.948	888	78 85 44	29.799
839	70 39 21	28.965	889	79 03 21	29.816
840	70 56 00	28.983	890	79 21 00	29.833
841	70 72 81	29.000	891	79 38 81	29.850
842	70 89 64	29.017	892	79 56 64	29.866
843	71 06 49	29.034	893	79 74 49	29.883
844	71 23 36	29.052	894	79 92 36	29.900
845	71 40 25	29.069	895	80 10 25	29.917
846	71 57 16	29.086	896	80 28 16	29.933
847	71 74 09	29.103	897	80 46 09	29.950
848	71 91 04	29.120	898	80 64 04	29.967
849	72 08 01	29.138	899	80 82 01	29.983
850	72 25 00	29.155	900	81 00 00	30.000

Number	Square	Square Root	Number	Square	Square Root
901	81 18 01	30.017	951	90 44 01	30.838
902	81 36 04	30.033	952	90 63 04	30.854
903	81 54 09	30.050	953	90 82 09	30.871
904	81 72 16	30.067	954	91 01 16	30.887
905	81 90 25	30.083	955	91 20 25	30.903
906	82 08 36	30.100	956	91 39 36	30.919
907	82 26 49	30.116	957	91 58 49	30.935
908	82 44 64	30.133	958	91 77 64	30.952
909	82 62 81	30.150	959	91 96 81	30.968
910	82 81 00	30.166	960	92 16 00	30.984
911	82 99 21	30.183	961	92 35 21	31.000
912	83 17 44	30.199	962	92 54 44	31.016
913	83 35 69	30.216	963	92 73 69	31.032
914	83 53 96	30.232	964	92 92 96	31.048
915	83 72 25	30.249	965	93 12 25	31.064
916	83 90 56	30.265	966	93 31 56	31.081
917	84 08 89	30.282	967	93 50 89	31.097
918	84 27 24	30.299	968	93 70 24	31.113
919	84 45 61	30.315	969	93 89 61	31.129
920	84 64 00	30.332	970	94 09 00	31.145
921	84 82 41	30.348	971	94 28 41	31.161
922	85 00 84	30.364	972	94 47 84	31.177
923	85 19 29	30.381	973	94 67 29	31.193
924	85 37 76	30.397	974	94 86 76	31.209
925	85 56 25	30.414	975	95 06 25	31.225
926	85 74 76	30.430	976	95 25 76	31.241
927	85 93 29	30.447	977	95 45 29	31.257
928	86 11 84	30.463	978	95 64 84	31.273
929	86 30 41	30.480	979	95 84 41	31.289
930	86 49 00	30.496	980	96 04 00	31.305
931	86 67 61	30.512	981	96 23 61	31.321
932	86 86 24	30.529	982	96 43 24	31.337
933	87 04 89	30.545	983	96 62 89	31.353
934	87 23 56	30.561	984	96 82 56	31.369
935	87 42 25	30.578	985	97 02 25	31.385
936	87 60 96	30.594	986	97 21 96	31.401
937	87 79 69	30.610	987	97 41 69	31.417
938	87 98 44	30.627	988	97 61 44	31.432
939	88 17 21	30.643	989	97 81 21	31.448
940	88 36 00	30.659	990	98 01 00	31.464
941	88 54 81	30.676	991	98 20 81	31.480
942	88 73 64	30.692	992	98 40 64	31.496
943	88 92 49	30.708	993	98 60 49	31.512
944	89 11 36	30.725	994	98 80 36	31.528
945	89 30 25	30.741	995	99 00 25	31.544
946	89 49 16	30.757	996	99 20 16	31.559
947	89 68 09	30.773	997	99 40 09	31.575
948	89 87 04	30.790	998	99 60 04	31.591
949	90 06 01	30.806	999	99 80 01	31.607
950	90 25 00	30.822	1000	100 00 00	31.623

Table B

AREAS OF THE NORMAL CURVE

z	.00	.01	.02	.03	.04	.05	.06	.07	.08	.09
0.0	.0000	.0040	.0080	.0120	.0159	.0199	.0239	.0279	.0319	.0359
0.1	.0398	.0438	.0478	.0517	.0557	.0596	.0636	.0675	.0714	.0753
0.2	.0793	.0832	.0871	.0910	.0948	.0987	.1026	.1064	.1103	.1141
0.3	.1179	.1217	.1255	.1293	.1331	.1368	.1406	.1443	.1480	.1517
0.4	.1554	.1591	.1628	.1664	.1700	.1736	.1772	.1808	.1844	.1879
0.5	.1915	.1950	.1985	.2019	.2054	.2088	.2123	.2157	.2190	.2224
0.6	.2257	.2291	.2324	.2357	.2389	.2422	.2454	.2486	.2518	.2549
0.7	.2580	.2612	.2642	.2673	.2704	.2734	.2764	.2794	.2823	.2852
0.8	.2881	.2910	.2939	.2967	.2995	.3023	.3051	.3078	.3106	.3133
0.9	.3159	.3186	.3212	.3238	.3264	.3289	.3315	.3340	.3365	.3389
1.0	.3413	.3438	.3461	.3485	.3508	.3531	.3554	.3577	.3599	.3621
1.1	.3643	.3665	.3686	.3708	.3729	.3749	.3770	.3790	.3810	.3830
1.2	.3849	.3869	.3888	.3907	.3925	.3944	.3962	.3980	.3997	.4015
1.3	.4032	.4049	.4066	.4083	.4099	.4115	.4131	.4147	.4162	.4177
1.4	.4192	.4207	.4222	.4236	.4251	.4265	.4279	.4292	.4306	.4319
1.5	.4332	.4345	.4357	.4370	.4382	.4394	.4406	.4418	.4430	.4441
1.6	.4452	.4463	.4474	.4485	.4495	.4505	.4515	.4525	.4535	.4545
1.7	.4554	.4564	.4573	.4582	.4591	.4599	.4608	.4616	.4625	.4633
1.8	.4641	.4649	.4656	.4664	.4671	.4678	.4686	.4693	.4699	.4706
1.9	.4713	.4719	.4726	.4732	.4738	.4744	.4750	.4756	.4762	.4767
2.0	.4773	.4778	.4783	.4788	.4793	.4798	.4803	.4808	.4812	.4817
2.1	.4821	.4826	.4830	.4834	.4838	.4842	.4846	.4850	.4854	.4857
2.2	.4861	.4865	.4868	.4871	.4875	.4878	.4881	.4884	.4887	.4890
2.3	.4893	.4896	.4898	.4901	.4904	.4906	.4909	.4911	.4913	.4916
2.4	.4918	.4920	.4922	.4925	.4927	.4929	.4931	.4932	.4934	.4936
2.5	.4938	.4940	.4941	.4943	.4945	.4946	.4948	.4949	.4951	.4952
2.6	.4953	.4955	.4956	.4957	.4959	.4960	.4961	.4962	.4963	.4964
2.7	.4965	.4966	.4967	.4968	.4969	.4970	.4971	.4972	.4973	.4974
2.8	.4974	.4975	.4976	.4977	.4977	.4978	.4979	.4980	.4980	.4981
2.9	.4981	.4982	.4983	.4983	.4984	.4984	.4985	.4985	.4986	.4986
3.0	.49865	.4987	.4987	.4988	.4988	.4988	.4989	.4989	.4989	.4990
3.1	.49903	.4991	.4991	.4991	.4992	.4992	.4992	.4992	.4993	.4993
3.2	.49931									
3.3	.49952									
3.4	.49966									
3.5	.49977									
3.6	.49984									
3.7	.49989									
3.8	.49993									
3.9	.49995									
4.0	.49997									

Example: The proportion of area between the mean and $z = .42$ is .1628. (The same proportion of area lies between the mean and $z = -.42$.)

TABLE C

TABLE OF χ^2 VALUES*

PROBABILITY

df	.90	.80	.70	.50	.30	.20	.10	.05	.02	.01	.001
1	.016	.064	.15	.46	1.07	1.64	2.71	3.84	5.41	6.64	10.83
2	.21	.45	.71	1.39	2.41	3.22	4.60	5.99	7.82	9.21	13.82
3	.58	1.00	1.42	2.37	3.66	4.64	6.25	7.82	9.84	11.34	16.27
4	1.06	1.65	2.20	3.36	4.88	5.99	7.78	9.49	11.67	13.28	18.46
5	1.61	2.34	3.00	4.35	6.06	7.29	9.24	11.07	13.39	15.09	20.52
6	2.20	3.07	3.83	5.35	7.23	8.56	10.64	12.59	15.03	16.81	22.46
7	2.83	3.82	4.67	6.35	8.38	9.80	12.02	14.07	16.62	18.48	24.32
8	3.49	4.59	5.53	7.34	9.52	11.03	13.36	15.51	18.17	20.09	26.12
9	4.17	5.38	6.39	8.34	10.66	12.24	14.68	16.92	19.68	21.67	27.88
10	4.86	6.18	7.27	9.34	11.78	13.44	15.99	18.31	21.16	23.21	29.59
11	5.58	6.99	8.15	10.34	12.90	14.63	17.28	19.68	22.62	24.72	31.26
12	6.30	7.81	9.03	11.34	14.01	15.81	18.55	21.03	24.05	26.22	32.91
13	7.04	8.63	9.93	12.34	15.12	16.98	19.81	22.36	25.47	27.69	34.53
14	7.79	9.47	10.82	13.34	16.22	18.15	21.06	23.68	26.87	29.14	36.12
15	8.55	10.31	11.72	14.34	17.32	19.31	22.31	25.00	28.26	30.58	37.70
16	9.31	11.15	12.62	15.34	18.42	20.46	23.54	26.30	29.63	32.00	39.29
17	10.08	12.00	13.53	16.34	19.51	21.62	24.77	27.59	31.00	33.41	40.75
18	10.86	12.86	14.44	17.34	20.60	22.76	25.99	28.87	32.35	34.80	42.31
19	11.65	13.72	15.35	18.34	21.69	23.90	27.20	30.14	33.69	36.19	43.82
20	12.44	14.58	16.27	19.34	22.78	25.04	28.41	31.41	35.02	37.57	45.32
21	13.24	15.44	17.18	20.34	23.86	26.17	29.62	32.67	36.34	38.93	46.80
22	14.04	16.31	18.10	21.24	24.94	27.30	30.81	33.92	37.66	40.29	48.27
23	14.85	17.19	19.02	22.34	26.02	28.43	32.01	35.17	38.97	41.64	49.73
24	15.66	18.06	19.94	23.34	27.10	29.55	33.20	36.42	40.27	42.98	51.18
25	16.47	18.94	20.87	24.34	28.17	30.68	34.38	37.65	41.57	44.31	52.62
26	17.29	19.82	21.79	25.34	29.25	31.80	35.56	38.88	42.86	45.64	54.05
27	18.11	20.70	22.72	26.34	30.32	32.91	36.74	40.11	44.14	46.96	55.48
28	18.94	21.59	23.65	27.34	31.39	34.03	37.92	41.34	45.42	48.28	56.89
29	19.77	22.48	24.58	28.34	32.46	35.14	39.09	42.56	46.69	49.59	58.30
30	20.60	23.36	25.51	29.34	33.53	36.25	40.26	43.77	47.96	50.89	59.70

* Table C is abridged from Table IV of Fisher & Yates: *Statistical Tables for Biological, Agricultural and Medical Research* published by Oliver & Boyd Ltd., Edinburgh, and by permission of the authors and publishers.

Example: With 5 *df*, $\chi^2 \geq 6.06$ has probability .30.

Table D

TABLE OF t VALUES*

PROBABILITY (*two-tailed test*)

df	.50	.40	.20	.10	.05	.02	.01	.001	df
1	1.00	1.38	3.08	6.31	12.71	31.82	63.66	636.62	1
2	.82	1.06	1.89	2.92	4.30	6.96	9.92	31.60	2
3	.76	.98	1.64	2.35	3.18	4.54	5.84	12.94	3
4	.74	.94	1.53	2.13	2.78	3.75	4.60	8.61	4
5	.73	.92	1.48	2.02	2.57	3.36	4.03	6.86	5
6	.72	.91	1.44	1.94	2.45	3.14	3.71	5.96	6
7	.71	.90	1.42	1.89	2.36	3.00	3.50	5.40	7
8	.71	.89	1.40	1.86	2.31	2.90	3.36	5.04	8
9	.70	.88	1.38	1.83	2.26	2.82	3.25	4.78	9
10	.70	.88	1.37	1.81	2.23	2.76	3.17	4.59	10
11	.70	.88	1.36	1.80	2.20	2.72	3.11	4.44	11
12	.70	.87	1.36	1.78	2.18	2.68	3.05	4.32	12
13	.69	.87	1.35	1.77	2.16	2.65	3.01	4.22	13
14	.69	.87	1.34	1.76	2.14	2.62	2.98	4.14	14
15	.69	.87	1.34	1.75	2.13	2.60	2.95	4.07	15
16	.69	.87	1.34	1.75	2.12	2.58	2.92	4.02	16
17	.69	.86	1.33	1.74	2.11	2.57	2.90	3.96	17
18	.69	.86	1.33	1.73	2.10	2.55	2.88	3.92	18
19	.69	.86	1.33	1.73	2.09	2.54	2.86	3.88	19
20	.69	.86	1.32	1.72	2.09	2.53	2.85	3.85	20
21	.69	.86	1.32	1.72	2.08	2.52	2.83	3.82	21
22	.69	.86	1.32	1.72	2.07	2.51	2.82	3.79	22
23	.69	.86	1.32	1.71	2.07	2.50	2.81	3.77	23
24	.68	.86	1.32	1.71	2.06	2.49	2.80	3.74	24
25	.68	.86	1.32	1.71	2.06	2.48	2.79	3.72	25
26	.68	.86	1.32	1.71	2.06	2.48	2.78	3.71	26
27	.68	.86	1.31	1.70	2.05	2.47	2.77	3.69	27
28	.68	.85	1.31	1.70	2.05	2.47	2.76	3.67	28
29	.68	.85	1.31	1.70	2.04	2.46	2.76	3.66	29
30	.68	.85	1.31	1.70	2.04	2.46	2.75	3.65	30
40	.68	.85	1.30	1.68	2.02	2.42	2.70	3.55	40
60	.68	.85	1.30	1.67	2.00	2.39	2.66	3.46	60
120	.68	.85	1.29	1.66	1.98	2.36	2.62	3.37	120
∞	.6745	.842	1.282	1.645	1.960	2.326	2.576	3.291	∞

* Table D is abridged from Table III of Fisher & Yates: *Statistical Tables for Biological, Agricultural and Medical Research* published by Oliver & Boyd Ltd., Edinburgh, and by permission of the authors and publishers.

Example: For a two-tailed test with 5 *df*, $t \geq 2.02$ has probability .10. Probabilities are halved for a one-tailed test. For a one-tailed test with 5 *df*, $t \geq 2.02$ has probability .05.

Table E

VALUES OF *r* FOR DIFFERENT LEVELS OF SIGNIFICANCE*

df	LEVEL OF SIGNIFICANCE FOR ONE-TAILED TEST			
	.05	.025	.01	.005
	LEVEL OF SIGNIFICANCE FOR TWO-TAILED TEST			
	.10	.05	.02	.01
1	.988	.997	.9995	.9999
2	.900	.950	.980	.990
3	.805	.878	.934	.959
4	.729	.811	.882	.917
5	.669	.754	.833	.874
6	.622	.707	.789	.834
7	.582	.666	.750	.798
8	.549	.632	.716	.765
9	.521	.602	.685	.735
10	.497	.576	.658	.708
11	.476	.553	.634	.684
12	.458	.532	.612	.661
13	.441	.514	.592	.641
14	.426	.497	.574	.623
15	.412	.482	.558	.606
16	.400	.468	.542	.590
17	.389	.456	.528	.575
18	.378	.444	.516	.561
19	.369	.433	.503	.549
20	.360	.423	.492	.537
21	.352	.413	.482	.526
22	.344	.404	.472	.515
23	.337	.396	.462	.505
24	.330	.388	.453	.496
25	.323	.381	.445	.487
26	.317	.374	.437	.479
27	.311	.367	.430	.471
28	.306	.361	.423	.463
29	.301	.355	.416	.456
30	.296	.349	.409	.449
35	.275	.325	.381	.418
40	.257	.304	.358	.393
45	.243	.288	.338	.372
50	.231	.273	.322	.354
60	.211	.250	.295	.325
70	.195	.232	.274	.302
80	.183	.217	.256	.283
90	.173	.205	.242	.267
100	.164	.195	.230	.254

* Table E is abridged from Table VII of Fisher & Yates: *Statistical Tables for Biological, Agricultural and Medical Research* published by Oliver & Boyd Ltd., Edinburgh, and by permission of the authors and publishers.

Example: For a two-tailed test with 7 *df*, $r \geq .750$ has probability .02. For a one-tailed test with 7 *df*, $r \geq .750$ has probability .01.

Table F

THE 5% (ROMAN TYPE) AND 1% (BOLDFACE TYPE) POINTS FOR THE DISTRIBUTION OF F*

NUMERATOR df — each cell shows 5% (roman) / 1% (boldface)

Denominator df	1	2	3	4	5	6	7	8	9	10	11	12	14	16	20	24	30	40	50	75	100	200	500	∞
1	161 / 4,052	200 / 4,999	216 / 5,403	225 / 5,625	230 / 5,764	234 / 5,859	237 / 5,928	239 / 5,981	241 / 6,022	242 / 6,056	243 / 6,082	244 / 6,106	245 / 6,142	246 / 6,169	248 / 6,208	249 / 6,234	250 / 6,258	251 / 6,286	252 / 6,302	253 / 6,323	253 / 6,334	254 / 6,352	254 / 6,361	254 / 6,366
2	18.51 / 98.49	19.00 / 99.00	19.16 / 99.17	19.25 / 99.25	19.30 / 99.30	19.33 / 99.33	19.36 / 99.34	19.37 / 99.36	19.38 / 99.38	19.39 / 99.40	19.40 / 99.41	19.41 / 99.42	19.42 / 99.43	19.43 / 99.44	19.44 / 99.45	19.45 / 99.46	19.46 / 99.47	19.47 / 99.48	19.47 / 99.48	19.48 / 99.49	19.49 / 99.49	19.49 / 99.49	19.50 / 99.50	19.50 / 99.50
3	10.13 / 34.12	9.55 / 30.82	9.28 / 29.46	9.12 / 28.71	9.01 / 28.24	8.94 / 27.91	8.88 / 27.67	8.84 / 27.49	8.81 / 27.34	8.78 / 27.23	8.76 / 27.13	8.74 / 27.05	8.71 / 26.92	8.69 / 26.83	8.66 / 26.69	8.64 / 26.60	8.62 / 26.50	8.60 / 26.41	8.58 / 26.35	8.57 / 26.27	8.56 / 26.23	8.54 / 26.18	8.54 / 26.14	8.53 / 26.12
4	7.71 / 21.20	6.94 / 18.00	6.59 / 16.69	6.39 / 15.98	6.26 / 15.52	6.16 / 15.21	6.09 / 14.98	6.04 / 14.80	6.00 / 14.66	5.96 / 14.54	5.93 / 14.45	5.91 / 14.37	5.87 / 14.24	5.84 / 14.15	5.80 / 14.02	5.77 / 13.93	5.74 / 13.83	5.71 / 13.74	5.70 / 13.69	5.68 / 13.61	5.66 / 13.57	5.65 / 13.52	5.64 / 13.48	5.63 / 13.46
5	6.61 / 16.26	5.79 / 13.27	5.41 / 12.06	5.19 / 11.39	5.05 / 10.97	4.95 / 10.67	4.88 / 10.45	4.82 / 10.27	4.78 / 10.15	4.74 / 10.05	4.70 / 9.96	4.68 / 9.89	4.64 / 9.77	4.60 / 9.68	4.56 / 9.55	4.53 / 9.47	4.50 / 9.38	4.46 / 9.29	4.44 / 9.24	4.42 / 9.17	4.40 / 9.13	4.38 / 9.07	4.37 / 9.04	4.36 / 9.02
6	5.99 / 13.74	5.14 / 10.92	4.76 / 9.78	4.53 / 9.15	4.39 / 8.75	4.28 / 8.47	4.21 / 8.26	4.15 / 8.10	4.10 / 7.98	4.06 / 7.87	4.03 / 7.79	4.00 / 7.72	3.96 / 7.60	3.92 / 7.52	3.87 / 7.39	3.84 / 7.31	3.81 / 7.23	3.77 / 7.14	3.75 / 7.09	3.72 / 7.02	3.71 / 6.99	3.69 / 6.94	3.68 / 6.90	3.67 / 6.88
7	5.59 / 12.25	4.74 / 9.55	4.35 / 8.45	4.12 / 7.85	3.97 / 7.46	3.87 / 7.19	3.79 / 7.00	3.73 / 6.84	3.68 / 6.71	3.63 / 6.62	3.60 / 6.54	3.57 / 6.47	3.52 / 6.35	3.49 / 6.27	3.44 / 6.15	3.41 / 6.07	3.38 / 5.98	3.34 / 5.90	3.32 / 5.85	3.29 / 5.78	3.28 / 5.75	3.25 / 5.70	3.24 / 5.67	3.23 / 5.65
8	5.32 / 11.26	4.46 / 8.65	4.07 / 7.59	3.84 / 7.01	3.69 / 6.63	3.58 / 6.37	3.50 / 6.19	3.44 / 6.03	3.39 / 5.91	3.34 / 5.82	3.31 / 5.74	3.28 / 5.67	3.23 / 5.56	3.20 / 5.48	3.15 / 5.36	3.12 / 5.28	3.08 / 5.20	3.05 / 5.11	3.03 / 5.06	3.00 / 5.00	2.98 / 4.96	2.96 / 4.91	2.94 / 4.88	2.93 / 4.86
9	5.12 / 10.56	4.26 / 8.02	3.86 / 6.99	3.63 / 6.42	3.48 / 6.06	3.37 / 5.80	3.29 / 5.62	3.23 / 5.47	3.18 / 5.35	3.13 / 5.26	3.10 / 5.18	3.07 / 5.11	3.02 / 5.00	2.98 / 4.92	2.93 / 4.80	2.90 / 4.73	2.86 / 4.64	2.82 / 4.56	2.80 / 4.51	2.77 / 4.45	2.76 / 4.41	2.73 / 4.36	2.72 / 4.33	2.71 / 4.31
10	4.96 / 10.04	4.10 / 7.56	3.71 / 6.55	3.48 / 5.99	3.33 / 5.64	3.22 / 5.39	3.14 / 5.21	3.07 / 5.06	3.02 / 4.95	2.97 / 4.85	2.94 / 4.78	2.91 / 4.71	2.86 / 4.60	2.82 / 4.52	2.77 / 4.41	2.74 / 4.33	2.70 / 4.25	2.67 / 4.17	2.64 / 4.12	2.61 / 4.05	2.59 / 4.01	2.56 / 3.96	2.55 / 3.93	2.54 / 3.91
11	4.84 / 9.65	3.98 / 7.20	3.59 / 6.22	3.36 / 5.67	3.20 / 5.32	3.09 / 5.07	3.01 / 4.88	2.95 / 4.74	2.90 / 4.63	2.86 / 4.54	2.82 / 4.46	2.79 / 4.40	2.74 / 4.29	2.70 / 4.21	2.65 / 4.10	2.61 / 4.02	2.57 / 3.94	2.53 / 3.86	2.50 / 3.80	2.47 / 3.74	2.45 / 3.70	2.42 / 3.66	2.41 / 3.62	2.40 / 3.60
12	4.75 / 9.33	3.88 / 6.93	3.49 / 5.95	3.26 / 5.41	3.11 / 5.06	3.00 / 4.82	2.92 / 4.65	2.85 / 4.50	2.80 / 4.39	2.76 / 4.30	2.72 / 4.22	2.69 / 4.16	2.64 / 4.05	2.60 / 3.98	2.54 / 3.86	2.50 / 3.78	2.46 / 3.70	2.42 / 3.61	2.40 / 3.56	2.36 / 3.49	2.35 / 3.46	2.32 / 3.41	2.31 / 3.38	2.30 / 3.36
13	4.67 / 9.07	3.80 / 6.70	3.41 / 5.74	3.18 / 5.20	3.02 / 4.86	2.92 / 4.62	2.84 / 4.44	2.77 / 4.30	2.72 / 4.19	2.67 / 4.10	2.63 / 4.02	2.60 / 3.96	2.55 / 3.85	2.51 / 3.78	2.46 / 3.67	2.42 / 3.59	2.38 / 3.51	2.34 / 3.42	2.32 / 3.37	2.28 / 3.30	2.26 / 3.27	2.24 / 3.21	2.22 / 3.18	2.21 / 3.16

DENOMINATOR df

* Table F is reproduced from Snedecor, *Statistical Methods*, 5th edition, 1956, Iowa State University Press, Ames, Iowa, by permission of the author and publisher.

Table F (Cont.)

THE 5% (ROMAN TYPE) AND 1% (BOLDFACE TYPE) POINTS FOR THE DISTRIBUTION OF F*

NUMERATOR df

DENOMINATOR df	1	2	3	4	5	6	7	8	9	10	11	12	14	16	20	24	30	40	50	75	100	200	500	∞
14	4.60 **8.86**	3.74 **6.51**	3.34 **5.56**	3.11 **5.03**	2.96 **4.69**	2.85 **4.46**	2.77 **4.28**	2.70 **4.14**	2.65 **4.03**	2.60 **3.94**	2.56 **3.86**	2.53 **3.80**	2.48 **3.70**	2.44 **3.62**	2.39 **3.51**	2.35 **3.43**	2.31 **3.34**	2.27 **3.26**	2.24 **3.21**	2.21 **3.14**	2.19 **3.11**	2.16 **3.06**	2.14 **3.02**	2.13 **3.00**
15	4.54 **8.68**	3.68 **6.36**	3.29 **5.42**	3.06 **4.89**	2.90 **4.56**	2.79 **4.32**	2.70 **4.14**	2.64 **4.00**	2.59 **3.89**	2.55 **3.80**	2.51 **3.73**	2.48 **3.67**	2.43 **3.56**	2.39 **3.48**	2.33 **3.36**	2.29 **3.29**	2.25 **3.20**	2.21 **3.12**	2.18 **3.07**	2.15 **3.00**	2.12 **2.97**	2.10 **2.92**	2.08 **2.89**	2.07 **2.87**
16	4.49 **8.53**	3.63 **6.23**	3.24 **5.29**	3.01 **4.77**	2.85 **4.44**	2.74 **4.20**	2.66 **4.03**	2.59 **3.89**	2.54 **3.78**	2.49 **3.69**	2.45 **3.61**	2.42 **3.55**	2.37 **3.45**	2.33 **3.37**	2.28 **3.25**	2.24 **3.18**	2.20 **3.10**	2.16 **3.01**	2.13 **2.96**	2.09 **2.89**	2.07 **2.86**	2.04 **2.80**	2.02 **2.77**	2.01 **2.75**
17	4.45 **8.40**	3.59 **6.11**	3.20 **5.18**	2.96 **4.67**	2.81 **4.34**	2.70 **4.10**	2.62 **3.93**	2.55 **3.79**	2.50 **3.68**	2.45 **3.59**	2.41 **3.52**	2.38 **3.45**	2.33 **3.35**	2.29 **3.27**	2.23 **3.16**	2.19 **3.08**	2.15 **3.00**	2.11 **2.92**	2.08 **2.86**	2.04 **2.79**	2.02 **2.76**	1.99 **2.70**	1.97 **2.67**	1.96 **2.65**
18	4.41 **8.28**	3.55 **6.01**	3.16 **5.09**	2.93 **4.58**	2.77 **4.25**	2.66 **4.01**	2.58 **3.85**	2.51 **3.71**	2.46 **3.60**	2.41 **3.51**	2.37 **3.44**	2.34 **3.37**	2.29 **3.27**	2.25 **3.19**	2.19 **3.07**	2.15 **3.00**	2.11 **2.91**	2.07 **2.83**	2.04 **2.78**	2.00 **2.71**	1.98 **2.68**	1.95 **2.62**	1.93 **2.59**	1.92 **2.57**
19	4.38 **8.18**	3.52 **5.93**	3.13 **5.01**	2.90 **4.50**	2.74 **4.17**	2.63 **3.94**	2.55 **3.77**	2.48 **3.63**	2.43 **3.52**	2.38 **3.43**	2.34 **3.36**	2.31 **3.30**	2.26 **3.19**	2.21 **3.12**	2.15 **3.00**	2.11 **2.92**	2.07 **2.84**	2.02 **2.76**	2.00 **2.70**	1.96 **2.63**	1.94 **2.60**	1.91 **2.54**	1.90 **2.51**	1.88 **2.49**
20	4.35 **8.10**	3.49 **5.85**	3.10 **4.94**	2.87 **4.43**	2.71 **4.10**	2.60 **3.87**	2.52 **3.71**	2.45 **3.56**	2.40 **3.45**	2.35 **3.37**	2.31 **3.30**	2.28 **3.23**	2.23 **3.13**	2.18 **3.05**	2.12 **2.94**	2.08 **2.86**	2.04 **2.77**	1.99 **2.69**	1.96 **2.63**	1.92 **2.56**	1.90 **2.53**	1.87 **2.47**	1.85 **2.44**	1.84 **2.42**
21	4.32 **8.02**	3.47 **5.78**	3.07 **4.87**	2.84 **4.37**	2.68 **4.04**	2.57 **3.81**	2.49 **3.65**	2.42 **3.51**	2.37 **3.40**	2.32 **3.31**	2.28 **3.24**	2.25 **3.17**	2.20 **3.07**	2.15 **2.99**	2.09 **2.88**	2.05 **2.80**	2.00 **2.72**	1.96 **2.63**	1.93 **2.58**	1.89 **2.51**	1.87 **2.47**	1.84 **2.42**	1.82 **2.38**	1.81 **2.36**
22	4.30 **7.94**	3.44 **5.72**	3.05 **4.82**	2.82 **4.31**	2.66 **3.99**	2.55 **3.76**	2.47 **3.59**	2.40 **3.45**	2.35 **3.35**	2.30 **3.26**	2.26 **3.18**	2.23 **3.12**	2.18 **3.02**	2.13 **2.94**	2.07 **2.83**	2.03 **2.75**	1.98 **2.67**	1.93 **2.58**	1.91 **2.53**	1.87 **2.46**	1.84 **2.42**	1.81 **2.37**	1.80 **2.33**	1.78 **2.31**
23	4.28 **7.88**	3.42 **5.66**	3.03 **4.76**	2.80 **4.26**	2.64 **3.94**	2.53 **3.71**	2.45 **3.54**	2.38 **3.41**	2.32 **3.30**	2.28 **3.21**	2.24 **3.14**	2.20 **3.07**	2.14 **2.97**	2.10 **2.89**	2.04 **2.78**	2.00 **2.70**	1.96 **2.62**	1.91 **2.53**	1.88 **2.48**	1.84 **2.41**	1.82 **2.37**	1.79 **2.32**	1.77 **2.28**	1.76 **2.26**
24	4.26 **7.82**	3.40 **5.61**	3.01 **4.72**	2.78 **4.22**	2.62 **3.90**	2.51 **3.67**	2.43 **3.50**	2.36 **3.36**	2.30 **3.25**	2.26 **3.17**	2.22 **3.09**	2.18 **3.03**	2.13 **2.93**	2.09 **2.85**	2.02 **2.74**	1.98 **2.66**	1.94 **2.58**	1.89 **2.49**	1.86 **2.44**	1.82 **2.36**	1.80 **2.33**	1.76 **2.27**	1.74 **2.23**	1.73 **2.21**
25	4.24 **7.77**	3.38 **5.57**	2.99 **4.68**	2.76 **4.18**	2.60 **3.86**	2.49 **3.63**	2.41 **3.46**	2.34 **3.32**	2.28 **3.21**	2.24 **3.13**	2.20 **3.05**	2.16 **2.99**	2.11 **2.89**	2.06 **2.81**	2.00 **2.70**	1.96 **2.62**	1.92 **2.54**	1.87 **2.45**	1.84 **2.40**	1.80 **2.32**	1.77 **2.29**	1.74 **2.23**	1.72 **2.19**	1.71 **2.17**
26	4.22 **7.72**	3.37 **5.53**	2.98 **4.64**	2.74 **4.14**	2.59 **3.82**	2.47 **3.59**	2.39 **3.42**	2.32 **3.29**	2.27 **3.17**	2.22 **3.09**	2.18 **3.02**	2.15 **2.96**	2.10 **2.86**	2.05 **2.77**	1.99 **2.66**	1.95 **2.58**	1.90 **2.50**	1.85 **2.41**	1.82 **2.36**	1.78 **2.28**	1.76 **2.25**	1.72 **2.19**	1.70 **2.15**	1.69 **2.13**

* Table F is reproduced from Snedecor, *Statistical Methods*, 5th edition, 1956, Iowa State University Press, Ames, Iowa, by permission of the author and publisher.

Table F (Cont.)

THE 5% (ROMAN TYPE) AND 1% (BOLDFACE TYPE) POINTS FOR THE DISTRIBUTION OF F*

Numerator df

Denom. df	1	2	3	4	5	6	7	8	9	10	11	12	14	16	20	24	30	40	50	75	100	200	500	∞
27	4.21 / 7.68	3.35 / 5.49	2.96 / 4.60	2.73 / 4.11	2.57 / 3.79	2.46 / 3.56	2.37 / 3.39	2.30 / 3.26	2.25 / 3.14	2.20 / 3.06	2.16 / 2.98	2.13 / 2.93	2.08 / 2.83	2.03 / 2.74	1.97 / 2.63	1.93 / 2.55	1.88 / 2.47	1.84 / 2.38	1.80 / 2.33	1.76 / 2.25	1.74 / 2.21	1.71 / 2.16	1.68 / 2.12	1.67 / 2.10
28	4.20 / 7.64	3.34 / 5.45	2.95 / 4.57	2.71 / 4.07	2.56 / 3.76	2.44 / 3.53	2.36 / 3.36	2.29 / 3.23	2.24 / 3.11	2.19 / 3.03	2.15 / 2.95	2.12 / 2.90	2.06 / 2.80	2.02 / 2.71	1.96 / 2.60	1.91 / 2.52	1.87 / 2.44	1.81 / 2.35	1.78 / 2.30	1.75 / 2.22	1.72 / 2.18	1.69 / 2.13	1.67 / 2.09	1.65 / 2.06
29	4.18 / 7.60	3.33 / 5.42	2.93 / 4.54	2.70 / 4.04	2.54 / 3.73	2.43 / 3.50	2.35 / 3.33	2.28 / 3.20	2.22 / 3.08	2.18 / 3.00	2.14 / 2.92	2.10 / 2.87	2.05 / 2.77	2.00 / 2.68	1.94 / 2.57	1.90 / 2.49	1.85 / 2.41	1.80 / 2.32	1.77 / 2.27	1.73 / 2.19	1.71 / 2.15	1.68 / 2.10	1.65 / 2.06	1.64 / 2.03
30	4.17 / 7.56	3.32 / 5.39	2.92 / 4.51	2.69 / 4.02	2.53 / 3.70	2.42 / 3.47	2.34 / 3.30	2.27 / 3.17	2.21 / 3.06	2.16 / 2.98	2.12 / 2.90	2.09 / 2.84	2.04 / 2.74	1.99 / 2.66	1.93 / 2.55	1.89 / 2.47	1.84 / 2.38	1.79 / 2.29	1.76 / 2.24	1.72 / 2.16	1.69 / 2.13	1.66 / 2.07	1.64 / 2.03	1.62 / 2.01
32	4.15 / 7.50	3.30 / 5.34	2.90 / 4.46	2.67 / 3.97	2.51 / 3.66	2.40 / 3.42	2.32 / 3.25	2.25 / 3.12	2.19 / 3.01	2.14 / 2.94	2.10 / 2.86	2.07 / 2.80	2.02 / 2.70	1.97 / 2.62	1.91 / 2.51	1.86 / 2.42	1.82 / 2.34	1.76 / 2.25	1.74 / 2.20	1.69 / 2.12	1.67 / 2.08	1.64 / 2.02	1.61 / 1.98	1.59 / 1.96
34	4.13 / 7.44	3.28 / 5.29	2.88 / 4.42	2.65 / 3.93	2.49 / 3.61	2.38 / 3.38	2.30 / 3.21	2.23 / 3.08	2.17 / 2.97	2.12 / 2.89	2.08 / 2.82	2.05 / 2.76	2.00 / 2.66	1.95 / 2.58	1.89 / 2.47	1.84 / 2.38	1.80 / 2.30	1.74 / 2.21	1.71 / 2.15	1.67 / 2.08	1.64 / 2.04	1.61 / 1.98	1.59 / 1.94	1.57 / 1.91
36	4.11 / 7.39	3.26 / 5.25	2.86 / 4.38	2.63 / 3.89	2.48 / 3.58	2.36 / 3.35	2.28 / 3.18	2.21 / 3.04	2.15 / 2.94	2.10 / 2.86	2.06 / 2.78	2.03 / 2.72	1.98 / 2.62	1.93 / 2.54	1.87 / 2.43	1.82 / 2.35	1.78 / 2.26	1.72 / 2.17	1.69 / 2.12	1.65 / 2.04	1.62 / 2.00	1.59 / 1.94	1.56 / 1.90	1.55 / 1.87
38	4.10 / 7.35	3.25 / 5.21	2.85 / 4.34	2.62 / 3.86	2.46 / 3.54	2.35 / 3.32	2.26 / 3.15	2.19 / 3.02	2.14 / 2.91	2.09 / 2.82	2.05 / 2.75	2.02 / 2.69	1.96 / 2.59	1.92 / 2.51	1.85 / 2.40	1.80 / 2.32	1.76 / 2.22	1.71 / 2.14	1.67 / 2.08	1.63 / 2.00	1.60 / 1.97	1.57 / 1.90	1.54 / 1.86	1.53 / 1.84
40	4.08 / 7.31	3.23 / 5.18	2.84 / 4.31	2.61 / 3.83	2.45 / 3.51	2.34 / 3.29	2.25 / 3.12	2.18 / 2.99	2.12 / 2.88	2.07 / 2.80	2.04 / 2.73	2.00 / 2.66	1.95 / 2.56	1.90 / 2.49	1.84 / 2.37	1.79 / 2.29	1.74 / 2.20	1.69 / 2.11	1.66 / 2.05	1.61 / 1.97	1.59 / 1.94	1.55 / 1.88	1.53 / 1.84	1.51 / 1.81
42	4.07 / 7.27	3.22 / 5.15	2.83 / 4.29	2.59 / 3.80	2.44 / 3.49	2.32 / 3.26	2.24 / 3.10	2.17 / 2.96	2.11 / 2.86	2.06 / 2.77	2.02 / 2.70	1.99 / 2.64	1.94 / 2.54	1.89 / 2.46	1.82 / 2.35	1.78 / 2.26	1.73 / 2.17	1.68 / 2.08	1.64 / 2.02	1.60 / 1.94	1.57 / 1.91	1.54 / 1.85	1.51 / 1.80	1.49 / 1.78
44	4.06 / 7.24	3.21 / 5.12	2.82 / 4.26	2.58 / 3.78	2.43 / 3.46	2.31 / 3.24	2.23 / 3.07	2.16 / 2.94	2.10 / 2.84	2.05 / 2.75	2.01 / 2.68	1.98 / 2.62	1.92 / 2.52	1.88 / 2.44	1.81 / 2.32	1.76 / 2.24	1.72 / 2.15	1.66 / 2.06	1.63 / 2.00	1.58 / 1.92	1.56 / 1.88	1.52 / 1.82	1.50 / 1.78	1.48 / 1.75
46	4.05 / 7.21	3.20 / 5.10	2.81 / 4.24	2.57 / 3.76	2.42 / 3.44	2.30 / 3.22	2.22 / 3.05	2.14 / 2.92	2.09 / 2.82	2.04 / 2.73	2.00 / 2.66	1.97 / 2.60	1.91 / 2.50	1.87 / 2.42	1.80 / 2.30	1.75 / 2.22	1.71 / 2.13	1.65 / 2.04	1.62 / 1.98	1.57 / 1.90	1.54 / 1.86	1.51 / 1.80	1.48 / 1.76	1.46 / 1.72
48	4.04 / 7.19	3.19 / 5.08	2.80 / 4.22	2.56 / 3.74	2.41 / 3.42	2.30 / 3.20	2.21 / 3.04	2.14 / 2.90	2.08 / 2.80	2.03 / 2.71	1.99 / 2.64	1.96 / 2.58	1.90 / 2.48	1.86 / 2.40	1.79 / 2.28	1.74 / 2.20	1.70 / 2.11	1.64 / 2.02	1.61 / 1.96	1.56 / 1.88	1.53 / 1.84	1.50 / 1.78	1.47 / 1.73	1.45 / 1.70

Denominator df

* Table F is reproduced from Snedecor, Statistical Methods, 5th edition, 1956, Iowa State University Press, Ames, Iowa, by permission of the author and publisher.

Table F (Concluded)

THE 5% (ROMAN TYPE) AND 1% (BOLDFACE TYPE) POINTS FOR THE DISTRIBUTION OF F*

NUMERATOR df

DENOMINATOR df	1	2	3	4	5	6	7	8	9	10	11	12	14	16	20	24	30	40	50	75	100	200	500	∞
50	4.03 **7.17**	3.18 **5.06**	2.79 **4.20**	2.56 **3.72**	2.40 **3.41**	2.29 **3.18**	2.20 **3.02**	2.13 **2.88**	2.07 **2.78**	2.02 **2.70**	1.98 **2.62**	1.95 **2.56**	1.90 **2.46**	1.85 **2.39**	1.78 **2.26**	1.74 **2.18**	1.69 **2.10**	1.63 **2.00**	1.60 **1.94**	1.55 **1.86**	1.52 **1.82**	1.48 **1.76**	1.46 **1.71**	1.44 **1.68**
55	4.02 **7.12**	3.17 **5.01**	2.78 **4.16**	2.54 **3.68**	2.38 **3.37**	2.27 **3.15**	2.18 **2.98**	2.11 **2.85**	2.05 **2.75**	2.00 **2.66**	1.97 **2.59**	1.93 **2.53**	1.88 **2.43**	1.83 **2.35**	1.76 **2.23**	1.72 **2.15**	1.67 **2.06**	1.61 **1.96**	1.58 **1.90**	1.52 **1.82**	1.50 **1.78**	1.46 **1.71**	1.43 **1.66**	1.41 **1.64**
60	4.00 **7.08**	3.15 **4.98**	2.76 **4.13**	2.52 **3.65**	2.37 **3.34**	2.25 **3.12**	2.17 **2.95**	2.10 **2.82**	2.04 **2.72**	1.99 **2.63**	1.95 **2.56**	1.92 **2.50**	1.86 **2.40**	1.81 **2.32**	1.75 **2.20**	1.70 **2.12**	1.65 **2.03**	1.59 **1.93**	1.56 **1.87**	1.50 **1.79**	1.48 **1.74**	1.44 **1.68**	1.41 **1.63**	1.39 **1.60**
65	3.99 **7.04**	3.14 **4.95**	2.75 **4.10**	2.51 **3.62**	2.36 **3.31**	2.24 **3.09**	2.15 **2.93**	2.08 **2.79**	2.02 **2.70**	1.98 **2.61**	1.94 **2.54**	1.90 **2.47**	1.85 **2.37**	1.80 **2.30**	1.73 **2.18**	1.68 **2.09**	1.63 **2.00**	1.57 **1.90**	1.54 **1.84**	1.49 **1.76**	1.46 **1.71**	1.42 **1.64**	1.39 **1.60**	1.37 **1.56**
70	3.98 **7.01**	3.13 **4.92**	2.74 **4.08**	2.50 **3.60**	2.35 **3.29**	2.23 **3.07**	2.14 **2.91**	2.07 **2.77**	2.01 **2.67**	1.97 **2.59**	1.93 **2.51**	1.89 **2.45**	1.84 **2.35**	1.79 **2.28**	1.72 **2.15**	1.67 **2.07**	1.62 **1.98**	1.56 **1.88**	1.53 **1.82**	1.47 **1.74**	1.45 **1.69**	1.40 **1.62**	1.37 **1.56**	1.35 **1.53**
80	3.96 **6.96**	3.11 **4.88**	2.72 **4.04**	2.48 **3.56**	2.33 **3.25**	2.21 **3.04**	2.12 **2.87**	2.05 **2.74**	1.99 **2.64**	1.95 **2.55**	1.91 **2.48**	1.88 **2.41**	1.82 **2.32**	1.77 **2.24**	1.70 **2.11**	1.65 **2.03**	1.60 **1.94**	1.54 **1.84**	1.51 **1.78**	1.45 **1.70**	1.42 **1.65**	1.38 **1.57**	1.35 **1.52**	1.32 **1.49**
100	3.94 **6.90**	3.09 **4.82**	2.70 **3.98**	2.46 **3.51**	2.30 **3.20**	2.19 **2.99**	2.10 **2.82**	2.03 **2.69**	1.97 **2.59**	1.92 **2.51**	1.88 **2.43**	1.85 **2.36**	1.79 **2.26**	1.75 **2.19**	1.68 **2.06**	1.63 **1.98**	1.57 **1.89**	1.51 **1.79**	1.48 **1.73**	1.42 **1.64**	1.39 **1.59**	1.34 **1.51**	1.30 **1.46**	1.28 **1.43**
125	3.92 **6.84**	3.07 **4.78**	2.68 **3.94**	2.44 **3.47**	2.29 **3.17**	2.17 **2.95**	2.08 **2.79**	2.01 **2.65**	1.95 **2.56**	1.90 **2.47**	1.86 **2.40**	1.83 **2.33**	1.77 **2.23**	1.72 **2.15**	1.65 **2.03**	1.60 **1.94**	1.55 **1.85**	1.49 **1.75**	1.45 **1.68**	1.39 **1.59**	1.36 **1.54**	1.31 **1.46**	1.27 **1.40**	1.25 **1.37**
150	3.91 **6.81**	3.06 **4.75**	2.67 **3.91**	2.43 **3.44**	2.27 **3.14**	2.16 **2.92**	2.07 **2.76**	2.00 **2.62**	1.94 **2.53**	1.89 **2.44**	1.85 **2.37**	1.82 **2.30**	1.76 **2.20**	1.71 **2.12**	1.64 **2.00**	1.59 **1.91**	1.54 **1.83**	1.47 **1.72**	1.44 **1.66**	1.37 **1.56**	1.34 **1.51**	1.29 **1.43**	1.25 **1.37**	1.22 **1.33**
200	3.89 **6.76**	3.04 **4.71**	2.65 **3.88**	2.41 **3.41**	2.26 **3.11**	2.14 **2.90**	2.05 **2.73**	1.98 **2.60**	1.92 **2.50**	1.87 **2.41**	1.83 **2.34**	1.80 **2.28**	1.74 **2.17**	1.69 **2.09**	1.62 **1.97**	1.57 **1.88**	1.52 **1.79**	1.45 **1.69**	1.42 **1.62**	1.35 **1.53**	1.32 **1.48**	1.26 **1.39**	1.22 **1.33**	1.19 **1.28**
400	3.86 **6.70**	3.02 **4.66**	2.62 **3.83**	2.39 **3.36**	2.23 **3.06**	2.12 **2.85**	2.03 **2.69**	1.96 **2.55**	1.90 **2.46**	1.85 **2.37**	1.81 **2.29**	1.78 **2.23**	1.72 **2.12**	1.67 **2.04**	1.60 **1.92**	1.54 **1.84**	1.49 **1.74**	1.42 **1.64**	1.38 **1.57**	1.32 **1.47**	1.28 **1.42**	1.22 **1.32**	1.16 **1.24**	1.13 **1.19**
1000	3.85 **6.66**	3.00 **4.62**	2.61 **3.80**	2.38 **3.34**	2.22 **3.04**	2.10 **2.82**	2.02 **2.66**	1.95 **2.53**	1.89 **2.43**	1.84 **2.34**	1.80 **2.26**	1.76 **2.20**	1.70 **2.09**	1.65 **2.01**	1.58 **1.89**	1.53 **1.81**	1.47 **1.71**	1.41 **1.61**	1.36 **1.54**	1.30 **1.44**	1.26 **1.38**	1.19 **1.28**	1.13 **1.19**	1.08 **1.11**
∞	3.84 **6.64**	2.99 **4.60**	2.60 **3.78**	2.37 **3.32**	2.21 **3.02**	2.09 **2.80**	2.01 **2.64**	1.94 **2.51**	1.88 **2.41**	1.83 **2.32**	1.79 **2.24**	1.75 **2.18**	1.69 **2.07**	1.64 **1.99**	1.57 **1.87**	1.52 **1.79**	1.46 **1.69**	1.40 **1.59**	1.35 **1.52**	1.28 **1.41**	1.24 **1.36**	1.17 **1.25**	1.11 **1.15**	1.00 **1.00**

* Table F is reproduced from Snedecor, *Statistical Methods*, 5th edition, 1956, Iowa State University Press, Ames, Iowa, by permission of the author and publisher.

Table G

TABLE OF RANDOM NUMBERS*

COLUMN NUMBER

1st Thousand

Row	00000 01234	00000 56789	11111 01234	11111 56789	22222 01234	22222 56789	33333 01234	33333 56789
00	23157	54859	01837	25993	76249	70886	95230	36744
01	05545	55043	10537	43508	90611	83744	10962	21343
02	14871	60350	32404	36223	50051	00322	11543	80834
03	38976	74951	94051	75853	78805	90194	32428	71695
04	97312	61718	99755	30870	94251	25841	54882	10513
05	11742	69381	44339	30872	32797	33118	22647	06850
06	43361	28859	11016	45623	93009	00499	43640	74036
07	93806	20478	38268	04491	55751	18932	58475	52571
08	49540	13181	08429	84187	69538	29661	77738	09527
09	36768	72633	37948	21569	41959	68670	45274	83880
10	07092	52392	24627	12067	06558	45344	67338	45320
11	43310	01081	44863	80307	52555	16148	89742	94647
12	61570	06360	06173	63775	63148	95123	35017	46993
13	31352	83799	10779	18941	31579	76448	62584	86919
14	57048	86526	27795	93692	90529	56546	35065	32254
15	09243	44200	68721	07137	30729	75756	09298	27650
16	97957	35018	40894	88329	52230	82521	22532	61587
17	93732	59570	43781	98885	56671	66826	95996	44569
18	72621	11225	00922	68264	35666	59434	71687	58167
19	61020	74418	45371	20794	95917	37866	99536	19378
20	97839	85474	33055	91718	45473	54144	22034	23000
21	89160	97192	22232	90637	35055	45489	88438	16361
22	25966	88220	62871	79265	02823	52862	84919	54883
23	81443	31719	05049	54806	74690	07567	65017	16543
24	11322	54931	42362	34386	08624	97687	46245	23245

* Table G is reproduced from M. G. Kendall and B. B. Smith. Randomness and random sampling numbers. *J. R. statist. Soc.,* **101** (1938), 147–166, by permission of the Royal Statistical Society.

Table G

TABLE OF RANDOM NUMBERS* (Cont.)

COLUMN NUMBER

Row	00000 01234	00000 56789	11111 01234	11111 56789	22222 01234	22222 56789	33333 01234	33333 56789
				2nd Thousand				
00	64755	83885	84122	25920	17696	15655	95045	95947
01	10302	52289	77436	34430	38112	49067	07348	23328
02	71017	98495	51308	50374	66591	02887	53765	69149
03	60012	55605	88410	34879	79655	90169	78800	03666
04	37330	94656	49161	42802	48274	54755	44553	65090
05	47869	87001	31591	12273	60626	12822	34691	61212
06	38040	42737	64167	89578	39323	49324	88434	38706
07	73508	30908	83054	80078	86669	30295	56460	45336
08	32623	46474	84061	04324	20628	37319	32356	43969
09	97591	99549	36630	35106	62069	92975	95320	57734
10	74012	31955	59790	96982	66224	24015	96749	07589
11	56754	26457	13351	05014	90966	33674	69096	33488
12	49800	49908	54831	21998	08528	26372	92923	65026
13	43584	89647	24878	56670	00221	50193	99591	62377
14	16653	79664	60325	71301	35742	83636	73058	87229
15	48502	69055	65322	58748	31446	80237	31252	96367
16	96765	54692	36316	86230	48296	38352	23816	64094
17	38923	61550	80357	81784	23444	12463	33992	28128
18	77958	81694	25225	05587	51073	01070	60218	61961
19	17928	28065	25586	08771	02641	85064	65796	48170
20	94036	85978	02318	04499	41054	10531	87431	21596
21	47460	60479	56230	48417	14372	85167	27558	00368
22	47856	56088	51992	82439	40644	17170	13463	18288
23	57616	34653	92298	62018	10375	76515	62986	90756
24	08300	92704	66752	66610	57188	79107	54222	22013

* Table G is reproduced from M. G. Kendall and B. B. Smith. Randomness and random sampling numbers. *J. R. statist. Soc.*, 101 (1938), 147–166, by permission of the Royal Statistical Society.

Table G

TABLE OF RANDOM NUMBERS* (Cont.)

Row	COLUMN NUMBER							
	00000 01234	00000 56789	11111 01234	11111 56789	22222 01234	22222 56789	33333 01234	33333 56789
				3rd Thousand				
00	89221	02362	65787	74733	51272	30213	92441	39651
01	04005	99818	63918	29032	94012	42363	01261	10650
02	98546	38066	50856	75045	40645	22841	53254	44125
03	41719	84401	59226	01314	54581	40398	49988	65579
04	28733	72489	00785	25843	24613	49797	85567	84471
05	65213	83927	77762	03086	80742	24395	68476	83792
06	65553	12678	90906	90466	43670	26217	69900	31205
07	05668	69080	73029	85746	58332	78231	45986	92998
08	39302	99718	49757	79519	27387	76373	47262	91612
09	64592	32254	45879	29431	38320	05981	18067	87137
10	07513	48792	47314	83660	68907	05336	82579	91582
11	86593	68501	56638	99800	82839	35148	56541	07232
12	83735	22599	97977	81248	36838	99560	32410	67614
13	08595	21826	54655	08204	87990	17033	56258	05384
14	41273	27149	44293	69458	16828	63962	15864	35421
15	00473	75908	56238	12242	72631	76314	47252	06347
16	86131	53789	81383	07868	89132	96182	07009	86432
17	33849	78359	08402	03586	03176	88663	08018	22546
18	61870	41657	07468	08612	98083	97349	20775	45091
19	43898	65923	25078	86129	78491	97653	91500	80786
20	29939	39123	04548	45985	60952	06641	28726	46473
21	38505	85555	14388	55077	18657	94887	67831	70819
22	31824	38431	67125	25511	72044	11562	53279	82268
23	91430	03767	13561	15597	06750	92552	02391	38753
24	38635	68976	25498	97526	96458	03805	04116	63514

* Table G is reproduced from M. G. Kendall and B. B. Smith. Randomness and random sampling numbers. *J. R. statist. Soc.,* **101** (1938), 147–166, by permission of the Royal Statistical Society.

Table G

TABLE OF RANDOM NUMBERS* (Cont.)

COLUMN NUMBER

4th Thousand

Row	00000 01234	00000 56789	11111 01234	11111 56789	22222 01234	22222 56789	33333 01234	33333 56789
00	02490	54122	27944	39364	94239	72074	11679	54082
01	11967	36469	60627	83701	09253	30208	01385	37482
02	48256	83465	49699	24079	05403	35154	39613	03136
03	27246	73080	21481	23536	04881	89977	49484	93071
04	32532	77265	72430	70722	86529	18457	92657	10011
05	66757	98955	92375	93431	43204	55825	45443	69265
06	11266	34545	76505	97746	34668	26999	26742	97516
07	17872	39142	45561	80146	93137	48924	64257	59284
08	62561	30365	03408	14754	51798	08133	61010	97730
09	62796	30779	35497	70501	30105	08133	00997	91970
10	75510	21771	04339	33660	42757	62223	87565	48468
11	87439	01691	63517	26590	44437	07217	98706	39032
12	97742	02621	10748	78803	38337	65226	92149	59051
13	98811	06001	21571	02875	21828	83912	85188	61624
14	51264	01852	64607	92553	29004	26695	78583	62998
15	40239	93376	10419	68610	49120	02941	80035	99317
16	26936	59186	51667	27645	46329	44681	94190	66647
17	88502	11716	98299	40974	42394	62200	69094	81646
18	63499	38093	25593	61995	79867	80569	01023	38374
19	36379	81206	03317	78710	73828	31083	60509	44091
20	93801	22322	47479	57017	59334	30647	43061	26660
21	29856	87120	56311	50053	25365	81265	22414	02431
22	97720	87931	88265	13050	71017	15177	06957	92919
23	85237	09105	74601	46377	59938	15647	34177	92753
24	75746	75268	31727	95773	72364	87324	36879	06802

* Table G is reproduced from M. G. Kendall and B. B. Smith. Randomness and random sampling numbers. *J. R. statist. Soc.*, 101 (1938), 147–166, by permission of the Royal Statistical Society.

Table G

TABLE OF RANDOM NUMBERS* (Concluded)

COLUMN NUMBER

5th Thousand

Row	00000 01234	00000 56789	11111 01234	11111 56789	22222 01234	22222 56789	33333 01234	33333 56789
00	29935	06971	63175	52579	10478	89379	61428	21363
01	15114	07126	51890	77787	75510	13103	42942	48111
02	03870	43225	10589	87629	22039	94124	38127	65022
03	79390	39188	40756	45269	65959	20640	14284	22960
04	30035	06915	79196	54428	64819	52314	48721	81594
05	29039	99861	28759	79802	68531	39198	38137	24373
06	78196	08108	24107	49777	09599	43569	84820	94956
07	15847	85493	91442	91351	80130	73752	21539	10986
08	36614	62248	49194	97209	92587	92053	41021	80064
09	40549	54884	91465	43862	35541	44466	88594	74180
10	40878	08997	14286	09982	90308	78007	51587	16658
11	10229	49282	41173	31468	59455	18756	08908	06660
12	15918	76787	30624	25928	44124	25088	31137	71614
13	13403	18796	49909	94404	64979	41462	18155	98335
14	66523	94596	74908	90271	10009	98648	17640	68909
15	91665	36469	68343	17870	25975	04662	21272	50620
16	67415	87515	08207	73729	73201	57593	96917	69699
17	76527	96996	23724	33448	63392	32394	60887	90617
18	19815	47789	74348	17147	10954	34355	81194	54407
19	25592	53587	76384	72575	84347	68918	05739	57222
20	55902	45539	63646	31609	95999	82887	40666	66692
21	02470	58376	79794	22482	42423	96162	47491	17664
22	18630	53263	13319	97619	35859	12350	14632	87659
23	89673	38230	16063	92007	59503	38402	76450	33333
24	62986	67364	06595	17427	84623	14565	82860	57300

* Table G is reproduced from M. G. Kendall and B. B. Smith. Randomness and random sampling numbers. *J. R. statist. Soc.*, 101 (1938), 147–166, by permission of the Royal Statistical Society.

Index

Random samples *see* Samples
Ranges
  interquartile, 59–60
  measure of variability and, 59–60, 94–95
Ranks, 11–15, 277–279
  centiles and, 45, 50–60
  comparing two sets of, 13–14
  data and, 3
  defined, 11
  graphs, 11–15
  relative position and, 11
  reliability and, 14
  tables, 11–15
Raw score formula, 138
Reliability
  measures and, 16
  ranks and, 14
Representative values, 46
Representativeness
  random sampling and, 71–72
Research methods
  needs for, 3–4
Regression equations, 142

Samples
  data and, 67
  defined, 69
  distributions, probability and, 171–174
  large populations and large, 168–171
  large populations and small, 163–165
  random, 69–72
    defined, 69–70
    properties of, 70
    representativeness and, 71–72
    statistical inference and, 71–72
    stratified, 70
  range and, 69
  sampling and, 69–72
Sampling distributions *see* Distributions
Scatter diagram, 130–132
  linearity and, 137
Scores
  coded

frequency distributions and, 89–94
  mean deviations and, 89–94
  standard deviations and, 89–94
  transformation of, 139–141
Semi-interquartile range, 60
Siegel, S., 277
Significance levels
  choosing of, 188–190
Skewed distribution *see* Distributions
Standard deviations *see* Deviations
Statistical hypotheses *see* Statistics
Statistical Principles in Experimental Design (Winer), 256n
Statistical probability *see* Probability
Statistical tests *see* Statistics
Statistics
  categories of, 67
  defined, 69
  descriptive, 67, 71, 274–275
    deviations and, 81
    non-symmetrical distribution and, 95
    shape of distribution and, 94–97
    symmetrical distributions and, 95
    variance and, 81
  deviations, 81
  distributions and, 95
  errors
    standard, 120
  estimates
    biased, 120–121
    unbiased, 120–121
  expectations and, 120–121
  hypotheses
    alternatives, 183
    choosing the appropriate, 183
    critical regions, 186–188
    definition of, 182–183
    examples of, 185
    expectation and, 182
    formulating, 181–191